Inorganic Ion Exchange Materials

Editor

Abraham Clearfield, Ph.D.
Professor of Inorganic Chemistry
Department of Chemistry
Texas A & M University
College Station, Texas

CRC Press, Inc.
Boca Raton, Florida

Library of Congress Cataloging in Publication Data
Main entry under title:

Inorganic ion exchange materials.

Bibliography

Includes index.
1. Ion exchange resins. I. Clearfield, Abraham.
QD561.I55   541.3'723   81-6109
ISBN 0-8493-5930-9   AACR2

International Standard Book Number 0-8493-5930-9

Library of Congress Card Number 81-6109
Printed in the United States

PREFACE

The early synthetic ion exchangers were largely gelatinous aluminosilicates termed permutits. They were troublesome to obtain in reproducible form and unstable in acid solution. Thus, they were subsequently replaced by the synthetic organic resins. Organic resins by virtue of their desirable physical, chemical, and mechanical properties have until recently dominated the field. However, the advent of synthetic crystalline zeolites has once again turned attention towards utilization of inorganic ion exchange materials. The use of zeolites in detergents and water pollution control will far outweigh in tonnage the amount of organic resins utilized annually. Nevertheless, the versatility and remarkable combination of desirable properties which can be built into organic resins has made their position in ion exchange technology secure.

What then is the role of the inorganic ion exchange materials described in this book? Originally they were sought out as a means of providing ion exchangers which would be stable to high radiation fields and high temperatures. This role has generally not been filled. However, investigators have continued to seek out new materials until now there is a bewildering array of new inorganic ion exchangers available. A turning point came when it was shown in 1964 that the gelatinous group IV phosphates and arsenates could be prepared in crystalline forms. The solution of the crystal structure of α-zirconium phosphate followed and established the layered nature of these compounds. These layered structures readily undergo phase changes during exchange so that their behavior is neither that of organic resins, where solid solutions are obtained, nor that of zeolites which retain a rigid framework with a multiplicity of exchange sites. We are thus presented with a new class of compounds, somewhat resembling clays in behavior, but of simpler structure and more amenable to quantitative treatment.

The preparation and study of semicrystalline exchangers provides a link between the crystalline layered compounds and the amorphous gels. Thus, indirectly we may be led to a better understanding of the nature of gels including hydrous oxides. From a practical standpoint these compounds will not only be utilized as ion exchangers because of their specialized properties and behavior but are promising as membranes for proton conduction, superion conductors and as catalysts or catalyst supports. Thus, a reading of this book may reward the effort by extending the frontiers for the ion exchange technologist and highlighting new materials for the future.

Abraham Clearfield
April 8, 1981

THE EDITOR

Abraham Clearfield is currently Professor of Inorganic Chemistry and Chairman of the Inorganic Division at Texas A&M University, College Station, Texas.

Dr. Clearfield obtained his B.A. and M.A. in chemistry from Temple University in Philadelphia. In 1954 he received his Ph.D. in Physical Chemistry and Crystallography from Rutgers University, New Brunswick, N.J. He is a member of the American Chemical Society, the American Crystallographic Association, and the New York Academy of Sciences.

Dr. Clearfield has published over 100 research papers, written chapters for several books, and presented numerous invited and submitted papers at international meetings. While a Professor at Ohio University he was elected a University Professor for excellence in teaching and a Research Institute Fellow for excellence in research. His current research interests center around the use of inorganic ion exchange materials as catalysts and fast ion conductors.

Dedication

To my beloved wife Ruth who, though schooled in the Liberal Arts, must suffer my affection for the sciences.

CONTRIBUTORS

Mitsuo Abe, Ph.D.
Professor
Department of Chemistry
Faculty of Science
Tokyo Institute of Technology
Tokyo, Japan

Giulio Alberti, Ph.D.
Full Professor of General and Inorganic
  Chemistry
Member of the Italian Chemical Society
University of Perugia
Perugia, Italy

Umberto Costantino, Ph.D.
Assistant and Professor of General and
  Inorganic Chemistry
Department of Chemistry
University of Perugia
Perugia, Italy

Arthur T. Howe, Ph.D. *
Department of Inorganic and Structural
  Chemistry
University of Leeds
Leeds, England

Aleksandar Ruvarac, Ph.D.
The Head of Chemical Dynamics
  Laboratory
Institute for Nuclear Sciences
"Boris Kidric" Institute
Belgrade, Yugoslavia

* Present Address
  Amoco Research Center
  Naperville, Illinois

TABLE OF CONTENTS

Chapter 1

ZIRCONIUM PHOSPHATES

Abraham Clearfield

TABLE OF CONTENTS

I. INTRODUCTION

It is now more than twenty years since reports of ion exchange behavior of zirconium phosphate gels first appeared in the chemical literature.[1-3] Since that time, research into the nature of this and similar compounds has continued unabated. Part of the impetus for this effort resulted from the discovery that zirconium and titanium phosphates could be prepared in crystalline form.[4,5] In the interim many other layered group (IV) phosphates and arsenates have been crystallized and studied as well as dozens of exchanged forms.[6,7,8] In addition, there are now quite a number of known phases of zirconium phosphate.[9] Furthermore, the original one, zirconium bis(monohydrogen orthophosphate), can be obtained as a gel, as single crystals, and in all intermediate stages of crystallinity.[10] For all of these products the ion exchange behavior differs, being a function of the crystallinity and structure. Thus, it is a mistake to consider zirconium phosphates as a single compound. It is essential to an understanding of the observed behavior that the exchanger be properly characterized. We shall attempt to do this as far as possible so that some reasonable correlation between structure and behavior may emerge.

Several excellent reviews have already appeared.[6,7,9,11] However, in the recent past, exciting new developments in the areas of surface chemistry, catalysis, electrochemistry, and fast ion conduction have taken place. These new findings need to be integrated with the already extensive knowledge of zirconium phosphates in a systematic way. It is hoped that the present treatment will achieve this objective.

II. STRUCTURAL STUDIES ON ZIRCONIUM BIS(MONOHYDROGEN ORTHOPHOSPHATE) MONOHYDRATE

A. Crystal Structure

Addition of a soluble Zr(IV) salt to phosphoric acid results in the precipitation of a gelatinous, amorphous solid of variable composition and properties (see Section III.A). However, a stoichiometric crystalline compound, $Zr(HPO_4)_2 \cdot H_2O$, can be prepared by refluxing these gels in strong phosphoric acid.[4,9] The crystals so formed range in size between 0.1 and 10 μm and are too small for single crystal studies. Larger crystals may be grown hydrothermally in quartz tubes or teflon-lined pressure vessels at 170 to 200°C.[12] A novel way of growing large crystals was developed by Alberti and Torracca.[13] It depends upon the fact that Zr(IV) forms soluble complexes with excess fluoride ions. To such a solution is added phosphoric acid, but not to the point of precipitation. On heating this mixture, the fluoride reacts with silicon from the glass container and is slowly removed as a volatile silicon fluoride. Thus, slow precipitation of zirconium phosphate occurs as the fluoride is depleted. The crystals prepared by either of the above methods will be referred to as α-ZrP.

The crystal structure of α-ZrP was initially solved by X-ray film methods[12] and later using a data set obtained with an automated diffractometer.[14] In the first case the space group was chosen as $P2_1/c$ and later it was more convenient to refine the structure in $P2_1/n$. Both sets of unit cell dimensions are given in Table 1, together with cell dimensions determined by others. The observed variation in unit cell dimensions will be discussed after a description of the structure is given.

α-Zirconium phosphate has a layered structure.[12,14] The metal atoms lie very nearly in a plane (± 0.25 Å to the mean plane) and are bridged by phosphate groups. These are situated alternately above and below the metal atom plane. Three oxygen atoms of each phosphate group are bonded to three different zirconium atoms which form a distorted equilateral triangle. Each zirconium atom is thus octahedrally coordinated by oxygens. An idealized picture of a portion of the layer is shown in Figure 1. It is seen that if the metal atoms were located in the mean plane that a psuedohexagonal arrangement would result with a unit cell $a_h \cong 5.24$ Å, $c_h \cong 22.6$ Å and D_{3d} point symmetry. The actual interlayer distance is 7.55 Å.

The two phosphate groups are not equivalent, one of them being more tilted in relation to the mean plane of the layer than the other. Reference to Figure 1 shows that the alternating metal and phosphate arrangement forms twelve-membered rings in a crown arrangement. These rings consist of three phosphorus atoms, three metal atoms, and six oxygen atoms (heavy outline in Figure 1). If the phosphorus atoms are below the mean plane, then the ring is capped by a phosphate group above the plane and vice versa. The whole arrangement assumes an open cup-like form. Adjacent layers are shifted relative to each other by 1/3 a_h, 2/3c_h. This places one twelve-membered ring capped on the top over another capped on the bottom, the whole making a six-

Table 1

UNIT CELL DIMENSIONS OF ZIRCONIUM PHOSPHATES

| Compound | Cell dimensions | | | | Ref. |
	a(Å)	b(Å)	c(Å)	β(deg)	
α-ZrP(1) (FILM)	9.076(3)	5.298(6)	16.22(2)	111.5(1)	12
α-ZrP(2)	9.060(2)	5.297(1)	15.414(3)	101.71(2)[a]	14
α-ZrP(3)	9.097(5)	5.307(1)	16.284(3)	111.38(1)	15
α-ZrP(4)	9.076	5.298	45.27[b]	—	16
	9.070	5.298	16.22	111.5	
α-ZrP(5)	9.0602(9)	5.2895(6)	15.455(2)	101.695(10)[a]	17
ζ-ZrP	9.20	5.35	16.14	112.1	40
η-ZrP	9.26	5.34	15.77	113.5	40
γ-ZrP	5.376(2)	6.636(4)	24.56(1)	93.94(5)	168

[a] Space Group P2$_1$/n.
[b] In orthorhombic system.

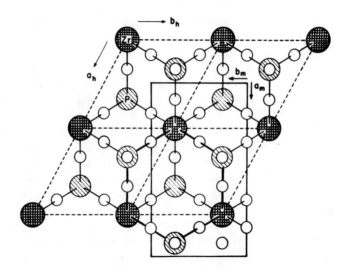

FIGURE 1.   Idealized layer in the α-ZrP structure showing relationship of psuedohexagonal cell (dashed lines) to the monoclinic cell (solid lines). The bottom half of one cavity is shown in heavy outline. (From Clearfield, A. and Smith, G. D., *Inorg. Chem.*, 8, 431, 1969. With permission.)

sided cavity (see Figure 2). The water molecule sits inside the cavity very near its center. There is just one mol of cavities per formula weight of α-ZrP or two exchange sites per cavity. Each of the phosphate oxygens which is not bonded to zirconium bears a proton. The O—H distances average 0.99 Å and thus the hydrogen is covalently bonded to oxygen.[18]

Two strong and one weak hydrogen bonds are formed between water and the phosphate groups.[14,19] The water molecule accepts two hydrogen bonds from the two distinct phosphate groups (O—O distances 2.769 and 2.807 Å), and in turn donates a hydrogen to one of them. The second water hydrogen atom is not involved in hydrogen bonding and points towards the top (or bottom) of the cavity. This produces a roughly tetrahedral arrangement of hydrogens about the water. There are no hydrogen bonds between layers; they are held together by van der Waals' forces only. This model of

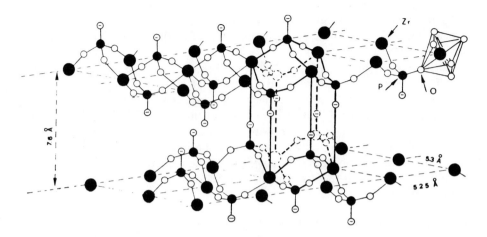

FIGURE 2.   Idealized structure of α-zirconium phosphate showing one of the zeolitic cavities created by the arrangement of the layers. (From Alberti, G., in *Study Week on Membranes,* Passino, R., Ed., Pontificiae Academie Scientarum Scripta Varia, Rome, 1976, 629. With permission.)

the structure has been found useful in describing the ion exchange behavior of α-ZrP as will be detailed in Section IV.

Recently some objection[16] was raised to the structure as reported above, based upon indexing of a X-ray powder pattern. Re-indexing was carried out in the orthorhombic system with a c-axis distance which corresponds to six layers. Therefore, we carried out a determination of the unit cell dimensions by the Guinier method. The pattern contained in excess of 100 lines whose 2θ values were corrected with an internal standard (NBS-641 Si). A least squares analysis of the data yielded the cell dimensions listed in Table 1 as α-ZrP (5). All of the lines could be indexed with no exceptions. Therefore, it is unlikely that the orthorhombic cell is correct. Apparent agreement with the orthorhombic cell resulted from the low accuracy of the listed d-spacings.[16]

Clearfield et al.[20] have shown that α-ZrP exhibits variations in cell dimensions as a function of the crystallinity of the preparation. For example, the c-axis varied from 16.284(3) Å for crystals obtained by refluxing a gel 24 hr in 12 $M\,H_3PO_4$ to 16.191(1) for single crystals. This shows that the unit cell dimensions depend upon the degree of perfection of the crystals which in turn affects the ion exchange behavior as will be discussed in Section III.B.6.

B. Infrared Studies

A relatively complete listing of the infrared absorption bands and their assignments was presented in an earlier review.[9] Since then, two new studies have appeared[21,22] and these need to be commented upon, particularly since the hydrogen bonding scheme is now known. According to Dushin et al.,[9] bands in the region 965 cm^{-1} to 1120 cm^{-1} represent phosphate vibrations of symmetry group C_{3v} (asymmetric and symmetric stretch) while those at 375 cm^{-1} to 600 cm^{-1} represent the various bending motions. The very sharp bands at 3590 and 3510 cm^{-1} are assigned to the asymmetric and symmetric water stretching while the one at 1620 cm^{-1} is the bending vibration (ν_2).

Horsley et al.[21] found that the bands at 3590, 3510, 3150, and 1620 cm^{-1} were all removed upon dehydration at 100°C. These bands were thus attributed to water. It was calculated, by combination of the water point group C_{2v} with the site symmetry C_1, that 4 bands at 3590, 3510, 3150, and 1620 cm^{-1} should arise from a single type of water molecule. All other hypotheses led to the conclusion that two kinds of water molecules are present and this would disagree with the crystal structure results. However, the lowered symmetry of the water molecule requires two different O−H bond lengths and there is as yet no evidence for this. What is to be noted is that one water hydrogen does not partake of hydrogen bonding while the other forms a weak hydrogen bond (O–H––O of 3.11 Å).

On dehydration the shoulder at 3280 cm^{-1} becomes a single strong band (at 3280 cm^{-1}). Thus, this band is assigned to the P–O–H hydroxyl stretch. Dushin et al.[22] assigned the band at 3150 cm^{-1} to this stretch. Since both P–O–H groups strong hydrogen bond to water, it would be expected that this stretching vibration would shift to a higher frequency upon dehydration. The fact that it doesn't may be due to the onset of hydrogen bonding between layers as the interlayer distance decreases with formation of the zeta phase.[23] The out of plane deformation for the P–O–H group occurs at 1250 cm^{-1} and this band is diagnostic for the presence of a monohydrogen phosphate group.

III. PREPARATION AND CHARACTERIZATION OF α-ZIRCONIUM PHOSPHATE

It is a mistake to consider zirconium phosphate as a single compound and this is nowhere more evident than in the different behaviors exhibited by the many preparations described in the literature. A listing of the different types of zirconium phosphates which behave as ion exchangers has been given earlier.[9] In this section we will be concerned with α-ZrP and its less crystalline forms.

A. Preparation

We have already mentioned that α-ZrP may be prepared by either refluxing a gel in strong phosphoric acid for long periods of time,[4,10] or by the direct precipitation method using HF.[13] In the latter procedure very large, well-formed crystals are obtained (see Section III.B.4). Reproducible behavior is to be expected from such preparations provided sufficient time is allowed to achieve equilibrium. Much smaller particles are obtained by the refluxing procedure (0.1 to 10 μm).

The ion exchange behavior of a particular zirconium phosphate depends very markedly upon how it was prepared. This is true both for gels and the crystalline materials. Amorphous gels are obtained by rapid addition of phosphate ion containing solutions to Zr(IV) salt solutions. The use of phosphoric acid is preferred because it avoids contamination of the precipitate with foreign ions and permits control of accompanying hydrolysis. If the mol ratio of phosphate to zirconium is less than two, quantitative precipitation of the zirconium still occurs (unless the ratio is less than one), but the product is a hydroxyphosphate, $Zr(OH)_x(HPO_4)_{2-\frac{x}{2}}$. Products in which x ranges from 3 to 0 have been obtained.[24-28] In such gels the ion exchange properties of the hydroxyl group must be considered as well as those of the monohydrogen phosphate groups. Even when the ratio of phosphate to zirconium exceeds two in the initial mix, the precipitate which first forms may have a ratio lower than two.[27] This arises particularly when the phosphate solution is added to the Zr(IV) solution. In such cases excess of zirconium is always present and hydroxy-phosphates precipitate. If the precipitate is aged in the mother liquor, its phosphate content continues to increase with time until equilibrium is reached.[27] Increased acidity and phosphate ion concentration favor a higher PO$_4$-Zr ratio. The maximum ratio even in the gels, is 2.[4] Higher ratios are the result of sorbed phosphate, although crystalline compounds with P/Zr greater than two are known.[9] Dehydration and ion exchange studies show that gels containing two phosphates per zirconium atom are correctly formulated as $Zr(HPO_4)_2 \cdot nH_2O$.[4,29] The value of n depends upon the drying procedure used, but is close to one when dried to constant weight over P$_2$O$_5$ and approximately five at 90% humidity. Even when the P/Zr ratio is less than 2, the phosphate groups are present as monohydrogen phosphate, in conformity with the formula given above.[30]

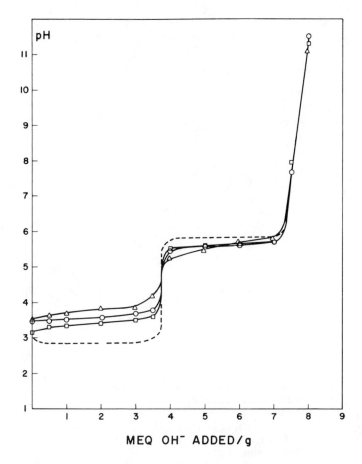

FIGURE 3. Potentiometric titration curves (batch method) for α-ZrP preparations of different crystallinities. Titrant: 0.1 *M* NaOH + 0.1 *M* NaCl; sample designation: 12:48 -△, 12:96 -○, 12:190 -□, 12:336 dashed line. (From Clearfield, A., Kullberg, L., and Oskarsson, Å., *J. Phys. Chem.*, 78, 1150, 1974. With permission.)

Heating and/or the presence of excess phosphoric acid during precipitation, as well as aging produces a gel with four distinct but broad X-ray reflections.[4,10,27] These reflections correspond to the four most intense reflections in α-ZrP crystals. The first reflection exhibited by the crystals occurs at d = 7.55 Å and represents the interlayer distance. In the gels this reflection can occur at a d-spacing as large as 11.2 Å when fully wet or as low as ∼8 Å when dry (n = 1).[4,10,31] By refluxing the gels in phosphoric acid of different concentrations for different lengths of time it is possible to build in any desired amount of crystallinity. It will be shown in the next section that the behavior of the products strongly depends upon the degree of crystallinity. In addition to this factor, the PO_4–Zr ratio, aging and temperature of precipitation influence the behavior of the gels. Therefore, it is imperative that a complete description of the synthetic method used always be given when describing zirconium phosphate behavior. Furthermore, methods of characterizing the exchanger are necessary so that correlations of behavior with structure and preparative procedure can be made. This will be discussed at length in Section III.B.

One of the difficulties encountered in practical applications of zirconium phosphate is the poor hydrodynamic properties of the gels or crystals. Normally the particles obtained are so fine that clogging of columns with attendant slow flow of fluid occurs.

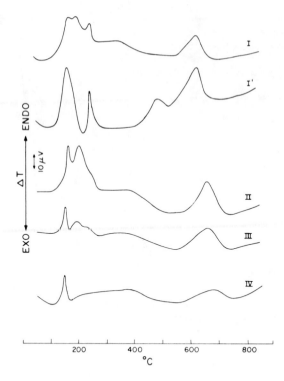

FIGURE 4.   Differential thermal analysis curves for
α-ZrP samples. Heating rates: 5°C/min for I; 17°/min
for all others. Sample designations are I and I', 12:176;
II, 14:330; III, 12:24; IV, 12:384. (From Clearfield, A.
and Pack, S. P., *J. Inorg. Nucl. Chem.*, 37, 1283, 1975.
With permission.)

Many methods of overcoming this problem have been tried. In the case of amorphous
gels small spheres about 1 to 2 mm in diameter have been prepared.[32,33] Zirconyl chloride solutions are mixed with urea and hexamethylene tetramine and the viscous solution is propelled through a needle into a hot silicone oil. Tiny, transparent spheres of
zirconium hydroxide are thus produced. These are then washed and treated with phosphoric acid to convert them to the phosphate.

B. Methods of Characterizing Zirconium Phosphate

In the early literature of zirconium phosphate, many authors did not report analyses
for their preparations nor characterize them in any meaningful way. I suppose this
stemmed from their subjective feeling that all zirconium phosphates were alike. A per-
fect example of the differences that one encounters is illustrated in a study carried out
by Ahrland et al.[31,34] These workers examined the influence of composition, crystallinity, aging of the gel, water content, and heat treatment in an attempt to obtain reproducible products. They found that this was not possible since even the best standard-
ization techniques produced gels with slightly different behaviors. The range of
differences for any one gel was not great so that one could expect reasonably similar
behavior if careful attention was paid to each step of the process. These results are
not unlike those experienced with polystyrene sulfonic acid resins where variations in
behavior from batch to batch are also observed.

Even with the crystalline preparations significant differences in exchange behavior
can be noted. This is illustrated in Figure 3 where sodium ion titration curves are shown
for different preparations of crystalline α-ZrP.[19] Gels refluxed from 48 to more than

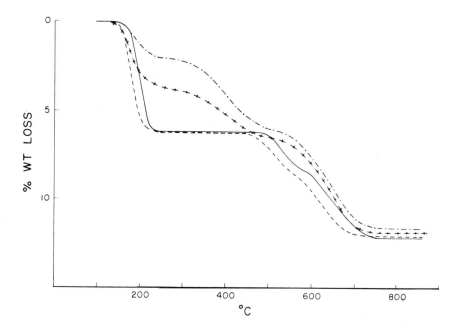

FIGURE 5. Weight loss (TG) curves for several α-ZrP samples obtained by the refluxing procedure. Samples are the same as those of Figure 4: I, —; II, ---; III, + + +; IV, -·-·. Heating rate 5°/min. (From Clearfield, A. and Pack, S. P., *J. Inorg. Nucl. Chem.*, 37, 1283, 1975. With permission.)

300 hr in 12 M H$_3$PO$_4$ exhibited lower pH values for Na$^+$ uptake with increased reflux time in the first 50% of exchange. This behavior difference is connected with crystal perfection as manifested by the changes in unit cell dimensions which occur on refluxing. Thus, even with the crystals, proper characterization is necessary. A fuller treatment of this subject is given below.

1. Thermal Methods

Differences in structure of the exchanger which result from the many small variations in preparative method are likely to manifest themselves in thermal effects. Thus DTA and TGA curves are likely to be sensitive indicators of these differences. Typical DTA curves for crystalline α-zirconium phosphate samples are shown in Figure 4.[23,35,36] Three endothermic peaks are obtained in the temperature range 100 to 250°C. The first one with a maximum at 150° has been ascribed to a phase transition from α-ZrP to ζ-ZrP.[23] This was shown by using a high temperature X-ray camera. The heated sample transformed to ζ-ZrP (7.41 Å) below 150°C and before the water of hydration was released. The second endotherm with maximum ∼190°C is due to the water loss and finally at ∼230° the zeta phase is converted to the η-phase (7.15 Å). The numbers in parenthesis represent the interlayer distances of the new phases.

Figure 5 reproduces the TG curves corresponding to the DTA curves of Figure 4.[23] The loss of one mol of water takes place in the neighborhood of 100 to 200°C for two of the samples while for two others this water loss extends to 450°C. At that temperature a second mol of water begins to split out. This water loss is the result of condensation of monohydrogen phosphate groups to form pyrophosphate,[4] and is accompanied by the endotherm with a maximum at ∼650°C. Somewhat higher temperatures may be required for crystallization of ZrP$_2$O$_7$. Otherwise a semiamorphous product is obtained.[4,38]

General agreement with the above results was obtained by La Ginestra et al.,[35] who examined a large number of samples. Much of the differences in the size and position of the endotherms below 300°C are due to the rate at which the hydration water is lost. In static experiments it is possible to remove this water at 80 to 100°C with no phase change.[37] However, if the phase change to ζ-ZrP occurs first, the water may have difficulty in escaping from the lattice. The endotherm due to water loss is then spread over a broad temperature region. Thus, kinetic effects may have more influence on the shape of the DTA-TG curves than actual structural differences of the exchangers. This is clearly shown by samples I and I′ in Figure 4 and by the thermograms of Horsley and Nowell.[38] These latter workers as well as others[39] have attributed the first endotherm to movement of zeolitic water within the lattice. However, there is now no doubt that the two phase changes are represented by the endotherms at 150° and 220 to 240°C. In fact Chernorukov[40] has derived unit cell dimensions for the two phases and these are given in Table 1. The transformation ζ-ZrP to η-ZrP is reversible with $\Delta H = 1.71 \pm 0.01$ kcal mol⁻¹.[40] The lower temperature phase change, α-ZrP $\rightleftharpoons$ ζ-ZrP is only reversible if water is present, i.e., the composition is $Zr(HPO_4)_2 \cdot H_2O$. If dehydration occurs, then ζ-ZrP is obtained on cooling to room temperature.

An example of the difficulty that one can encounter using thermal methods is illustrated by the work of Horsley and Nowell.[38] They prepared α-ZrP by four different methods and obtained three different DTA curves. A gel which had been refluxed for 150 hr in 10 $M\,H_3PO_4$ (10:150) gave a single endotherm at about 125°C as did a sample homogeneously precipitated from oxalic acid solution. However, the TGA curves for these two samples were somewhat dissimilar. A sample which had been crystallized from HF at 80°C gave three endotherms similar to those described for highly crystalline α-ZrP above. However, another sample crystallized from HF at room temperature exhibited only two endotherms below 300°C, one of which was broad and may be a doublet. Again the TG curves for these two samples showed significant differences. Finally, Inoue and Yamada[41] and La Ginestra et al.[35] also observed only two endotherms for a sample prepared by the HF method. However, the latter workers clearly showed by X-ray powder patterns that crystals prepared by the reflux method (12:400) underwent the phase transformation sequence

$$\alpha-ZrP \longrightarrow \zeta-ZrP \longrightarrow \eta-ZrP$$

In the case of the crystals prepared by the HF method a somewhat different X-ray pattern was obtained for the η-phase which underwent further transformations at 300°C and 400°C. It would appear then that the phase changes undergone by the HF preparations need further study. However, as we shall see in what follows, other significant differences are observed in the behavior of samples prepared by refluxing in H_3PO_4 and direct precipitation from HF.

DTA data on amorphous and semicrystalline samples is meager. The amorphous solid exhibits a broad endotherm due to water loss at about 165°C.[39] The size of this peak depends upon the water content of the gel and this has generally not been specified. Both TG curves and static weight loss data for amorphous and semicrystalline samples have been determined by many workers.[4,30,31,34,42-45] A typical set of weight loss curves is shown in Figure 6. It is seen that the air-dried gel contains on the order of 5 mol of water per formula weight whereas the more crystalline samples contain two (this includes the water due to phosphate condensation). Albertsson's data[42] show that the water content increases steadily with decrease in crystallinity. Crystallinity has generally been indicated by specifying the time and the concentration of H_3PO_4 used in refluxing the gel. Thus, 4.5:48 (4.5 $M\,H_3PO_4$, 48 hr reflux time) contained exactly two moles of water, Figure 6, but 9:1 contained 2.1 moles and 6:1, 2.28 moles.[42]

The temperature at which condensation of phosphate groups occurs also depends

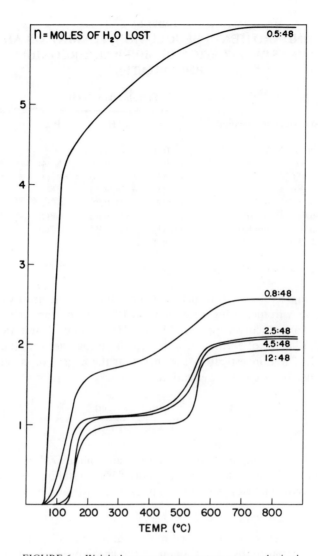

FIGURE 6. Weight loss versus temperature curves, obtained thermogravimetrically, for zirconium phosphate samples whose X-ray patterns are shown in Figure 7. Samples were dried at 45-50°C except for 0.5:48 which was equilibrated at $a_w = 0.997$. (From Clearfield, A., Oskarsson, Å., and Oskarsson, C., *Ion Exch. Membr.*, 1, 9, 1972. With permission.)

upon the crystallinity. Temperatures as low as 180°C have been reported for the onset of condensation.[44] However, one must be sure that no excess phosphate is present as this considerably lowers the temperature of condensation.[4] Only a portion of the water is split out at this low temperature but the amount increases with increasing temperature. In common with other gels, condensation continues to about 1000°C. However, the ion exchange capacity is almost zero after heating to 450°C. While considerable capacity is lost even by heating at 260°C, a large portion of this loss can be recovered by soaking the gel in water for long periods of time. It was shown from the condensation behavior of the gel that the amount of pyrophosphate formed corresponded to that expected from monohydrogenphosphate groups.[30]

2. Heat of Formation

Allulli, Massucci, and Tomassini[46] measured the heats of solution (in NaF) calori-

Table 2
STANDARD HEATS OF SOLUTION, FORMATION AND
CRYSTALLIZATION OF SEVERAL ZIRCONIUM
PHOSPHATES

| Compound and prep method | Enthalpy (kcal/mol) | | | X Fractional cryst. |
	ΔH_s	ΔH_f	$\Delta H^a_{cryst.}$	
Amorphous ZrP	−21.1(2)	−821.2(10)	—	0
α-ZrP(1:48)	−18.3(3)	−824.3(10)	−3.1(4)	0.47
α-ZrP(3.5:48)	−17.2(3)	−825.1(10)	−3.9(3)	0.58
α-ZrP(12:330)	−15.4(3)	−826.9(10)	−5.8(4)	0.86
α-ZrP-fast ppt from HF	−14.9(2)	−827.4(10)	−6.2(3)	0.94
α-ZrP Slow ppt from HF	−14.8(1)	−827.5(10)	−6.3(2)	0.95
α-ZrP(c) very slow ppt from HF	−14.5(1)	−827.8(10)	−6.7(2)	1.0
ζ-ZrP (12:330)	−17.9(2)	−756.2(10)	—	

^{a} $\Delta H_{cryst} = \Delta H_f(c) - \Delta H_f(amorp)$.

metrically on samples of α-ZrP of increasing crystallinity. The heats of solution were found to increase with increasing crystallinity reaching a constant value for the 100% crystalline material (which was prepared by the HF method). These values were converted to standard heats of formation which are given together with the heats of solution in Table 2. These investigators assumed that the degree of crystallinity of any sample would then be given by the equation

$$X_\eta = \frac{\Delta H_f^\circ(\eta) - \Delta H_f^\circ(am)}{\Delta H_f^\circ(Cr) - \Delta H_f^\circ(am)}$$

where (η) refers to the sample of interest (am) to amorphous ZrP and (Cr) to the fully crystalline sample. On this basis 12:330 is only 86% crystalline. Heats of formation for several unspecified phases of zirconium phosphate have also been published.[47]

3. X-Ray Methods

X-ray powder patterns were first used to distinguish crystalline from semicrystalline and amorphous preparations.[4,10,31,42] Figure 7 shows the progression of changes which occur upon refluxing. Application of the Scherrer equation was made to obtain relative crystallite sizes from the broadened reflections.[10,42] The crystallites vary in size from about 36 Å (3:1) to 400 Å (4.5:48) in the direction perpendicular to the layers. This method becomes relatively insensitive for crystallite sizes in the neighborhood of 1000 Å and also contains errors due to strain. Thus, any samples more crystalline than say 12:48 cannot be distinguished by this method. However, as we have seen in the preceeding section, even 12:330 is only 86% crystalline. Thus, a more sensitive X-ray method is required. Peak profile analysis of broadened reflections offers a possible solution to this problem.[48]

4. Particle Size Determination

An electron microscopic study of the particles obtained by the refluxing procedure was carried out by Clearfield.[9] The initially precipitated gel particles are typical of an amorphous structure. The individual particles are quite small, certainly less than 0.1 μm and exhibit no regular structure. Upon refluxing in H_3PO_4 dense nuclei are seen to form and these eventually grow into smooth triangular-shaped particles. Further refluxing in 2 to 6 $M H_3PO_4$ produces prismatic platelets of monoclinic symmetry. The bulk of the particles average about 1 μm across and ∼0.1 μm thick.

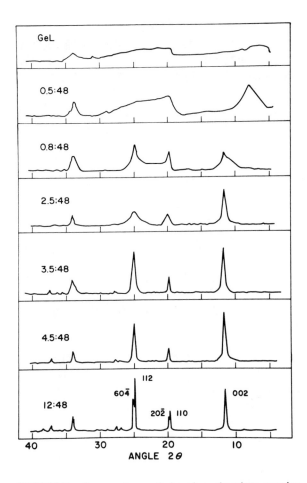

FIGURE 7.   X-ray patterns of zirconium phosphate samples
having different degrees of crystallinity. (From Clearfield, A.,
Oskarsson, Å., and Oskarsson, C., *Ion Exch. Membr.*, 1, 9,
1972. With permission.)

Several workers prepared crystalline α-ZrP by the HF method and measured the
particle size distribution. Horsley and Nowell[38] found a mean particle size of 3 to 6
μm with negligible porosities (surface areas of 2.4 to 2.7 M²/g). Of the particles, 95%
were larger than 1 μm and the largest were about 20 μm. Costantino et al.[49] measured
the particle size distribution of $Zr(NaPO_4)_2 \cdot 3H_2O$ and $Zr(KPO_4)_2 \cdot 2H_2O$ by the method
of centrifugal aerosol spectrometry. The mean particle size was about 4 μm with the
distribution showing a skewed distribution towards larger sizes (up to 40 μm). Much
larger crystals, 50 to 450 μm long and 8 to 90 μm thick, with some up to several milli-
meters in length were obtained by slow decomposition of the soluble fluoro-complex
of zirconium in the presence of phosphoric acid.[50]

5. Surface Titrations

Larger ions such as Cs^+ and NH_4^+ are known not to exchange with α-ZrP in acid
solution.[4,51] However, when solutions of these ions are added to α-ZrP, the pH decreases. This was ascribed to the displacement of surface protons and a rough correlation between surface area and pH lowering was demonstrated.[52] Operating on this
assumption Clearfield and Djuric[53] exhaustively treated zirconium phosphates of suc-
cessively decreasing crystallinity with NH_4Cl until no further change in pH was ob-

Table 3

THE SURFACE AREAS AND SURFACE PROTON
CONTENTS OF α-ZIRCONIUM PHOSPHATES
POSSESSING DIFFERENT CRYSTALLINITIES

α-ZrP Sample	Total NH_4^+ uptake (meq/g)	Surface area (M^2/g)	
		NH_4^+ Exchange	B.E.T.
2.5:48	0.498	72	90
3.5:48	0.440	64	—
4.5:48	0.180	26	34.6
6:48	0.135	20	—
9:48	0.054	7.8	7.8
12:50	0.038	5.5	—
12·100	0.022	3.2	—
12:336	0.021	3.0	1.8

served. The liberated protons were then either titrated or calculated from the pH changes and volumes of solution used. Since each proton (or P—OH group) occupies 23.99 $Å^2$, the surface area could be calculated from the number of protons liberated. The results are shown in Table 3. It is seen that there is a good correlation between surface areas measured by the B.E.T. gas adsorption method and surface titrations. Thus, it is possible to relate the surface area to the degree of crystallinity as shown in Table 3. Therefore, by proper control of the refluxing procedure surface areas of 100 M^2/g and greater may be obtainable. These high surface areas greatly affect the ion exchange behavior, conductivity, and catalytic properties of the exchangers as will be described in succeeding sections.

6. Ion Exchange Characterization

We have already mentioned that the degree of crystallinity of α-ZrP strongly influences its ion exchange behavior. It is thus possible to obtain a measure of the degree of crystallinity of a particular exchanger by carrying out a sodium ion titration with it. The titration curves are shown in Figures 3 and 8.[10,19] These curves were obtained using 0.1 N NaCl as supporting electrolyte. Other pH values would result if the concentration of electrolyte were altered. It is seen that each increase in acid concentration or reflux time is reflected in the curves. In the fully crystalline sample, which would be 12:500 (see below) or crystals slowly precipitated from HF, the plateaus in the titration curve are perfectly flat. Along the first plateau the reaction is[20]

$$Zr(HPO_4)_2 \cdot H_2O(7.6\ Å) + Na^+ \longrightarrow ZrNaH(PO_4)_2 \cdot 5H_2O(11.8\ Å) + H^+ \qquad (1)$$

Sodium hydroxide is required to neutralize the protons and allow the reaction to go to completion. There are three phases present along the plateau; α-ZrP, the half-exchanged phase, and the aqueous solution. Three components are necessary to describe the system; the sodium ion and hydrogen ion concentration of the solution and the total amount of exchanger. Thus, according to the phase rule the system is invariant at constant temperature and pressure and the titration curves should have a zero slope.[55] The second plateau also has a zero slope as the reaction is

$$ZrHNa(PO_4)_2 \cdot 5H_2O + Na^+ \rightleftharpoons Zr(NaPO_4)_2 \cdot 3H_2O(9.8\ Å) + H^+ \qquad (2)$$

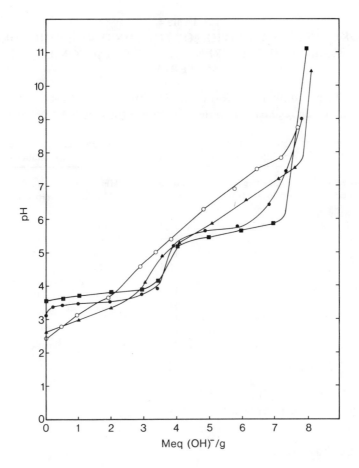

FIGURE 8. Potentiometric titration curves of α-ZrP of low and intermediate crystallinities. Titrant: 0.1 M NaOH + 0.1 M NaCl; sample designations are 0.8:48-○; 2.5:48-▲, 4.5:48-●, 12:48-■. (From Clearfield, A., Oskarsson, Å., and Oskarsson, C., *Ion Exch. Membr.*, 1, 9, 1972. With permission.)

However, all the other titration curves exhibit a positive slope indicating that the restriction on zero degrees of freedom is removed. X-ray examination of the solids indeed shows that partial solid solution occurs with the composition range increasing with decreasing crystallinity. Thus, the degree of order in the solid is reflected in the extent of solid solution formation and hence the titration curve.

It should also be noted that the back titration curves show deviations from reversibility at low sodium contents. This is due to the formation of a phase of composition $Zr(HPO_4)_2 \cdot 6H_2O$, which has been termed θ-ZrP.[9,20,56] The exact water content of this phase is still in doubt but is close to 6. However, only under special circumstances is 100% of θ-ZrP obtained. Rather a mixture of α-ZrP and θ-ZrP are more likely as is shown in Table 4.[57] With decreasing crystallinity of the exchanger the amount of θ-ZrP increases relative to α-ZrP becoming 100% with sample 10:100. At still lower crystallinities α-ZrP is no longer obtained but now a mixture of θ-ZrP and a phase having an interlayer spacing of 11.5 Å are observed. This latter phase is similar to that obtained when zirconium phosphate has a very low crystallinity.[4,10,57] With samples of the highest crystallinity the titration curve is reversible[41] and 100% of the sodium free phase is α-ZrP.[57] Thus, careful analysis of the phase mixture obtained in the back-titration of the half-exchanged sodium ion phase can serve as a sensitive measurement of the crystallinity of the exchanger.

Table 4
APPROXIMATE COMPOSITION OF THE MIXTURE OF DIHYDROGEN PHASES OBTAINED BY DIFFERENT STARTING ZIRCONIUM PHOSPHATE MATERIALS

Conditions: 0.5 g of dihydrogen form titrated with 0.1 N(NaCl + NaOH) to pH 5-6 and then regenerated to the dihydrogen form with 0.1 N HCl

Starting zirconium phosphate material	First interlayer distance (Å) of the:		Approximate phase composition after regeneration (%)		
	Starting dihydrogen form	Monosodium form	HH·H$_2$O (7.6 Å)	θ-ZP (10.4 Å)	ZP(11.5 Å)
$\overline{HH}$·H$_2$O by d.p. method					
Slow ppt.	7.6	11.8	100	0	0
Normal ppt.	7.6	11.8	95	5	0
Fast ppt.	7.6	11.8	78	22	0
ZP (12:466)	7.6	11.8	26	74	0
ZP (12:100)	7.6	11.8	25	75	0
ZP (10:100)	7.6	11.8	0	100	0
ZP (12:48)	7.6	11.8	0	95	5
ZP (10:48)	7.6	11.8	0	71	29
ZP (7:48)	7.6	11.8	0	72	28
ZP (4.5:48)	7.6	11.7, 11.5, 10.0	0	40	60
ZP (2.5:48)	10.6^a, 7.7	10.5	0	30	70
ZP (1.2:48)	11.6	—	0	0	100
ZP (1.0:48)	11.6	—	0	0	100
ZP (0.5:48)	12.6 (Very broad)	—	0	0	100 (Very broad)

^{a} Peak having the highest intensity.

IV. ION EXCHANGE PROPERTIES

A. Amorphous Zirconium Phosphate

A great variety of ion exchange studies and ion separations have been carried out with amorphous zirconium phosphate.[1,2,9,11] Isotherms, from which thermodynamic data were derived, were also determined. However, many of these studies suffer from the fact that the gels used were poorly characterized and/or the correct exchange capacity was not employed.[9,58-63] In order to obtain thermodynamically meaningful results the gel has to be well characterized and the preparative method standardized. Therefore, Clearfield and his co-workers chose to reflux a precipitated gel for 48 hr in 0.5 M H$_3$PO$_4$ (0.5:48). Such samples exhibited no inflection points in their titration curves and only broad, indistinct X-ray reflections.[10,64-67] In these respects they resembled the unrefluxed gels but they were more resistant to hydrolysis and their behavior was more reproducible than the gels. In spite of these precautions there was about a 15% variation in exchange behavior for the same cation exhibited by four different batches of 0.5:48. Therefore, for comparison purposes all measurements for the alkali metal cations were carried out on one and the same batch. The results, plotted as log K_c versus $\bar{X}_M$, are shown in Figure 9.[68]

It is seen from the data in Figure 9 that only about 90% maximum cation loading is achieved. At higher loads hydrolysis becomes severe. However, this cation uptake is sufficient to show all the selectivity sequences. These are listed in Table 5 together with the sequences predicted by Eisenman's theory.[69] The only discrepancies are found in the omission of sequences II and III and a reversed order where sequence VIII is pre-

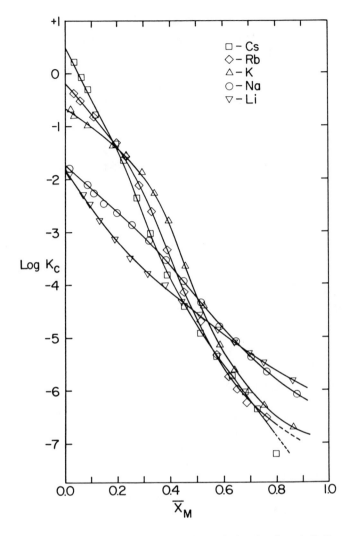

FIGURE 9.   log Kc as a function of the equivalent fraction of alkali
metal cation in the solid for exchanger 0.5:48. (From Kullberg, L. and
Clearfield, A., *J. Phys. Chem.*, 85, 1578, 1981. With permission.)

dicted. Figure 9 shows that the Cs^+, Rb^+, and K^+ exchange isotherms all cross each
other at the same loading. Consequently, sequences II and III cannot be distinguished.
It is noteworthy that Eisenman[69] also found the curves for these ions to intersect at
about the same anionic field strength. Thus, he gave two possible sequences for II and
III. For sequence VIII the data show a reversal of the Rb^+-Li^+ curves before the reversal
of the K^+-Na^+ curves, which is in contrast to Eisenman's prediction. All of these discrepancies are within the error limits of the experimental data. Thus, it can be stated
that amorphous zirconium phosphate exhibits low field strength characteristics at low
load, which gradually changes to high field strength at high loads. This can be ration-
alized by remembering that the interlayer distance in amorphous zirconium phosphate
is large[10,57] and the ions taken up initially are far from the fixed negative sites. The
interlayer spacing reaches a maximum at $X_M \cong 0.07$ and then steadily declines with
loading.[10] Thus, the ions are brought closer and closer to the negative sites with consequent steady increase in field strength.

Table 5
SELECTIVITY SEQUENCES AND CORRESPONDING ION LOAD RANGES FOR ALKALI METAL ION EXCHANGE ON ZrP 0.5:48

Loading range	Selectivity sequence observed	Eisenman sequence
$\bar{X}_M < 0.19$	Cs > Rb > K > Na > Li	I
$0.19 < \bar{X}_M < 0.34$	K > Rb > Cs > Na > Li	IV
$0.34 < \bar{X}_M < 0.42$	K > Rb > Na > Cs > Li	V
$0.42 < \bar{X}_M < 0.44$	K > Na > Rb > Cs > Li	VI
$0.44 < \bar{X}_M < 0.48$	K > Na > Rb > Li > Cs	VII
$0.48 < \bar{X}_M < 0.52$	K > Na > Li > Rb > Cs	—
$0.52 < \bar{X}_M < 0.54$	Na > K > Li > Rb > Cs	IX
$0.54 < \bar{X}_M < 0.62$	Na > Li > K > Rb > Cs	X
$\bar{X}_M > 0.62$	Li > Na > K > Rb > Cs	XI

The distribution of Na$^+$, K$^+$, and Cs$^+$ on amorphous ZrP (0.5:48) from a mixed solution of these ions was also determined.[68] It was demonstrated that the uptake of these ions, as a function of loading, followed the same sequences predicted by Eisenman's theory. In fact the load ranges for each sequence agreed closely with those obtained from the study of binary systems.

1. Enthalpy and Entropy Changes

Figure 10 shows the standard heats of exchange, ΔH_x, as a function of loading for alkali metal ion exchange on amorphous ZrP(0.5:48).[66-68,70,75] Enthalpy changes for the exchange reactions arise from three main sources, namely, (1) the heat consumed in breaking the PO—H covalent bonds, (2) the heat released in the formation of bonds to the incoming cations, and (3) the enthalpy changes accompanying hydration and dehydration of the exchanging ions.

The observed heat changes can be explained on the basis that amorphous ZrP contains cavities of different sizes.[71] Thus, the exchange sites are not energetically equivalent. The incoming ions would occupy the most favorable sites initially, i.e., the largest cavities, because they require the least amount of dehydration of the ions to occur. For the hydrated ions the size order is Li$^+$ > Na$^+$ > K$^+$ > Rb$^+$ > Cs$^+$. The heat released for the bonding of an alkali ion in the exchanger will depend upon the amount of water the ion must give up in order to accommodate itself to the cavity size. This should be in the same order as the hydrated ionic radii. Since the enthalpy changes accompanying O—H bond breaking and hydration of the proton remain relatively constant throughout the exchange reaction, we expect initially the most exothermic effect with Cs$^+$ and the least exothermic reaction with Li$^+$. One would expect then that the size of the hydrated ions filling the cavities at first would be roughly the same no matter what the size of the original unhydrated cation. That is, the size of the species bound in the exchanger is determined by the cavity size. As this decreases the amounts of water shed by each ion should be about the same (after the initial larger loss of the more highly hydrated ones). Thus, the reactions should become progressively more endothermic and the slopes of the heat curves should be about the same. This is what is actually observed as seen in Figure 11.[68]

Differential entropies of exchange, $\Delta \bar{S}_x$, were obtained from the relation

$$\Delta \bar{G}_x = \Delta \bar{H}_x - T \Delta \bar{S}_x \tag{3}$$

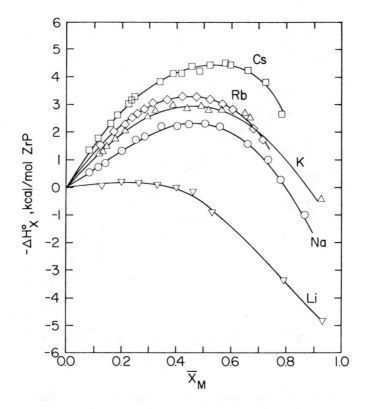

FIGURE 10. Standard heats of partial exchange as a function of alkali metal cation loading for exchanger 0.5:48. (From Kullberg, L. and Clearfield, A., *J. Phys. Chem.*, 85, 1578, 1981. With permission.)

The entropy contributions all disfavor the replacement of a hydrogen ion by an alkali metal cation. A large part of the observed entropy values is due to the entropy differences of the hydrated ions. Thus, it is more instructive to consider $\Delta \bar{S}_{ex}$ values from Equation 4

$$\Delta \bar{S}_{ex} = \Delta \bar{S}_x - (S_H^{\circ}{}^+ - S_M^{\circ}{}^+) \tag{4}$$

where the term in parenthesis is the difference in the entropies of the exchanging ions. Figure 12 shows $\Delta \bar{S}_{ex}$ as a function of loading.

The degrees of freedom possessed by water are lower in the exchanger phase than in the solution phase. Thus, sorption of water must result in a decrease of entropy while release of water results in an entropy increase. The entropy decrease on freezing of a mol of water at 25°C, 6.1 eu,[72] may be used as an estimate for the binding of water in the exchanger.

According to our model the exchange initially takes place in the largest cavities so that the alkali ions can enter more or less fully hydrated. The cavities are initially filled with (or the space between layers contains) water. Thus, at low loads the exchange is accompanied by a fixing of water in the exchanger. This amounts to about 1 to 1.5 mol for K^+, Rb^+, and Cs^+ and 2 mol of water for the smaller, more hydrated, ions. As exchange proceeds and smaller cavities are occupied the more loosely held water by the larger cations is squeezed out and a progressive increase in entropy occurs. In contrast the small ions, which bind their water strongly, continue to fix more wter in the exchanger. This is accompanied by an increase in the interlayer spacing. For Na^+

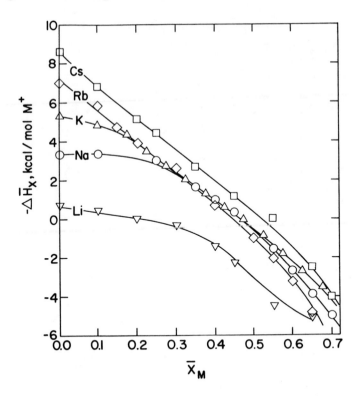

FIGURE 11.   Differential heats of exchange as a function of alkali metal cation loading for exchanger 0.5:48. (From Kullberg, L. and Clearfield, A., *J. Phys. Chem.*, 85, 1578, 1981. With permission.)

X-ray patterns showed an increase from 11.2 Å at zero load to 12.0 Å to 12.6 Å at $\bar{X}_{Na}$ = 0.1 to 0.25 and a decline in interlayer spacing thereafter. Beyond 50% of exchange two cations must approach each other closely as they occupy the same cavity. Thus, all excess water is eliminated with consequent increase in entropy. However, part of this entropy increase must be due to lattice disorder as evidenced by the greater release of phosphate to the solution.[68]

B. Crystalline α-Zirconium Phosphate
1. Exchange of Alkali Metal Cations
a. Thermodynamics of Exchange
Figure 13 shows the titration curves for alkali metal ion — hydrogen ion exchange on crystalline α-ZrP.[55,64-67,73] All the data except that for Cs$^+$-H$^+$ were obtained with 12:336. Cesium ion exchange with this sample gave data of low reproducibility.[64] Therefore, the cesium ion data were obtained for sample 4.5:48. Alberti and Costantino[6,7] have published similar curves based on α-ZrP crystals precipitated from HF. The exchanger selectivity greatly favors hydrogen ion over the alkali metal cations. Thus, the exchange reactions must be carried out by additions of base. Each curve was obtained at constant alkali metal ion concentration of 0.1 *M*. Along each plateau the solution composition is constant and one phase is being converted into another. There is some disagreement on the exact number and composition of phases formed. This information is summarized in Table 6. The differences noted may well be due to the greater crystallinity of the HF-precipitated material. For example, in the case of Cs$^+$ uptake a solid solution of the cation in α-ZrP forms initially. The limit of solubility appeared to be about the same in the two exchangers. However, with the less crystalline exchanger a half-exchanged phase was not obtained. Rather a phase with interlayer

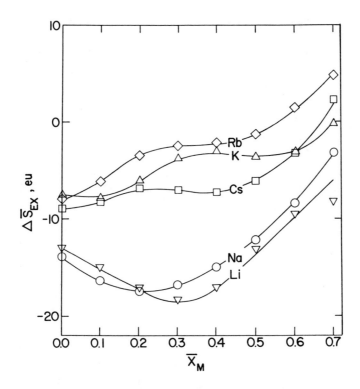

FIGURE 12. Exchanger phase entropy changes, $\overline{\Delta S}_{ex}$, for M^+-H^+ exchange at different alkali metal ion loadings. (From Kullberg, L. and Clearfield, A., *J. Phys. Chem.*, 85, 1578, 1981. With permission.)

spacing of 11.0 Å was observed to form and this interlayer spacing increased continuously with Cs^+ uptake to 11.6 Å at 50% of exchange and thereafter remained constant. Thus, it would appear that a second solid solution with a broad composition range is formed. This is confirmed by the ΔH_x curve for Cs^+ uptake (see Figure 14)[64] which shows a single straight line up to 75% of exchange. The straight line indicates a constant amount of heat released per unit of Cs^+ uptake regardless of whether the Cs^+ is taken into the 7.6 Å phase or the 11.6 Å phase. Only at 75% of loading does one observe a sharp break indicating a phase change. Thus, the half-exchanged phase observed by Alberti et al.[74] may be peculiar only to fully (100%) crystalline α-ZrP.

As will be shown when discussing semicrystalline α-ZrP, solid solutions are a feature of the exchange process. Thus, with 4.5:48 a single solid solution of Li^+ composition ranging from 50 to 80% of exchange was observed. Only with the more crystalline exchanger are three distinct Li^+-containing phases obtained as indicated in Table 6. However, even with 12:336, a fairly broad solid solution of composition $ZrLi_{1.33-1.5}$ $H_{0.67-0.5}(PO_4)_2 \cdot 4H_2O$ was found to exist.[65]

Figure 14 presents the standard heats, ΔH_x, as a function of metal ion loadings.[73] The linear parts of the heat functions show clearly that the reactions proceed in distinct and separate steps except as already noted for the initial solid solution regions for Cs^+ and Rb^+ and to a lesser extent for K^+ and Li^+.

Exchange reactions on crystalline α-ZrP are, as previously mentioned, generally not reversible (except for Na^+ exchange on highly crystalline α-ZrP). However, one can think of the ion exchange reactions as being ideally

$$\overline{RH} + M^+(aq) \rightleftharpoons \overline{RM} + H^+(aq) + nH_2O \qquad (5)$$

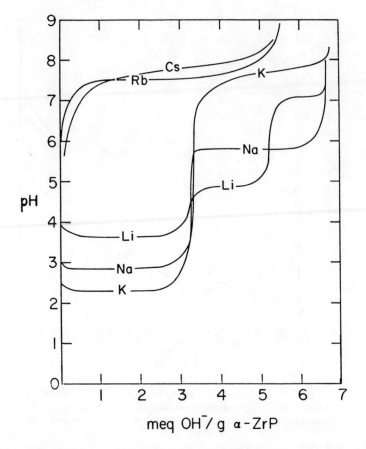

FIGURE 13.   Variation of pH with amount of alkali metal hydroxide added for M^+-H^+ exchange on α-ZrP, 4.5:48 for Cs^+ and 12:336 for the other ions. (From Kullberg, L. and Clearfield, A., *J. Phys. Chem.*, 85, 1585, 1981. With permission.)

The thermodynamic equilibrium constant for this reaction is given by

$$K_{M/H} = \frac{\overline{a}_M \cdot a_{H^+} \cdot a_W^n}{\overline{a}_H \cdot a_{M^+}} \qquad (6)$$

where the barred quantities represent activities in the solid phase and the unbarred ones of ions in the aqueous phase. Along a plateau one solid of constant composition is converted into another of constant composition. If we choose as the standard reference state an activity of 1 for the pure solids, then

$$K_{M/H} = \frac{a_{H^+} \cdot a_W^n}{\overline{a}_{M^+}} \qquad (7)$$

The water activity is close to one at $\mu = 0.1$. Thus, the ratios of the aqueous ion activities determines the value of $K_{M/H}$[55] (however, see Section IV.E).

Free energies were calculated as

$$\Delta G^\circ = -RT \ln K_{M/H} \qquad (8)$$

Table 6
SOLID PHASES OBTAINED BY ALKALI METAL ION EXCHANGE
OF α-ZrP

Phases and interlayer spacings (Å)

System	Clearfield	d_{002}	Alberti	d_{002}
$H^+ - Li$	$ZrHLi(PO_4)_2 \cdot 4H_2O$	10.3	$ZrHLi(PO_4)_2 \cdot 4H_2O$	10.1
	$ZrH_{0.34}Li_{1.66}(PO_4)_2 \cdot 4H_2O$	10.2	$ZrH_{0.5}Li_{1.5}(PO_4)_2 \cdot 4H_2O$	10.1
	$Zr(LiPO_4)_2 \cdot 4H_2O$	10.2	$Zr(LiPO_4)_2 \cdot 4H_2O$	10.0
$H^+ - Na^+$	$ZrHNa(PO_4)_2 \cdot 5H_2O$	11.8	$ZrHNa(PO_4)_2 \cdot 5H_2O$	11.8
	$Zr(NaPO_4)_2 \cdot 3H_2O$	9.8	$Zr(NaPO_4)_2 \cdot 3H_2O$	9.9
$H^+ - K^+$	$ZrHK(PO_4)_2 \cdot H_2O$	8.0	$ZrHK(PO_4)_2 \cdot H_2O$	8.0
	$Zr(KPO_4)_2 \cdot 3H_2O$	10.8	$Zr(KPO_4)_2 \cdot 3H_2O$	10.8
$H^+ - Rb^+$	$ZrH_{1.8}Rb_{0.2}(PO_4)_2 \cdot nH_2O^a$	7.6	$ZrH_{1.5}Rb_{0.5}(PO_4)_2 \cdot 0.5H_2O^a$	7.6
	$ZrH_{0.5}Rb_{1.5}(PO_4)_2 \cdot 3H_2O$	10.6	$ZrH_{0.5}Rb_{1.5}(PO_4)_2 \cdot 2H_2O$	10.6
			$Zr(RbPO_4)_2 \cdot H_2O$	9.2
$H^+ - Cs^+$	$ZrH_{1.8}Cs_{0.2}(PO_4)_2 \cdot nH_2O^a$	7.6	$ZrH_{1.5}Cs_{0.5}(PO_4)_2 \cdot 0.5H_2O^a$	7.6
	$ZrH_{0.5}Cs_{1.5}(PO_4)_2 \cdot 4H_2O^a$	11.6	$ZrHCs(PO_4)_2 \cdot 2H_2O$	11.3
			$ZrH_{0.5}Cs_{1.5}(PO_4)_2 \cdot 3H_2O$	11.7
			$Zr(CsPO_4)_2 \cdot 6H_2O$	14.2

^{a} Solid solution. Composition given is that near the limit of cation solubility.

The enthalpy changes for the same reactions were obtained from the slopes of the ΔH_x° curves divided by a factor of 2. This was necessary because the ΔH_x° values are expressed in kcal per mol of exchanger while the thermodynamic parameters of Reaction 5 are given in kcal per mol of exchanged alkali metal. Finally, the standard entropies of exchange were calculated from the relation

$$\Delta G^\circ = \Delta H^\circ - T\Delta S^\circ \qquad (9)$$

The thermodynamic quantities are given in Table 7.[73] Values of ΔS_{ex}° are also included in the table along with the change in number of moles of water, Δn_{H2O}, in the exchanger accompanying the exchange reaction.

Figure 15 is a plot of ΔS_{ex}° vs. Δ_{H_2O}. The data fit very well to two straight lines, the top one for exchange of the first hydrogen ion and the lower one for exchange of the second one as listed in Table 7. The two curves have identical slopes of $\geqslant 6.8$ eu/mol H_2O, which shows that the entropy of the exchanger decreases by 6.8 eu for each mol of water taken up. This agrees well with the entropy decrease accompanying the freezing of water. Since the upper curve has a value of zero at $\Delta \bar{n}_{H_2O} = 0$, the entropy of a half-exchanged phase is very much the same as that of the α-ZrP phase provided the two phases have the same water content. The bottom straight line is separated from the upper one by -7.2 eu. This means that the high cation-containing phases have lower entropies by this amount than the half-exchanged phase at the same water content and probably reflects restrictions due to closer packing of the ions in the high cation-containing phases.

The ΔS_{ex}° values for Rb^+ and Cs^+ suggest that 2 and 3 moles of H_2O, respectively are transferred during exchange to form the 75%-exchanged phases. Thus, these phases should contain 3 and 4 mol of water, respectively, rather than the 2 and 3 mol reported by Alberti et al.[74] To clarify this discrepancy we examined the interlayer distances in different alkali metal ion exchanged α-ZrP phases as determined in our own work and that of Alberti.[7] The interlayer distance was found to be a function of the size of the cations in the phase and its water content. The effect of the water content can be

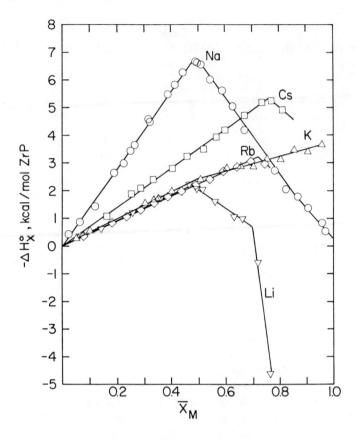

FIGURE 14.   Standard heats of partial exchange as a function of alkali metal ion loading. Exchangers same as for Figure 13. (From Kullberg, L. and Clearfield, A., *J. Phys. Chem.*, 85, 1585, 1981. With permission.)

obtained by a simple subtraction of the ionic diameters of the ions present in the phase as shown in Equation 10.[73]

$$d_{corr} = d_{int} - \tfrac{1}{2}(n_1 d_{M_1} + n_2 d_{M_2}) \tag{10}$$

d_{int} is the interlayer spacing, n_1 and n_2 are the number of moles of the two cations in the exchanger phase, and d_{M_1} and d_{M_2} are their ionic diameters. For hydrogen a diameter of 0.7 Å was chosen. Figure 16 shows that d_{corr} is a straight line function of the water content, which can be represented by the relation (all terms are in Å)

$$d_{corr} = 0.95 n H_2 O + 5.25 \tag{11}$$

This means that the interlayer distance increases by 0.95 Å for each added mol of water taken up. Thus,

$$d_{int} = 0.95 n H_2 O + 5.25 + \tfrac{1}{2}(n_1 d_{M_1} + n_2 d_{M_2}) \tag{12}$$

The interlayer spacings for the rubidium and cesium ion phases fall on the straight line only if n_{H_2O} is 3 and 4, respectively.

b. Ion Exchange Mechanism
The principal feature of the α-ZrP layered structure is the fact that the layers arrange

Table 7

STANDARD THERMODYNAMIC QUANTITIES OF EXCHANGE
FOR CRYSTALLINE α-ZrP

Reaction[a]	$\Delta G°$ (kcal/mol)	$-\Delta H°$ (kcal/mol)	$T\Delta S°$ (kcal/mol)	$\Delta S°_{ex}$ (eu)	Δn_{H_2O}
$\overline{HH} \rightarrow \overline{LiH}$	3.5	2.3	−5.8	−21.9	3
$\overline{HH} \rightarrow \overline{NaH}$	2.4	6.9	−9.3	−26.1	4
$\overline{HH} \rightarrow \overline{KH}$	1.6	2.5	−4.1	−0.2	0
$\overline{HH} \rightarrow \overline{Rb_{1.5}H_{0.5}}$	8.8	2.2	−11.0	−20.4	
$\overline{HH} \rightarrow \overline{Cs_{1.5}H_{0.5}}$	9.1	3.4	−12.5	−24.7	
$\overline{LiH} \rightarrow$ $\overline{Li_{1.33}H_{0.67}}$	5.2	−3.6	−1.6	−7.8	0
$\overline{NaH} \rightarrow \overline{NaNa}$	6.4	−7.0	0.6	−7.1	−2
$\overline{KH} \rightarrow \overline{KK}$	9.0	1.2	−10.2	−20.6	2

[a] $\overline{HH}$ means $Zr(HPO_4)_2 \cdot H_2O$ and $\overline{LiH}$ is $ZrLiH(PO_4)_2 \cdot 4H_2O$, etc. as listed in Table 6 and 5.

themselves in such a way as to create cavities between the layers. The largest entrance-ways into the cavities would allow a spherical cation of 2.61 Å diameter to diffuse unobstructed into the cavities.[14,20] This should allow Li[+], Na[+], and K[+] to enter, if un-hydrated, but exclude Rb[+] and Cs[+]. Figure 13 indeed shows that the three smaller ions exchange in acid solution but not the larger two. This suggests that unhydrated, or for small cations, partially hydrated cations are exchanged in acid solution and that expansion of the layers occurs when base is added.[55,73] The mechanism of exchange, without base added, is therefore thought to occur in the following way. At the surface of the crystal the hydrated cation gives up most of its water and diffuses into the cavity as either an unhydrated or partially hydrated species. The cation goes into solid solution, i.e., is statistically distributed throughout the exchanger, and no phase change occurs. The pH observed at equilibrium is determined by the amount of cation present as solid solution. Thus, a cation with a high solubility in the α-ZrP phase will give a titration curve exhibiting a low pH for the first plateau.

Exchange of large cations on α-ZrP is possible if base is added. Under the influence of the hydroxide ions the layers presumably move apart.[18] Hydroxide ion can diffuse to the exchange sites and there neutralize the protons. The accumulating negative charge would then force the layers apart so that hydrated ions may enter. This process continues until all or almost all of the hydroxide is consumed. Parallel to this process a second and presumably much slower exchange process also takes place. Here, metal ions present as part of the supporting electrolyte diffuse into the cavities of the α-ZrP phase and exchange with hydrogen ions. Thus, a solid solution is formed in the same manner as described above when no base was added. More cations will exchange than hydroxide neutralized and this effect should be greatest with K[+]. Indeed it has been observed that more K[+] is taken up than hydroxide neutralized in the first 50% of exchange.[75] Under such circumstances the final solution will be acidic.

If the amount of base added is such that the pH remains high for a period of time, the phase that forms may have a high metal content, i.e., be greater than a half-exchanged phase. Such phases are stable at relatively high pH. As the pH falls the high-metal-ion-containing phase reverts to a phase stable in acid solution, e.g., a half-exchanged phase. Indeed such a conversion has been observed in the K[+]−H[+] system.[76] When the base is added slowly so that the pH does not rise above 5, then only the acid stable form is observed.

Rubidium and cesium ions cannot enter the cavities of α-ZrP due to their large size. Thus, no drop in pH accompanies addition of Rb[+] or Cs[+] as neutral electrolyte solu-

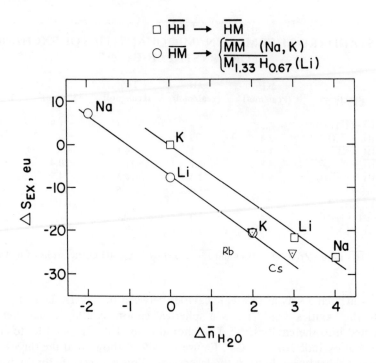

FIGURE 15.   Plot of $\overline{\Delta S}_{ex}$ as a function of the water transferred Δn_{H2O}, in the exchange reaction. Squares refer to the formation of half-exchanged phases from HH and circles to reactions $\overline{HM} \rightarrow \overline{MM}$ (M = Na$^+$ or K$^+$), HM $\rightarrow \overline{H0.5M_{1.5}}$ (M = Rb$^+$ or Cs$^+$) and $\overline{HM} \rightarrow \overline{H_{0.67}M_{1.33}}$ (M = Li$^+$).[73] (From Kullberg, L. and Clearfield, A., *J. Phys. Chem.*, in press. With permission.)

tions to the exchanger. However, when base is added the pH rises sufficiently to form the 75%-exchanged phase but not the fully exchanged phase. The pH never drops below 5 during the equilibration period. Thus, the half-exchanged phase does not form but rather a solid solution. That is, a small portion of each crystal must form the crystalline $\overline{M_{1.5}H_{0.5}}$ phase* but as the pH falls below the value at which this phase is stable, the M$^+$ ions diffuse throughout the crystal forming a solid solution. When the solubility limit of the cations is reached, the pH is now sufficient for the 75%-exchanged phase to be stable.

Along the plateaus of the titration curves, two phases with different interlayer spacings coexist. Indirect evidence has been presented above to indicate that each of the two phases are present in a single crystal. For example, when a sample of α-ZrP exchanged to the 25% level with Na$^+$ was dried in a desiccator for long periods of time a rearrangement of the Na$^+$ occurred. Some Na$^+$ from the half-exchanged phase converted some of the α-ZrP to ZrNa$_{0.2}$H$_{1.8}$(PO$_4$)$_2$ forming in turn ZrNa$_{0.8}$H$_{1.2}$(PO$_4$)$_2$.[23] It is unlikely that Na$^+$ from one crystal migrated to another. Rather a rearrangement of Na$^+$ in the cavities of a single crystal must have taken place.

The idea of two coexisting phases present in a single crystal means that the crystal has two different interlayer distances.[7] Since ion exchange begins at the surface of the crystal, it may be expected that the new phase also forms in the outer parts of the crystal. The phase boundary then always moves from the external toward the center of the crystal. This idea will be used later to explain certain phenomena in ternary cation exchange systems and exchange in salt forms of α-ZrP.

---

*   For α-ZrP crystals it is convenient to represent the phases as $\overline{HH} \cdot H_2O$ for α-ZrP, $\overline{MH} \cdot nH_2O$ for half-exchanged phases, etc.[7]

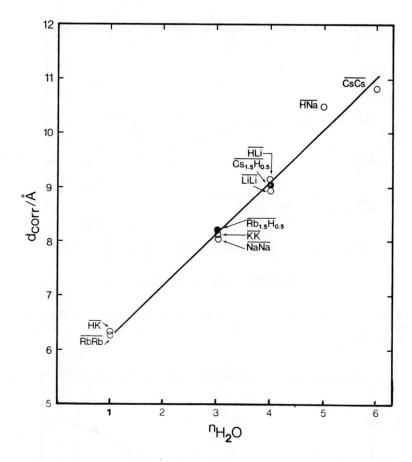

FIGURE 16. The corrected interlayer distance, d_{corr}, as a function of moles of water, n_{H_2O}, in the crystalline exchanged phase of α-ZrP. (From Kullberg, L. and Clearfield, A., *J. Phys. Chem.*, 15, 1585, 1981. With permission.)

The titration curves for the alkali metal cations suggest that the solubility of these ions in α-ZrP is in the order $K^+ > Na^+ > Li^+$. This decrease is in the same order as the increase in heat of hydration of these ions. Thus, the extent of exchange between a cation and hydrogen ions in α-ZrP depends upon both the size of the cation and its heat of hydration. Hence the low uptake of bi- and trivalent metal ions by α-ZrP is, in most cases, due to the high heats of hydration of the ions rather than that they are too large to enter the cavities.

Alkali metal ion exchange on crystalline α-ZrP shows that the exchange behavior towards each ion is unique and does not depend upon the acidity of the protons. Rather the phases formed depend upon the solution composition and upon the way in which the exchanger can accommodate different cations in the cavities. Furthermore, it will be shown in Section IV.B.1.c below that data obtained from binary exchange systems, as a rule cannot be used in predicting the relative metal ion uptake in polynary systems. Exchange on α-ZrP is, therefore, a much more complicated process than exchange on amorphous ZrP. For the latter solid, the ion exchange reactions are reversible and the relative metal ion uptake from a mixture of ions can be predicted from the results of the binary systems. Smoothly curved isotherms and enthalpy functions are observed for amorphous ZrP supporting the view that the exchange sites are of continuously varying size. In contrast exchange on crystalline α-ZrP gives rectilinear isotherms and enthalpy curves consisting of linear parts with different slopes which reflect phase tran-

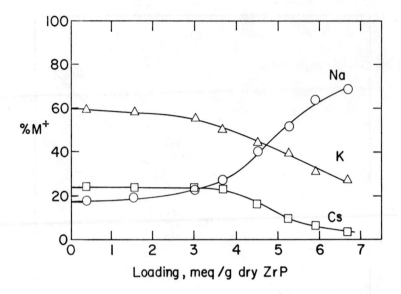

FIGURE 17.   Distribution of Na$^+$, K$^+$, and Cs$^+$ on crystalline α-ZrP (12:336) at different metal loadings. (From Kullberg, L. and Clearfield, A., *J. Phys. Chem.*, 15, 1585, 1981. With permission.)

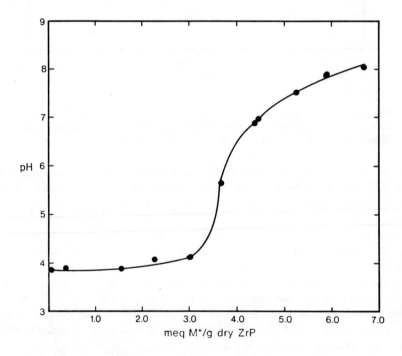

FIGURE 18.   Potentiometric titration curve (pH versus total metal ion loading) for Na$^+$-K$^+$-Cs$^+$-H$^+$ exchange on crystalline α-ZrP(12:336). (From Kullberg, L. and Clearfield, A., *J. Phys. Chem.*, 15, 1585, 1981. With permission.)

sitions occurring upon exchange and also the uniformity of the exchange sites within each phase.

c. Multiple Ion Systems

In order to obtain information on the ion exchange behavior of solutions containing more than one univalent cation Kullberg and Clearfield[73] examined the uptake by α-ZrP from a mixture of Na$^+$, K$^+$, and Cs$^+$ chlorides.[73] The ions were present in equal amounts at ionic strength, $\mu = 0.2$ and 25°C. The hydroxide added also consisted of an equimolar solution of the ions. The distribution of ions on the exchanger at different loadings is shown in Figure 17 and the titration curve in Figure 18. Three solid phases were present throughout the exchange. During the first half of exchange the phases were α-ZrP, the half-exchanged K$^+$ phase ($\overline{KH} \cdot H_2O$), and a 9.1 Å phase, most likely a sodium-cesium-containing phase. In the second half of exchange the phases were $\overline{KH} \cdot H_2O$, the 9.1 Å phase, and the fully exchanged sodium phase ($\overline{NaNa} \cdot 5H_2O$).

The pH at which the first plateau in the titration curve is observed, 3.9, is considerably higher than those observed for the K$^+$–H$^+$ and Na$^+$–H$^+$ systems. In a study of Na$^+$–K$^+$–H$^+$ exchange on α-ZrP it was found that the uptake of K$^+$ closely followed what was predicted from the results of the K$^+$–H$^+$ binary system.[77] This suggests that the presence of Cs$^+$ inhibits the uptake of K$^+$. A most likely cause is the sorption of Cs$^+$ on the surface of the crystals which decreases the potassium ion activity on the surface of the crystals. This in turn decreases the solubility of K$^+$ in α-ZrP and keeps the pH high. Alberti et al.[78] found that the surface sites on α-ZrP greatly prefer Cs$^+$ to K$^+$ and Na$^+$, a fact which supports the view presented here.

The results with the Na$^+$–K$^+$–Cs$^+$–H$^+$ exchange system show that exchange on the surface of the crystals plays a large part in governing the total exchange process. Moreover, data obtained from binary systems, in some cases, cannot be used in predicting the relative metal ion uptake in multiple ion systems. The general irreversibility of the exchange reactions will also make such predictions invalid.

2. Exchange of Alkaline Earth Cations

Both magnesium and barium ions were found to exchange very slowly or not at all on α-ZrP.[79,80] This is attributed to the very high heat of hydration of magnesium and in the case of Ba^{2+}, its large size. Conversely, unhydrated Ca^{2+} and Sr$^+$ are small enough (Sr^{2+} just barely) to enter the layers through the narrow passageways. The heats of hydration of these ions are apparently sufficiently smaller than that of Mg^{2+} for the water to be removed from the ions by the overall exchange reaction. In both cases a half-exchanged phase is formed by addition of M(OH)$_2$.[81-83] At higher additions of base the pH rises and precipitation of the metal phosphates takes place.[81] However, it is possible to form more highly exchanged products by extremely slow addition of base.[87,84] Thus, the titration curves are in a sense misleading. When 50% cation loading has been achieved, the rate of further cation uptake becomes so slow that macroscopic additions of base cause the pH to rise to where metal phosphates precipitate. The necessary phosphate ion is obtained from solubilization or hydrolysis of the exchanger phosphate groups at the high pH of the medium.

In order to obviate the precipitation of alkali metal phosphates, Clearfield and Hagiwara[85] used metal acetate solutions to exchange alkali metal ions onto α-ZrP.[5] Calcium and strontium ions formed both half and fully exchanged phases but Mg^{2+} and Ba^{2+} only a single phase. The composition of the phases is given in Table 8. It should be noted that the phases exist over a range of compositions and this seems to be a feature of exchange with these cations.[80,81] With alkaline earth acetates at room temperature about half the added cation is taken up rapidly, followed by a slow approach to equilibrium. However, only about 2/3 of the total cation added is exchanged at equilibrium. The process is speeded up enormously by carrying out the exchange at 100°C. Near quantitative uptake of cations occurs at this temperature in a few hours except for Mg^{2+} which still exchanges very slowly.[85] On cooling none of the exchanged cations are re-exchanged but remain fixed in the solid. The pH of the solution, at room temperature, is in the neighborhood of 3. This is higher than the equilibrium pH for

Table 8

COMPOSITION OF ALKALINE EARTH ION PHASES OF α-ZrP

Half-exchanged phase	d_{002}	Fully exchanged phase	d_{002}
—		$ZrMg_{0.75-1}H_{0.5-0}(PO_4)_2 \cdot 4H_2O$	9.64
$ZrCa_{0.5-0.65}H_{1-0.7}(PO_4)_2 \cdot 3H_2O$	9.94	$ZrCa_{0.85-1}H_{0.3-0}(PO_4)_2 \cdot 4H_2O$	9.83
$ZrSr_{0.45-0.55}H_{1.1-0.9}(PO_4)_2 \cdot 3.5H_2O$	10.2	$ZrSr_{0.65-1}H_{0.7-0}(PO_4)_2 \cdot 2.5H_2O$	10.2
		$ZrBa_{0.8-1}H_{0.4-0}(PO_4)_2 \cdot 2H_2O$	—

the 50% phases, but probably lower than that for the 100% phases. Therefore, enough M^{2+} should re-enter the solution to conform to this pH. That is, the equilibrium at 25°C favors the replacement of some M^{2+} by H^+. However, we have seen that exchange of alkali metal cations into the half-exchanged phase is very slow. Similarly, the removal of hydrated cations from the interior of the crystals to the solution on cooling must also be a very slow process. It will be shown in Section IV.B.3 below that M^{2+}, first row transition metals exist as tetrahydrates in the exchanger. Such large ions would be expected to diffuse very slowly at room temperature and thus they remain relatively fixed in the exchanger. This "sitebinding" is expected to pertain to the alkali metal cations also. Upon addition of acid in a back titration procedure, equilibrium is not achieved even in 4 days. Thus, even though the pH falls below 2, not all of the expected M^{2+} ions are exchanged out in this time. An excess of strong acid is required to remove all the cations.[82]

It will be shown in Section IV.C that more facile exchange of the alkaline earth cations as well as other large cations is possible if the interlayer spacing of α-ZrP is first expanded by special methods.

3. Exchange of First Row Transition Metal Ions

The M(II) cations of the first row transition elements from Mn^{2+} to Zn^{2+} all have ionic radii in a narrow range of values (0.7 to 0.9 Å) which are not too different from that of Mg^{2+}. Thus, they bind water strongly and in addition there is a significant contribution due to crystal field stabilization energy. Thus, these cations exchange only with difficulty on α-ZrP. For example, at room temperature only a few tenths of a milliequivalent of Cu^{2+} was exchanged on 12:336. This increased at reflux temperature where slightly more than 2 meq of a total of 7.5 added was exchanged.[86] However, when solutions of acetates were used, near quantitative uptake was observed for Cu^{2+}, Zn^{2+}, Mn^{2+}, and Co^{2+} in the temperature range 75 to 100°C. Even at room temperature high uptakes were possible. However, Ni(II) which has the highest heat of hydration, exchanged to a much lesser degree under the same conditions.

The ions initially form a solid solution which may contain up to 12 to 15% cation. The solid is then converted to a fully exchanged phase but these phases have broad composition ranges being about $ZrCu_{0.85-1}H_{0.4-0}(PO_4)_2 \cdot 4H_2O$ for Cu(II) and even broader for Mn(II).[86] These fully converted forms exhibit UV-visible spectra which indicate octahedral stereochemistry for Mn(II), Co(II), Ni(II), and Cu(II) [tetragonally distorted in the case of Cu(II)].[87] Undoubtedly the water molecules form part of the coordination sphere of the cation and help to fix the cations in the lattice.[82]

4. Ammonium Ion Exchange

The titration curve for both the forward and reverse exchange processes is shown in Figure 19.[88] A distinguishing feature of this exchange is the single plateau at the relatively high pH of 5.7 ($\mu = 0.1$) indicating the formation of a single exchanged phase. Its composition was determined as $Zr(NH_4PO_4)_2 \cdot H_2O$. The initial steeply rising portion of the curve represents a region of solid solution formation. Similar curves were

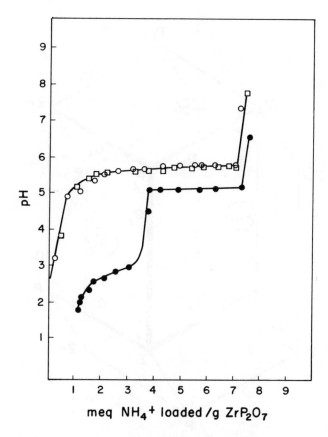

FIGURE 19. Forward and reverse ammonium ion (ammonia) potentiometric titration curves for α-ZrP. Titrant: forward direction, 0.1 NH$_4$OH + 0.1 N NH$_4$Cl for 12:384 -● and 12:190 -□; reverse direction, HCl + NH$_4$Cl at μ = 0.1 for 12:384 -●. (From Clearfield, A. and Hunter, R. A., *J. Inorg. Nucl. Chem.*, 38, 1085, 1976. With permission.)

obtained by other workers.[51,89] In the reverse titration a half-exchanged phase of composition Zr(NH$_4$PO$_4$)(HPO$_4$)·xH$_2$O, where x is 0.5 or less, was obtained.[88,90]

Alberti et al.[51] pointed out that the single plateau at pH = 5.6 must result from intercalation of NH$_3$ rather than exchange of NH$_4^+$. They found that almost no NH$_4^+$ exchanged even when α-ZrP was equilibrated with 5 M NH$_4$Cl. Furthermore, ammonium ion was preferred to Na$^+$ when NH$_4$Cl was equilibrated with ZrNaH(PO$_4$)$_2$·5H$_2$O (see Section IV.C.1.f) and converted it to Zr(NH$_4$PO$_4$)(HPO$_4$)·H$_2$O. Thus, if NH$_4^+$ were being exchanged on α-ZrP, the pH of the plateau should be lower than that of sodium ion. Apparently ammonium ion is not taken up for steric reasons but the smaller NH$_3$ molecule can diffuse into the layers. Ammonia molecules then react with protons to produce ammonium ions with direct formation of Zr(NH$_4$PO$_4$)$_2$·H$_2$O. The half-exchanged phase is formed in the reverse titration because the interlayer spacing of the exchanger is now 9.4 A and H$^+$ can replace NH$_4^+$ in a one for one exchange. The reported formation of Zr(NH$_4$PO$_4$)$_{1.33}$(HPO$_4$)$_{0.61}$·H$_2$O in the forward titration appears unlikely.[91]

The inability of NH$_4^+$ to exchange with α-ZrP does not apply to exchange with surface hydroxyl groups. Thus, surface exchange was used to determine the number of surface protons and from this information the surface area of the exchanger.[53,54]

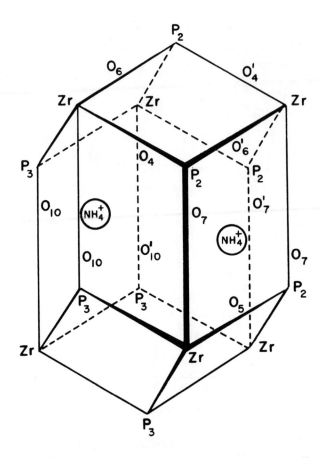

FIGURE 20.   Idealized picture of a cavity formed by two adjacent layers of α-ZrP showing the approximate location of the ammonium ions in $Zr(NH_4PO_4)_2 \cdot H_2O$. A water molecule lies between the ammonium ions. (From Clearfield, A. and Troup, J. M., *J. Phys. Chem.*, 77, 243, 1973. With permission.)

The structure of the diammonium ion phase has been determined.[92] This compound is monoclinic as is the parent α-ZrP but with the interlayer distance expanded to 9.36 Å to accommodate the ions. The integrity of the layers is retained and the ions site themselves in two different locations as shown in Figure 20. One of the ions lies about halfway between and above the oxygen atoms of two P(3)-O(10) groups in the same layer while the other lies halfway between and below two oxygens of the P(2) to O(7) groups in the same layer. Each NH_4^+ has five neighbors, consisting of four oxygens from P—O groups and a water oxygen. The coordination for the first NH_4^+ ion includes the two O(10) atoms and an O(10) and O(7) from an adjacent layer, while for the second NH_4^+ it includes three O(7) atoms and one O(10). The coordination is a highly distorted trigonal bipyramid. Each P—O—oxygen is in turn surrounded by four NH_4^+ at distances ranging from 2.72 to 3.03 Å for the O(7) atoms to 2.77 to 3.17 Å for each O(10). This arrangement serves as indirect proof that ammonium ions rather than NH_3 exists within the crystals.

5. Silver Ion Exchange

Silver ion is slightly larger than Na^+ but with a heat of hydration some 17 kcal/mol larger.[93] Thus, it would be expected to be somewhat less preferred than sodium ion. However, it was found that it is readily taken up even in acid solution.[94] The exchange

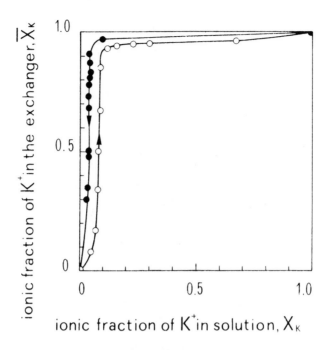

FIGURE 21. Forward and reverse ion exchange isotherms obtained by using ZrNaH(PO₄)₂·5H₂O and ZrKH(PO₄)₂·H₂O as exchangers. (From Alberti, G., Costantino, U., and Gupta, J. P., *J. Inorg. Nucl. Chem.*, 36, 2103, 1974. With permission.)

for protons is almost quantitative from acetate solutions even at room temperature. A fully exchanged monohydrate was the only phase obtained both in the forward and in the reverse process in which H⁺ replaced Ag⁺. The greater preference for Ag⁺ over Na⁺ may be due to its greater polarizability.

Bernasconi et al.[95] did obtain a half-exchanged phase when Ag⁺ was exchanged onto ZrNaH(PO₄)₂·5H₂O. However, it occurred as part of a mixture resulting from a complicated series of reactions. This type of exchange reaction is discussed in the next section.

C. Ion Exchange Reactions on Expanded Layer Zirconium Phosphates

It is clear from the discussion thus far that only a few ions are small enough and possess low enough heats of hydration to exchange with α-ZrP. This number can be increased by the use of base or buffered media. However, the hydroxides of many cations are insoluble in neutral or alkaline solutions which serves as a limitation to their use. This limitation may be overcome by first expanding the layers of α-ZrP permitting larger ions or highly charged ions with tightly held hydration shells to exchange. These procedures are discussed in this section.

1. Exchange with ZrNaH(PO₄)₂·5H₂O($\overline{NaH·5H_2O}$)
a. Alkali Metal Ions

The half-exchanged sodium ion form is a pentahydrate with interlayer spacing of 11.8 Å.[20] Thus, it should be able to exchange large ions without appreciable barriers to diffusion. The hydrogen ions in $\overline{NaH·5H_2O}$ are not appreciably exchanged by alkali metal cations below pH ~5 while sodium ion is not exchanged by H⁺ above pH 3. Thus, $\overline{NaH·5H_2O}$ behaves as a monofunctional exchanger with a capacity of 2.53 meq/g.[96]

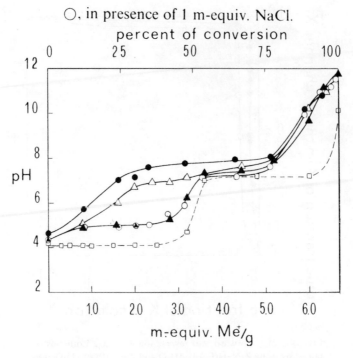

FIGURE 22.   Potentiometric titration curves for exchange of Cs⁺ as catalysed with different amounts of NaCl as catalyst. Conditions: 1 g of α-ZrP in 200 ml of solution at 25 ± 1°C. ●, No added NaCl; △, 0.05 meq NaCl; ▲, 0.2 meq NaCl; ○, 1 meq NaCl. Dashed curve refers to Na⁺ titration (5 × 10⁻³ N NaCl + NaOH). (From Alberti, G., Costantino, U., and Gupta, J. P., *J. Inorg. Nucl. Chem.*, 36, 2109, 1974. With permission.)

Forward and reverse Na⁺−K⁺ ion exchange isotherms at 25°C and μ = 0.1 M are shown in Figure 21. Initially the K⁺ goes into solid solution but at X_K = 0.09 a steep rise in the isotherm is observed as K⁺ is preferentially taken up. The exchange reaction is

$$\text{ZrNaH(PO}_4)_2 \cdot 5\text{H}_2\text{O} + \text{K}^+(\text{aq}) \longrightarrow \text{ZrKH(PO}_4)_2 \cdot \text{H}_2\text{O} + \text{Na}^+(\text{aq}) \qquad (13)$$

In the vertical portion of the isotherm both the sodium and potassium phases coexist. A small hysteresis loop is observed as the reverse isotherm has its vertical portion at $X_K \cong 0.04$. This is attributed to supersaturation[96] in which excess K⁺ remains in the solid phase when Na⁺ replaces K⁺ compared to the amount exchanged when K⁺ replaces Na⁺.

Similar isotherms are exhibited with other alkali metals yielding the selectivity sequence K⁺ > Cs⁺ > Na⁺ > Li⁺. In the case of Cs⁺ a half-exchanged phase ZrCsH(PO₄)₂ was obtained in contrast to the three-quarters-exchanged phase observed in the normal titration of α-ZrP with CsOH.

b. Sodium Ion Catalysed Exchange

It has been found that the presence of small amounts of Na⁺ in solution catalyse the uptake of Cs⁺ by α-ZrP.[97] Figure 22 shows the titration curves for (CsCl + CsOH) on α-ZrP in the presence of different amounts of Na⁺. When the sodium ion content was below 0.05 meq, the curve resembled that of the ordinary titration with CsOH. That is, the three-quarters-exchanged phase was formed in alkaline solution. However, with increase in the Na^+ concentration, exchange took place at acid pH values with formation of a half-exchanged phase. These results are explained by the preferential uptake of Na^+ to form $\overline{NaH} \cdot 5H_2O$ (Equation 14) followed by displacement of Na^+ by Cs^+ (Equation 15).

$$Zr(HPO_4)_2 \cdot H_2O + Na^+(aq) \longrightarrow ZrNaH(PO_4)_2 \cdot 5H_2O + H_3O^+(aq) \tag{14}$$

$$ZrNaH(PO_4)_2 \cdot 5H_2O + Cs^+(aq) \longrightarrow ZrCsH(PO_4)_2 + Na^+ + 5H_2O \tag{15}$$

A similar set of reactions can occur with Mg^{2+}. As shown in Figure 23 Mg^{2+} does not exchange when MgO is used as the base.[97] However, in the presence of Na^+ a titration curve indicating uptake of Mg^{2+} in acid solution is observed. The reaction is formulated as

$$Zr(HPO_4)_2 \cdot H_2O + 0.72Mg^{2+}(aq) \longrightarrow ZrMg_{0.72}H_{0.56}(PO_4)_2 \cdot 4H_2O + 1.44H_3O^+ \tag{16}$$

A schematic diagram, based upon the expansion of the α-ZrP layers to form $\overline{NaH} \cdot 5H_2O$ followed by uptake of Mg^{2+}, has been presented.[7]

c. Alkaline Earth Cations

Alkaline earth cations readily exchange with $ZrNaH(PO_4)_2 \cdot 5H_2O$.[98] In the case of Mg^{2+} and Sr^{2+} only the sodium ions are exchanged yielding phases of the type $ZrM_{0.5}H(PO_4)_2 \cdot XH_2O$. The reaction with Sr^{2+} is rapid but exchange of Mg^{2+} is slow requiring about 24 hr for equilibrium to be attained. This is attributed to the very high heat of hydration of magnesium ion.

Barium ions are able to exchange both Na^+ and H^+ simultaneously. The accumulation of hydronium ions in solution results in the replacement of sodium ions by protons to form both α-ZrP and θ-ZrP. This latter phase has an interlayer spacing of 10.4 Å and is also able to exchange Ba^{2+} (see Section IV.C.2). Thus, as many as five different phases may be observed. However, kinetic experiments indicate the following sequence of reactions

$$ZrNaH(PO_4)_2 \cdot 5H_2O + 0.5 Ba^{2+}(aq) \longrightarrow ZrBa_{0.5}H(PO_4)_2 \cdot 4H_2O + Na^+(aq) \tag{17}$$

$$ZrNaH(PO_4)_2 \cdot 5H_2O + 0.8 Ba^{2+}(aq) \longrightarrow ZrBa_{0.8}H_{0.4}(PO_4)_2 \cdot 2.5H_2O + Na^+(aq) + 0.6H_3O^+ \tag{18}$$

$$ZrBa_{0.5}H(PO_4)_2 \cdot 4H_2O + 0.3Ba^{2+} \longrightarrow ZrBa_{0.8}H_{0.4}(PO_4)_2 \cdot 2.5H_2O + 0.6H_3O^+ \tag{19}$$

The $\overline{Ba_{0.5}H}$ phase is unstable decomposing into α-ZrP and $\overline{Ba_{0.8}H_{0.4}}$.

Calcium ion is intermediate in behavior to Ba^{2+} and Sr^{2+}. The amount of hydrogen ion exchanged depends upon the concentration and amount of Ca^{2+} added. At low concentrations a half-exchanged phase forms but with increased amounts of Ca^{2+} added, more Ca^{2+} is taken up to form a solid solution of composition $ZrCa_{0.55-0.65}H_{0.9-0.7}(PO_4)_2 \cdot 3.3H_2O$. Both the separation factor and rational selectivity coefficients were found to be very high (1100 and 2.6×10^4, respectively) for Ca^{2+} in 0.01 N NaCl.

d. Transition Metal Ions

First row divalent transition metal ions can be exchanged on $ZrNaH(PO_4)_2 \cdot 5H_2O$ to quite high (greater than 50%) levels by static equilibrations.[99] The reactions are similar to those described for exchange of Ba^{2+} (preceding section). In the first step Na^+ is replaced by M^{2+} to form phases of the type $ZrM_{0.5}H(PO_4)_2 \cdot nH_2O$.[100] However,

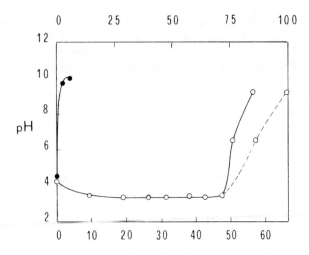

FIGURE 23. Comparison between the H^+-Mg^{2+} ion exchange process on α-ZrP in the absence and presence of NaCl as catalyst. Conditions as for Figure 22. •, No added NaCl; ○, 1 meq NaCl. Dashed curve gives total Mg^{2+} + Na^+ uptake. (From Alberti, G., Costantino, U., and Gupta, J. P., *J. Inorg. Nucl. Chem.*, 36, 2109, 1974. With permission.)

such phases are unstable and tend to disproportionate to a phase containing more M^{2+} and α-ZrP. The Na^+ liberated can then catalyse the uptake of M^{2+} by α-ZrP. This latter reaction liberates protons which then remove Na^+ from $\overline{NaH} \cdot 5H_2O$ to yield θ-ZrP and some α-ZrP. The stable transition metal phase formed by the disproportionation reaction and by the sodium ion-catalysed reaction has the approximate composition $ZrM_{0.8}H_{0.4}(PO_4)_2 \cdot 4H_2O$. It is the same phase formed by α-ZrP when contacted with hot transition metal acetate solutions (see Section IV.B.3).[86] Further uptake of M^{2+} does not result in the formation of a new phase. Rather a solid-solution containing 80 to 100% M^{2+} is obtained.

The results described above were obtained with nitrate solutions. However, less complicated reactions are observed when metal acetate solutions are used. Due to the buffering action of acetate ions the acidity of the solutions is never great enough to produce α- and θ-ZrP. Thus, the reaction proceeds smoothly to the formation of the 80 to 100% exchanged phase.[100]

The selectivity of the exchanger for the transition metal cations was found to be in the order $Cu^{2+} > Zn^{2+} \gg Mn^{2+} > Co^{2+} > Ni^{2+}$. The same selectivity sequence was noted with α-ZrP.[86] This order cannot be related to the stability of the hexa-aquo ions nor to the stereochemistry adopted by the M^{2+} ions in the solid, which is distorted octahedral.[87] However, it can be correlated to the rate at which $M(H_2O)_6^{2+}$ dissociates which is also in the order $Cu^{2+} > Zn^{2+}, Mn^{2+} > Fe^{2+} > Co^{2+} > Ni^{2+}$.[101]

e. Trivalent Cations

Trivalent (and many polyvalent) cations are exchanged at room temperature by amorphous[102] but not by fully crystalline α-ZrP. Apparently insufficient energy is available at room temperature to dehydrate the cations so that diffusion into the crystals can occur. However, Cr^{3+} is taken up rapidly at 25° by $\overline{NaH} \cdot 5H_2O$. More than 80% exchange was achieved in a few minutes.[103] Initially the chromium displaces Na^+ in the required 1:3 ratio. Since θ-ZrP was detected as one of the phases which formed during exchange, the process taking place up to 50% exchange is thought to be represented by Equation 20

$$3ZrNaH(PO_4)_2 \cdot 5H_2O + Cr^{3+}(aq) \longrightarrow 2ZrCr_{0.5}H_{0.5}(PO_4)_2 \cdot 4H_2O + Zr(HPO_4)_2 \cdot 6H_2O + 3Na^+ \quad (20)$$

This reaction is followed by further exchange of Cr^{3+} for the protons of θ-ZrP. The formation of θ-ZrP could be avoided by increasing the Na^+ content of the exchanging solution. Loadings up to 90% of capacity were achieved with no phase change, i.e., with formation of a chromium-containing solid solution.

The uptake of La^{3+} was much slower than that for Cr^{3+} and only 60% loading was achieved in 45 days. The process could be speeded up by heating, but even at 75°C only 60% exchange was achieved. The exchanged phase is thought to be $ZrLa_{0.5}H_{0.5}(PO_4)_2 \cdot 4H_2O$ occuring together with some La^{3+} dissolved in θ-ZrP. Similar results were obtained with Tl^{3+}.

f. Exchange of Ammonium and Silver Ions

While NH_4^+ did not exchange with the protons of α-ZrP, it is exchanged by $\overline{NaH} \cdot 5H_2O$.[51] A half-exchanged monohydrate phase with interlayer spacing of 8.3 Å is formed by displacement of the Na^+ only.

A complicated sequence of reactions takes place when Ag^+ is contacted with $\overline{NaH} \cdot 5H_2O$. Both Na^+ and H^+ are exchanged in a 1:0.7 ratio. Initially the selectivity is so high that the uptake is quantitative.[95] The major reaction is the exchange of Ag^+ for Na^+ to form a half-exchanged phase with a 9.9 A interlayer spacing. At the same time some protons are also exchanged and this produces some α- and θ-ZrP. These phases also take up Ag^+ yielding the fully exchanged phase. Thus, the pure half-exchanged phase is not obtained but rather a mixture of the silver-containing phases together with small amounts of $\overline{NaH} \cdot 5H_2O$, α-ZrP and θ-ZrP.

g. Exchange of Oxocations

Both UO_2^{2+} and VO^{2+} were found to exchange with $ZrNaH(PO_4)_2 \cdot 5H_2O$.[104] The reactions resembled those described above. With uranyl ion the exchange at room temperature was extremely slow and therefore was run at 80°C in both acetate and nitrate solutions. In acetate solution the exchange process took place in three steps consisting of 0 to 25%, 25 to 90% and 90 to 100% loading. The first step is fast and leads to a single phase, $ZrHNa_{0.5}(UO_2)_{0.25}(PO_4)_2 \cdot 2H_2O$, with interlayer spacing 9.1 Å. The second step is slower and both Na^+ and H^+ are exchanged. As many as four exchanged phases may be present at the same time but the main one and the only one obtained at 90% loading is $ZrH_{0.2}(UO_2)_{0.9}(PO_4)_2 \cdot 6H_2O(d_{002} = 10.5$ Å$)$. The third step, in which H^+ is displaced with no phase change, is extremely slow.

When nitrate solutions are used, the first step is the same as for acetate solutions. At higher loadings protons are liberated and since these are not buffered as with acetate ions some α-ZrP is formed at the expense of the 25% phase (Equation 21).

$$ZrHNa_{0.5}(UO_2)_{0.25} \cdot 2H_2O + H^+ \longrightarrow Zr(HPO_4)_2 \cdot H_2O + 0.25\,UO_2^{2+} + 0.5Na^+ \quad (21)$$

Vanadyl ion exchanges to a level of 55 to 60% loading at 80°C from a 0.01 N $VOSO_4$ solution. Up to 50% exchange the uptake is quantitative and some H^+ is displaced as well as Na^+. This results in formation of α- and θ-ZrP. The vanadyl-containing solid has an interlayer spacing of 9.5 Å. At higher loadings this phase forms a solid solution of composition $ZrH_{1-2x}(VO)_{0.5+x}(PO_4)_2 \cdot nH_2O$.

2. Exchange with θ-ZrP

The preparation of θ-ZrP by treating $\overline{NaH} \cdot 5H_2O$ with HCl has been described in Section III.B.6. This phase has an interlayer spacing of 10.4 Å and therefore should present less of a barrier to exchange than α-ZrP. This has been found to be the case.[57]

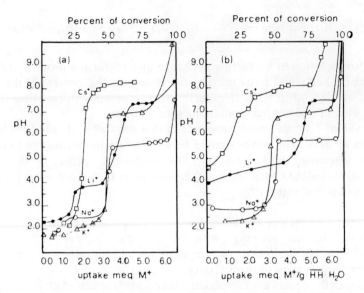

FIGURE 24(a).   Potentiometric titration curves of θ-ZrP Zr(HPO₄)₂·6H₂O, with alkali metal ions. Conditions: a weight of θ-ZrP equivalent to 1g α-ZrP in 200 mℓ of 0.1 N(MCl + MOH) - solid lines, or in 200 mℓ of 0.1 N MCl containing known amounts of HCl - dotted lines. (b) Similar results for α-ZrP. (From Alberti, G., Costantino, U., and Gill, J. S., *J. Inorg. Nucl. Chem.*, 38, 1783, 1976. With permission.)

a. Alkali Metal Cations

The titration curves obtained by equilibration of 0.1 M (MOH + MCl) with θ-ZrP are shown in Figure 24. Comparison with the data for exchange with α-ZrP shows that in the region of 0-50% of exchange, the pH values are lower for θ-ZrP. This is due to the formation of phases of the type ZrM$_{0.5}$H$_{1.5}$(PO₄)₂·nH₂O. Increased uptake results in conversion of these 25% phases to the regular half-exchanged phases obtained with α-ZrP. Thereafter the curves parallel those for α-ZrP with the same results. Although a cesium phase $\overline{HCs}$·2H₂O (d$_{002}$ = 11.3 Å) was reported to form,[57] the titration curve shows no inflection at half-exchange and the pH indicates that the 3/4 phase is formed.

b. Divalent Cations

The titration curves for alkaline earth cations is shown in Figure 25.[57] Only one endpoint was obtained for each cation at different loading levels. The phases obtained were ZrMg$_{0.5}$H(PO₄)₂·3H₂O(d$_{002}$ = 9.9 Å), ZrSr$_{0.75}$H$_{0.5}$(PO₄)₂·3.6H₂O(d$_{002}$ = 10.2 Å), ZrBa(PO₄)₂·2.5H₂O(d$_{002}$ = 9.5 Å). Barium ion exchange may be more complicated than indicated since phases with interlayer spacings of 11.3 Å and 13.4 Å were present at intermediate levels of exchange.

Transition metal ions such as Ni(II), Cu(II), and Co(II) were also readily exchanged.[57] The metal-containing phases were the same ones obtained by exchange with α-ZrP or $\overline{NaH}$·5H₂O.

Hg(II) is taken up slowly by α-ZrP even at 60°C and only very low loadings are possible. The situation is not much better if $\overline{NaH}$·5H₂O is used because the concentration of Hg²⁺ in solution at the pH required for exchange with the sodium ions is very low. However, θ-ZrP exhibits a very high affinity for Hg²⁺ and exchanges very rapidly with this ion even in 0.1 N HNO₃ solutions.[105]

3. Exchange with Amine Intercalates

Amines are readily intercalated by α-ZrP (see Chapter 3). In the process the layers

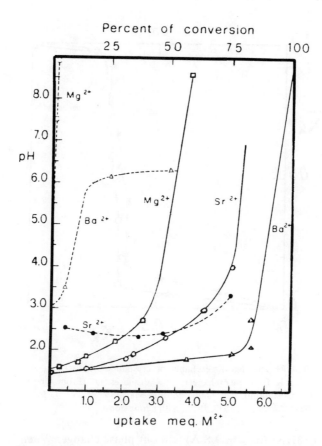

FIGURE 25. Potentiometric titration curves for alkaline earth cations on θ-ZrP (solid lines) and α-ZrP (dashed lines). Conditions same as for Figure 24. (From Alberti, G., Costantino, U., and Gill, J. S., *J. Inorg. Nucl. Chem.*, 38, 1783, 1976. With permission.)

are spread apart to accommodate a bilayer of amine. It is quite likely that the amines become protonated to form alkyl ammonium ions in the process. Thus, it is possible to exchange cations for the alkyl ammonium ions. For example, quantitative exchange of Ni(II) for butylammonium ion was found to occur.[106] Large complexes such as $Cu(NH_3)_4^{2+}$, $Co(NH_3)_6^{3+}$ and $Cu(en)_2^{2+}$ have also been exchanged.[107] It is appropriate to note at this point that $Co(NH_3)_6^{3+}$ was also exchanged with α-ZrP at 75°C to a loading of 45%[108] but higher loadings were achieved with amine intercalates.[107] The use of amine intercalates would appear to offer great promise as a means of incorporating a large number of diverse species between the layers of many inorganic exchangers with small interlayer spacings.

D. Exchange with $Zr(MPO_4)_2 \cdot nH_2O$ Phases

In Section IV.C.1 the exchange of various cations with $\overline{NaH} \cdot 5H_2O$ was discussed. It was shown that high degrees of selectivity are exhibited, resulting in rectilinear isotherms. Extensive investigations with totally exchanged salt forms have also been carried out. In order to avoid a ternary system the pH of the solution should always be well above 6, thus eliminating the possibility of incorporating small amounts of hydrogen ion into the exchanger.[109] Two general types of behavior are exhibited. The first is illustrated by the Na^+/H^+ system whose isotherm is shown in Figure 26.[109,110]

In a mixed Na^+-K^+ solution at X_{K^+} less than 0.5 a small amount of K^+ is incorporated

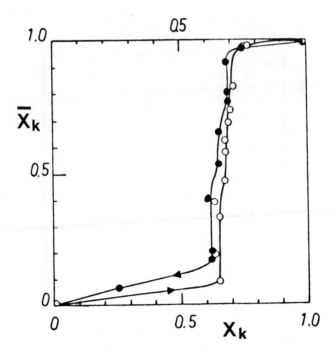

FIGURE 26. Na^+-K^+ exchange on crystalline α-ZrP: •, Na^+ displaces K^+ from the exchanger, O; K^+ displaces Na^+. (From Alberti, G., Costantino, U., Allulli, S., and Massucci, M. A., *J. Inorg. Nucl. Chem.*, 35, 1339, 1973. With permission.)

into $Zr(NaPO_4)_2 \cdot 3H_2O$ ($d_{002} = 9.8$ Å) without phase change. When $X_{K^+} = 0.66$, the uptake increases rapidly giving rise to a vertical line in the isotherm. Along this line two immiscible phases are present and the system has no degrees of freedom. The composition of the second phase is somewhat in doubt. According to Alberti et al.[110] it is $ZrNaK(PO_4)_2 \cdot 2.7H_2O$ ($d_{002} = 10.2$ Å) while Clearfield and Medina[109] found that $\overline{X}_K \cong 0.62$. The latter workers then showed that this phase has a composition range of $\overline{X}_K = 0.62$ to 0.76 whereas Alberti et al. indicate a single phase present from 50 to 72% K^+ uptake. These differences may be due to the crystallinity of the two exchangers used, 13:330 for Clearfield and Medina and 10:100 by Alberti. At higher loadings a second two-phase region is obtained. The two phases are the 10.2 Å phase and the fully exchanged potassium phase which contains a small amount of Na^+. As the mole fraction of K^+ in solution increases beyond 0.7 this dissolved Na^+ is replaced by K^+.

In the reverse process a small hysteresis loop is observed, by Alberti, over the whole range of compositions, but only over the lower portion of the curve by Clearfield and Medina. If the exchange is carried out on the anhydrous salts in aqueous media, a larger hysteresis is observed.[111]

Isotherms for the Li/K system on α-ZrP prepared in two different ways are shown in Figure 27. At first potassium ion is taken up by $Zr(LiPO_4)_2 \cdot 3H_2O$($d_{002} = 10.0$Å) to form a solid solution, but then at $X_{K^+} = 0.1$ a $\overline{LiK} \cdot 3H_2O$ phase ($d_{002} = 9.3$ Å) is obtained. However, a second phase of the same composition and an interlayer spacing of 10.0 Å was also present. This phenomenon, two phases of the same composition but different interlayer spacing, has not been observed previously. A second two phase region is obtained at $X_K = 0.7$ and here the 10.0 Å phase coexists with a phase whose composition is $Li_{0.33}K_{1.67} \cdot 3H_2O$($d_{002} = 10.4$ Å). A solid solution region also exists from this composition to $\overline{KK} \cdot 3H_2O$($d_{002} = 10.8$ Å). In the reverse process a much broader solid solution region extending from $\overline{KK} \cdot 3H_2O$ to $\overline{K_{1.5}Li_{0.5}}$ was obtained. At higher

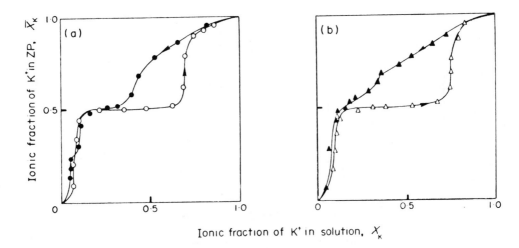

FIGURE 27. Li$^+$-K$^+$ exchange isotherms obtained with two different zirconium phosphates; (A) Direct precipitation from HF, (B) α-ZrP (10:100). O, ▲: K$^+$ displaces Li$^+$ from the exchanger, ●, △: Li$^+$ displaces K$^+$ from the exchanger. (From Allulli, S., Massucci, M. A., Costantino, U., and Bertrami, R., *J. Inorg. Nucl. Chem.*, 39, 659, 1977. With permission.)

lithium contents the 9.3 Å phase appears. The isotherm at this point is not perfectly vertical, indicating that one or both of the phases do not maintain a constant composition as Li$^+$ is added. The 10.0 Å LiK·3H$_2$O phase also appears at the same time as does the 9.3 Å phase but its relative amount is low until $\overline{X}_{K^+} = 0.5$. Thereafter, it increases rapidly while the amount of the 9.3 Å phase decreases correspondingly.

The major difference exhibited by the less crystalline 10:100 exchanger is the existence of a broader solid-solution region. Such behavior is typical of less crystalline zirconium phosphates and this is discussed more fully in Section E below. Thus, while the small hysteresis in the Na$^+$/K$^+$ system is ascribed to supersaturation phenomena, the large hysteresis in the Li$^+$/K$^+$ system is due to phases of different composition in the forward and reverse processes. The effect of temperature on this exchange has also been examined.[112] An increase in temperature was found to favor the uptake of the smaller ion and to decrease the hysteresis loop. It was concluded that the energy of phase formation and of hydration in the solid are the main factors determining the ion exchange behavior. NH$_4^+$/Na$^+$ and NH$_4^+$/Li$^+$ isotherms have also recently been determined,[113,114] as have Li$^+$/Cs$^+$, Na$^+$/Cs$^+$, and K$^+$/Cs$^+$ exchange isotherms.[115]

1. Exchange in Fused Salts

We have already discussed the role played by the amount of water fixed or released during exchange in determining the course of that exchange. It was therefore of interest to determine the course of exchange with water not present as solvent. Fused salts presented a medium for doing this since, unlike zeolites, no solvent is occluded by α-ZrP. It was necessary to carry out such studies with the salt forms as displacement of protons into the solvent from α-ZrP would result in volatilization by decomposition of the acids forms with the molten salt anions.

Isotherms for Na$^+$/K$^+$ exchange in molten KNO$_3$−NaNO$_3$ at 300°C and 450°C are shown in Figure 28.[116,117] At the higher temperature no hysteresis was observed. From $X_K = 0$ to ∼0.6 the exchanger strongly prefers sodium ion and only 0.05 mol fraction of K$^+$ is incorporated. At $X_K \cong 0.6$ two immiscible phases having approximate compositions Zr(Na$_{0.95}$K$_{0.05}$PO$_4$)$_2$ and Zr(Na$_{0.6}$K$_{0.4}$PO$_4$)$_2$ were found. The composition of the melt remained fixed until the exchanger was completely converted to the latter form. From $X_K \cong 0.6$ to $X_K \cong 0.9$ Zr(Na$_{0.6}$K$_{0.4}$PO$_4$)$_2$ becomes richer in K$^+$ until at $X_K \cong 0.95$

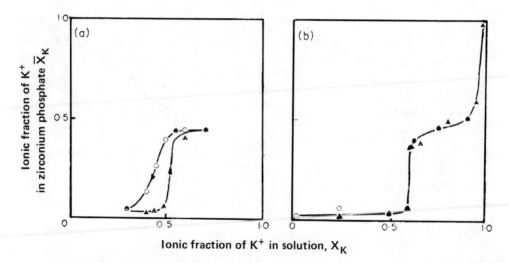

FIGURE 28.   Forward and reverse ion exchange isotherms at 300° (a), and 450°C (b) in molten NaNO₃-KNO₃ mixtures. ○, Na⁺ displaces K⁺; △, K⁺ displaces Na⁺. (From Allulli, S. and Cardini, G., *J. Inorg. Nucl. Chem.*, 34, 339, 1972. With permission.)

two immiscible phases, having the approximate compositions $Zr(Na_{0.5}K_{0.5}PO_4)_2$ and $Zr(Na_{0.02}K_{0.98}PO_4)_2$, are again present. Thus, the isotherm shows another vertical region until pure $Zr(KPO_4)_2$ is obtained.

At 300°C the range of solution compositions used was limited to 30 to 70% mol fraction owing to the higher melting points of the pure salts. The curve for K⁺ replacing Na⁺ resembled that obtained at 450°C except that the two-phase region was found to occur at $X_K \cong 0.5$. The exchanged phase has the composition $ZrNaK(PO_4)_2(d_{002} = 8.1$ Å). Further exchange did not take place and this was shown to be a rate phenomenon.[117] In the reverse direction (Na⁺ → K⁺) the X-ray patterns revealed the presence of two phases with d_{002} spacings of 8.1 ($\overline{NaK}$) and 7.8 Å ($\overline{NaNa}$). Since the original NaNa phases are not the same; this difference in interlayer spacing is then responsible for the observed hysteresis.

An interesting phenomenon was uncovered in the course of examining some Li⁺/M⁺ (M = Na⁺, K⁺) ion exchange isotherms in molten salts. Dehydration of $\overline{LiLi}\cdot 4H_2O$ yields an anhydrous phase with an interlayer spacing of 7.0 Å.[65] If this phase is used in the exchange study, the isotherms show extremely large hysteresis loops.[118] Only the half-transformed phases $\overline{LiNa}$ and $\overline{LiK}$ are obtained as the exchanger exhibits a very high preference for Li⁺. Replacement of K⁺ by Li⁺ in the reverse step leads to the formation of an $\overline{LiLi}$ phase with an interlayer spacing of 7.6 Å. Clearly this phase is different than the starting one and accounts for the hysteresis. However, when the 7.6 Å phase serves as the starting exchanger, the isotherms are reversible. This behavior is accounted for in the following way. The interlayer spacing of $\overline{LiK}$ is close to 7.6 Å. Thus, when the smaller Li⁺ replaces K⁺, it does so in such a way as to accommodate itself in the spaces left vacant by the larger ion. Conversely there is sufficient space for K⁺ in $\overline{LiLi}$ (7.6 Å) for K⁺ to be taken up without layer expansion. This is not the case for $\overline{LiLi}$ (7.0 Å). Here layer expansion is required and energetically less favorable. Thus, K⁺ uptake occurs at a greater value of X_{K^+}.

The selectivity sequences exhibited by both the amorphous and crystalline forms of zirconium phosphate (α-ZrP) in molten salts is Li⁺ ≫ Na⁺ > K⁺. This is Eisenman's strong field sequence and is the reverse of that exhibited in aqueous solution. It was also found that Tl⁺ is much more highly preferred to Rb⁺, indicating a strong dependence of selectivity on the polarizability of the cation (see also Section IV.B.5).[119]

E. Semicrystalline α-ZrP

We have seen in Section IV.A that amorphous zirconium phosphate gels exchange by forming a single continuous solid solution.[10] The pH rises steeply and continuously with increasing cation content. This is shown in Figure 8 for Na^+ exchange with α-ZrP 0.5:48. As the crystallinity of the exchanger increases, a definite curvature indicating a second endpoint is observed in the titration curve (0.8:48, 2.5:48, see Figure 8). X-ray analysis shows that two separate phases are present; the original gel (containing dissolved Na^+) and a new phase which has an X-ray pattern similar to that of the half-exchanged sodium ion phase, but with very broad reflections. As the crystallinity of the exchanger increases, the X-ray reflections sharpen and the composition ranges of the two phases become narrower. The initial pH of the exchange is seen to increase steadily as the crystallinity of the exchanger increases, but when it exceeds that of 12:48, begins to fall again (see Figure 3).[10,19]

The behavior described above seems to be quite general but is not exhibited in as great detail by other alkali metal ions.[64,65,67,81] Ideally, a fully crystalline exchanger would not exhibit any solid solution formation and the exchange process would consist of conversion of the pure hydrogen phase into a pure exchanged phase of constant composition. In such a case the slope of the titration curve should be zero as the system possesses no degrees of freedom.[55] This is almost the case for Na^+-H^+ exchange on 12:336. The equilibrium pH is then determined by the pK of the protons in pure α-ZrP.

Addition of an MCl solution (no added base) to the less crystalline forms of α-zirconium phosphate results in significant uptake of cations. This is possible because the exchanger contains a range of cavity sizes. The larger ones can accept hydrated cations so some exchange can occur without complete dehydration. Thus, the greater the proportion of large cavities, the more cations exchanged and the lower the pH. As the crystallinity of the exchanger increases, the size and number of larger cavities decreases, resulting in less exchange and higher pH values. The composition range must be determined by the deviation of the cavity sizes from regularity. That is, the highly (but not fully) crystalline solids, having only a few cavities slightly larger than normal, possess a very restricted solubility range. A greater dehydration of the cations is necessary for them to be able to occupy these cavities and exchange is therefore not favorable, the exchanger preferring hydrogen ions.

Another way of stating the case is that an exchanger with a wide range of cavity sizes (low crystallinity) means that the protons have a wide range of pK values. This could arise from the widely varying hydrogen bond lengths which result from displacement of the phosphate groups from their required equilibrium position in the true crystals. Thus, the most acidic hydrogens are exchanged first. At any loading the pH is determined primarily by the activities of the two ions in the solid and at low loads the acidity of the protons is still great so the pH is low. As more sites are filled the pH rises rapidly as only the less acidic protons remain. Thus, the least crystalline exchanger exhibits the broadest pH range in its titration curve and the curves get flatter as the crystallinity of the exchanger increases.

The effect of low crystallinity is evident in the results for Li^+-H^+ and Ca^{2+}-H^+ exchange. Exchanger 12:24 exhibited a broad positive slope from 50 to 75% of lithium ion uptake,[120] indicating a solid solution in this region of composition. When a more crystalline exchanger was used, a 50% phase and a 75% phase were formed.[65,81] A narrowing of the composition range for more crystalline samples was also observed for the Ca^{2+} exchanged phase.[81]

F. Surface Exchange

Large ions such as Cs^+ are incapable of exchange with the interior of α-ZrP since they are prevented from doing so by the narrow passageways of the exchanger.[4] However, no such barrier to exchange exists on the surface. Thus, if a dilute solution of Cs^+ is added to α-ZrP a rapid decrease in pH is observed and in a matter of seconds levels off to a practically constant value.[78] Other cations behave similarly and if conditions are kept the same the pH serves as a rough measure of the surface selectivity.

Ion exchange isotherms were determined for surface exchange by a representative number of ions.[78,121] The selectivity was found to increase with increased charge of the cation. Within a group of equal charge, the larger the unhydrated radius of the cation the greater the selectivity coefficient. For cations of the regular elements the selectivity coefficient decreased continuously with load. However, for more easily polarized ions such as those of the transition elements or those with filled d shells (Zn^{2+}), the selectivity remained relatively constant with loading. This implies that the interaction with the fixed charges is large compared to cation interactions. The observed large differences in separation factors indicate that many interesting separations are possible.

The crystals used in the study described above were prepared by the direct precipitation method and possessed surfaces with a capacity of 4 to 6 μeq. Thus, only microseparations are possible with these crystals. In Section III.B.4 it was shown that semi-crystalline α-ZrP can be prepared with high surface areas. An exchanger having a surface area of 100 M^2/g would contain 0.69 meq/g of surface protons or $\sim$10% of its exchange capacity on the surface. Thus, macroseparations as well as many other surface processes (chromatography, catalysis, etc.) should become accessible through the use of high surface area material.

G. Kinetics

1. Rates of Exchange

Very little quantitative rate data is available. Harvie and Nancollas[122] measured the rate of Na^+-H^+ exchange on 5:100. The rate was found to be particle diffusion controlled. Therefore, they applied the theory of Boyd et al.,[123] describing diffusion into spherical particles of radius r by the equation

$$F = 1 - \frac{6}{\pi^2} \sum_{n=1}^{\infty} \frac{1}{n^2} \exp^{-(n^2 Bt)}$$

where $B = \Pi^2 Di/r^2$ and Di is the effective diffusion coefficient. If Di is constant then a plot of F vs. Bt should be linear and pass through the origin. The data conformed to such a plot for the first 10 sec of exchange. This initial fast reaction was then followed by a slower one. Diffusion coefficients for the two processes are given in Table 9.

Subsequently, Harvie and Nancollas[83] obtained rate data for K^+/H^+, Na^+/H^+, and Li^+/H^+ exchange on α-ZrP (5:100). This time the plots of Bt vs. F were not linear which is quite puzzling as the exchanger was prepared in almost the same way for this study and the previous one. The nonlinearity was attributed to the dependence of the interdiffusion coefficient on F. It was assumed that the self-diffusion coefficient for each ion remains constant during exchange and that these correspond to the values of the interdiffusion coefficient as $F \rightarrow 0$ and $F \rightarrow 1$. The self-diffusion coefficients derived from the data based on this assumption are given in Table 9. It is seen that the exchange rates were in the order $K^+ > Na^+ > Li^+$.

In contrast to the above results, measurement of the rate of K^+/H^+ exchange on α-ZrP (12:360) yielded a two stage reaction, as shown in Figure 29.[75] It is seen that the Bt vs. t plots for the KOH reactions are linear over both stages of the reaction with the diffusion coefficients listed in Table 9. There was no difference in the rate over a

Table 9
DIFFUSION COEFFICIENTS FOR DIFFERENT
EXCHANGE PROCESSES ON α-ZIRCONIUM PHOSPHATE

Process	Di (cm²/sec)	Temp (°C)	Ref.
Na$^+$ → H$^+$ on α-ZrP(5:100)	0.8-5×10^{-11}	25	122
Na$^+$ → H$^+$ on NaH (5:100)	0.1-0.6×10^{-11}	25	122
Li$^+$ self-diffusion from exchange of Li$^+$ → H$^+$ on α-ZrP(5:100)	2.0×10^{-12}	25	83
Na$^+$ self-diffusion from Na$^+$ → H$^+$ exchange on α-ZrP (5:100)	1.9×10^{-11}	25	83
K$^+$ self diffusion from K$^+$ → H$^+$ exchange on α-ZrP(5:100)	4×10^{-11}	25	83
H$^+$ self diffusion	0.7×10^{-12}	25	83
K$^+$ → H$^+$ in α-ZrP(12:360)^a	7.6×10^{-13}	25	75
K$^+$ → H$^+$ in $\overline{KH}$·H$_2$O(12:360)^a	4.9×10^{-13}	25	75
K$^+$ → H$^+$ in α-ZrP(12:360)^b	1.2×10^{-12}	25	75
Na$^+$ self-diffusion in $\overline{NaNa}$·H$_2$O (10:24)	5.0×10^{-13}	25	125
K$^+$ self-diffusion in $\overline{KK}$·H$_2$O(10:24)	6.3×10^{-14}	25	125
Na$^+$ self-diffusion in $\overline{NaNa}$·3H$_2$O	6.7×10^{-15}	25	49
	6.7×10^{-13}	78.8	
K$^+$ self-diffusion in $\overline{KK}$·3H$_2$O	8.2×10^{-13}	25	49
	3.3×10^{-11}	65	
Na$^+$ self-diffusion in NaH·5H$_2$O	5.0×10^{-13}	31	127
	2.3×10^{-13}	0	
Na$^+$ self-diffusion in NaH·H$_2$O	1.9×10^{-13}	51	127
Gas-solid reactions			
H$^+$ → Na$^+$ in Zr(NaPO$_4$)$_2$	0.4×10^{-12}	140	131
	3.4×10^{-12}	220	
H$^+$ → Na$^+$ in ZrNaH(PO$_4$)$_2$	0.8×10^{-12}	140	131
	10.1×10^{-12}	220	
H$^+$ → Na$^+$ in ZrNa$_{0.8}$H$_{1.2}$(PO$_4$)$_2$	8.5×10^{-15}	77	131
	2.3×10^{-13}	137	

^{a} KOH as only source of K$^+$.
^{b} KOH + KCl used as source of K$^+$.

fivefold concentration change of KOH. However, when a mixture of KOH and KCl was used, the rate increased considerably. Furthermore, only the plot for the first stage was linear, that for the second showed a distinct curvature. A possible explanation for this effect is the following. When an increment of base is added to the solution containing α-ZrP and KCl, the pH rises to values exceeding 9. This value is above that required to completely exchange K$^+$ and causes a large amount of K$^+$ and some Cl$^-$ to be taken up.[75] In fact, the fully exchanged phase is obtained even when the amount of base added is significantly less than 3.3 meq/g (half-exchanged value).[76] However, the excess K$^+$ then diffuses back out as the pH is lowered by reaction of hydroxyl ion with the protons of the lattice. When no KCl is present, this sequence of events may not occur, since no excess K$^+$ is available. Thus, the actual reaction may be different in the two cases, accounting for the different rates of exchange.

A puzzling feature of K$^+$-H$^+$ exchange reaction is the slow (more than 30 days) approach to equilibrium exhibited by highly crystalline α-ZrP.[75,76] The reasons for this behavior are not apparent from the kinetic data which indicate that equilibrium should be attained in a few hours. The answer must lie in phenomena which are not connected with the particle-controlled diffusion reaction. For example, slow crystallization phe-

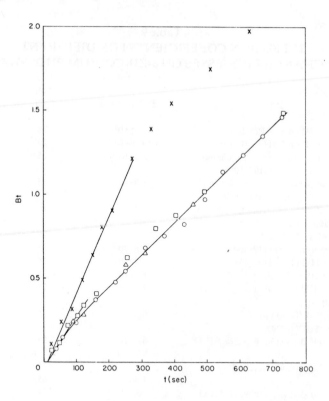

FIGURE 29.   Plots of Bt as a function of time. Exchange solutions: O, 0.02 M KOH; △, 0.04 M KOH; □, 0.1 M KOH; X, 0.02 M KOH + 0.08 M KCl. (From Ruvarac, A., Milonjic, S., Clearfield, A., and Garces, J. M., *J. Inorg. Nucl. Chem.*, 40, 79, 1978. With permission.)

nomena have been observed in zeolites.[124] The rapid uptake of large amounts of K[+] and its subsequent redistribution after KOH addition may disorder the crystal lattice which then undergoes a slow recrystallization.[7]

2. Self-Diffusion Studies

Dyer and associates[125-127] have carried out extensive measurements of self-diffusion in exchanged phases of α-ZrP and α-ZrP. In their early work, the α-ZrP used was 10:24 and not completely exchanged. Thus, some M[z+]/H[+] exchange may have occurred along with self-diffusion. In fact, they observed that more than one process was taking place. Self-diffusion coefficients were in the order Na[+] > K[+] > Ca[2+] > Cs[+] > Ba[2+] > Sr[2+].

Subsequently, self-diffusion experiments were carried out for Na[+] diffusion in $\overline{\text{NaH}} \cdot 5\text{H}_2\text{O}$ and $\overline{\text{NaH}} \cdot \text{H}_2\text{O}$.[127] A two-stage process was found to hold in $\overline{\text{NaH}} \cdot 5\text{H}_2\text{O}$, a low temperature exchange with an activation energy of 7.2 kcal/mol and a higher temperature one with ΔE of 10 kcal/mol. Diffusion coefficients are listed in Table 9. The self-diffusion of Na[+] in $\overline{\text{NaH}} \cdot \text{H}_2\text{O}$ (7.6 Å) requires an activation energy of only 5 kcal/mol and this may be connected with the fact very little dehydration and rehydration of Na[+] need occur in this phase.

Self-diffusion coefficients have recently been measured for Na[+] and K[+] in $\overline{\text{NaNa}} \cdot 3\text{H}_2\text{O}$ and $\overline{\text{KK}} \cdot 3\text{H}_2\text{O}$, respectively.[49] The α-ZrP was prepared from HF solutions. A solution to Fick's equation was used which incorporated the size distribution of the particles which was determined experimentally. Although the particles are hexagonal platelets, they were considered to be spheres. The average particle size was 3

μm, but a significant fraction was found to be greater than 10 μm. The self-diffusion processes were found to occur in a single step in contrast to the results of Dyer and Ocon.[125] Activation energies of 17.4 and 18.9 kcal/mol were obtained for Na^+ and K^+, respectively. These values are a little higher than those found for the monohydrates (15.2 and 16 kcal/mol)[125] even though the interlayer spacings in the trihydrates are significantly larger. A possible explanation could be that the less crystalline exchanger used by Dyer and Ocon contained a larger number of defects which decreased the energy barrier. Altenatively, stronger water binding in the trihydrates may be involved. These diffusion coefficients are given in Table 9.

Recently, Dyer and Yusof[128] have measured the rates of exchange for a large ion (Cs^+) on $\overline{HNa} \cdot 5H_2O$ (11.8 Å) and Na^+ on the resulting cesium ion phase. They found that the diffusion coefficient for Cs → Na^+ in $\overline{HNa} \cdot 5H_2O$ was 1.2×10^{-12} cm²/sec. (at 21°C), whereas the replacement of Cs^+ by Na^+ in the product (which had a narrower interlayer distance) yielded a diffusion coefficient of 2×10^{-15} cm²/sec at 25°C. From this they concluded that the Alberti mechanism,[7] in which it is proposed that both the original and exchanged phases occur in the same crystal, is correct.

3. Solid-Solid Ion Exchange

Zirconium phosphates, whether hydrated or dehydrated, are able to undergo ion exchange with salts.[129] For example, when a dry mixture of NaCl and ζ-ZrP is heated above 100°C, HCl is evolved and a sodium exchanged phase produced (Equation 22).

$$Zr(HPO_4)_2 + xNaCl \rightleftarrows ZrNa_xH_{2-x}(PO_4)_2 + xHCl \qquad (22)$$

Similar reactions are possible with zeolites in the hydrogen form.[130] The reactions are reversible with hydrogen ion being selectively favored by the exchanger. It will be shown in Section V that exchanged forms of zirconium phosphate yield a variety of phases at elevated temperatures. Thus, the product obtained in the solid-solid exchange reaction depends upon the temperature and the extent of exchange. Complete exchange is possible above 300°C provided the HCl is removed. The forward reactions are endothermic and hence higher temperatures favor the formation of exchanged forms.

Measurement of the rates of the reverse reactions represented by Equation 22 have been carried out.[131] The starting phase was $Zr(NaPO_4)_2$ (x = 2) and the sequence of reactions was as follows:

$$Zr(NaPO_4)_2 \xrightarrow[HCl]{(1)} ZrNaH(PO_4)_2 \xrightarrow{(2)} ZrNa_{0.8}H_{1.2}(PO_4)_2 \xrightarrow{(3)}$$

$$ZrNa_{0.2}H_{1.8}(PO_4)_2 \xrightarrow{(4)} Zr(HPO_4)_2 \qquad (23)$$

The reactions were diffusion controlled and could be fit by an equation for a spherical particle in a well-stirred fluid of limited volume.[132] Diffusion coefficients for the first three reactions are given in Table 9. Activation energies are 10.3, 12.7, and 15.9 kcal/mol for processes 1, 2, and 3, respectively. Extrapolation of the diffusion coefficients to 25°C yields values of the order of 10^{-15} cm²/sec. Thus, the gas-solid reactions are considerably slower than exchange reactions in aqueous solution (see Table 9).

Inoue and Yamada[133] measured the self-diffusion of Na^+ in $\overline{NaNa}$ from molten $NaNO_3$. The reaction reached equilibrium in a matter of minutes. Thus, the slow approach to equilibrium observed for Na^+/K^+ exchange in molten salts[117] must arise from other than a diffusion-controlled mechanism.

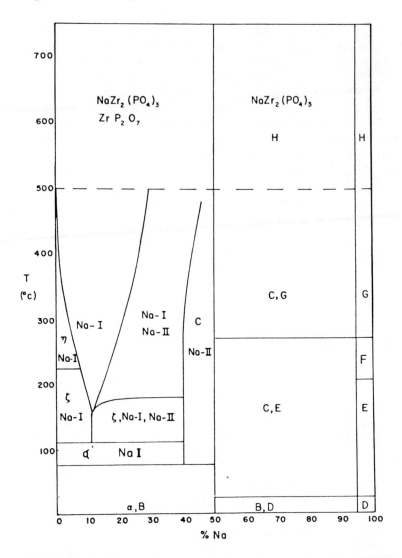

FIGURE 30.   Phases formed by $ZrNa_xH_{2-x}(PO_4)_2$, where X = O–2, upon heating to elevated temperatures. (From Clearfield, A. and Jirustithipong, P., in *Fast Ion Transport in Solids,* Vashista, P., Mundy, J. M., and Shenoy, G. K., Eds., North Holland, New York, 1979, 153. With permission.)

H. Zirconium-Titanium Phosphates

Coprecipitation of a mixture of Zr(IV) and Ti(IV) with phosphoric acid followed by refluxing in strong phosphoric acid leads to the formation of mixed zirconium-titanium phosphates.[134,135] X-ray powder patterns indicated that true solid solutions were formed over a broad range of compositions. The exchangers which were rich in Zr behaved like α-ZrP of intermediate crystallinity when exchanged with Na[+]. Likewise, behavior of the titanium rich solid solutions was similar to that of α-TiP (see Chapter 2) with perhaps a slightly better resistance to hydrolysis.

V. DEHYDRATED AND HIGH TEMPERATURE PHASES OF α-ZIRCONIUM PHOSPHATE

It is evident from the discussion of ion exchange properties in Section IV that the

Table 10
IDENTIFICATION OF THE PHASES IN
FIGURE 30

Designation	Composition of phase	Interlayer spacing (Å)
A	$ZrNaH(PO_4)_2 \cdot 5H_2O$	11.8
B	$ZrNaH(PO_4)_2 \cdot H_2O$	7.9
C	$ZrNaH(PO_4)_2$	7.3
D	$Zr(NaPO_4)_2 \cdot 3H_2O$	9.8
E	$Zr(NaPO_4)_2 \cdot H_2O$	8.4
F	$Zr(NaPO_4)_2$	8.4
G	$Zr(NaPO_4)_2$	7.6
H	$Zr(NaPO_4)_2$	7.6
Na-I	$ZrNa_{0.2}H_{1.8}(PO_4)_2$	6.9
Na-II	$ZrNa_{0.8}H_{1.2}(PO_4)_2$	7.2
ζ-ZrP	$Zr(HPO_4)_2$	7.41
η-ZrP	$Zr(HPO_4)_2$	7.2

amount of water taken up or released during the exchange plays a major role in determining the course of the exchange. Therefore, it is important to identify the actual degree of hydration of the phase in equilibrium with the exchanging solution. Many phases, i.e., $\overline{NaH} \cdot 5H_2O$, $\overline{KH} \cdot H_2O$, lose some or all of their waters of hydration at relative humidities lower than 90 to 100%. Thus, it is necessary to obtain X-ray data on the wet phases, i.e., those in equilibrium with the solution phase[20] and to determine the dehydration characteristics of these phases. Where these precautions were not taken lower hydrates or mixtures of hydrates were mistaken for the true exchanged phases.[84,136] Many dehydration studies were carried out in conjunction with the ion exchange studies.[20,65,74,87,137-140] These studies uncovered the existence of a variety of hydrates and anhydrous phases. In addition, new partially exchanged phases such as $ZrNa_{0.2}H_{1.8}(PO_4)_2$ and $ZrNa_{0.8}H_{1.2}(PO_4)_2$ were discovered (see Section IV.G.3).[23] These latter results indicated that for a complete understanding of the dehydration behavior and phase characterization it was necessary to examine the entire range of compositions from 0 to 100% cation content. The results for sodium ion are shown in Figure 30.[141] This figure is not an equilibrium phase diagram as the temperature range in which each phase occurs was determined by TGA and X-ray patterns taken at room temperature. The identification of the phases is given in Table 10. The α' phase has an X-ray pattern which resembles that of α-ZrP but may contain some Na$^+$. An interesting feature of the Na-I phase is the increase in its composition range at elevated temperature.

The sequence of phase changes which $\overline{NaH} \cdot 5H_2O$ undergoes on heating is the following:

$$\overline{NaH} \cdot 5H_2O \xrightarrow[50\%]{R.H.} \overline{NaH} \cdot 4H_2O \xrightarrow[<30\%]{R.H.} \overline{NaH} \cdot H_2O \xrightarrow{90^\circ}$$

$$\overline{NaH} \xrightarrow{500^\circ C} NaZr_2(PO_4)_3 \qquad (24)$$

Formation of sodium dizirconium triphosphate appears to take place by a decomposition reaction as shown in Equation 25.[20,142]

$$ZrNaH(PO_4)_2 \longrightarrow \tfrac{1}{2} NaZr_2(PO_4)_3 + \tfrac{1}{2} NaPO_3 + \tfrac{1}{2}H_2O \qquad (25)$$

The triphosphate is not a layered compound but a three-dimensional structure type.[143]

This phase has recently been synthesized hydrothermally from α-ZrP in the presence of sufficient Na^+.[142]

Even more complicated behavior is exhibited by $\overline{NaNa} \cdot 3H_2O$. This phase is relatively stable at room temperature although it slowly transforms to lower hydrates when kept in a desiccator for long periods of time. Phase H which appears still to be a layered compound is obtained by heating $\overline{NaNa} \cdot 3H_2O$ to 800°C. At higher temperatures phase H decomposes to yield $NaZr_2(PO_4)_3$ but above 1100°C a new phase, termed phase I, is obtained along with triphosphate.[142] A high temperature study of the silver exchange zirconium phosphate showed that $AgZr_2(PO_4)_3$ is formed in this system.[144] It can also be prepared hydrothermally.[146]

The hydrothermal and high temperature reactions are especially interesting in in the light of the discovery of fast ion conduction in compounds of the type $Na_{1+x}Zr_2Si_xP_{3-x}O_{12}$.[145] Apparently, it is also possible to prepare members of this series directly, either hydrothermally or by heating a mixture of sodium silicate and α-ZrP.[146]

Phase diagrams similar to the one presented in Figure 30 have been published for Li^+ and Cu^{2+} phases of α-ZrP.[139,147] We have already mentioned that UV-visible reflectance spectra of the fully exchanged phases, $ZrM(PO_4)_2 \cdot 4H_2O$ (M = Mn, Co, Ni, Cu, Zn) can be interpreted on the basis of the transition metal being octahedrally coordinated.[87] In the case of Cu(II) the coordination was tetragonally distorted. Marked changes in the spectra occurred with each water loss indicating that all four waters are coordinated to the metal ion. The dehydrated species are tetrahedral but become highly distorted at higher temperatures. Similar spectra were obtained for the corresponding partially M(II) exchanged α-ZrP solids, except for Ni(II).[148] For this ion the spectra indicated a five-coordinate stereochemistry, probably square pyramidal.

Horsley and Nowell[149] found that cation exchange of α-ZrP was accompanied by cleavage of the crystals parallel to the layers. This resulted in a marked increase in surface area and porosity of the crystals. A somewhat similar, but smaller effect, was caused by dehydrating the exchanged phases.

VI. ELECTROCHEMICAL PROPERTIES OF α-ZrP*

Solid electrolytes, having conductivities of 10^{-1} to 10^{-2} Ω^{-1} cm^{-1}, are required in several systems operating either with high current densities (electrolyzers, batteries, etc.), or at very low current levels (gauges, electrochemical memories, coulometers, etc.), in order to avoid excessive Joule-heat losses or excessive cell impedence.[150] Furthermore, high conductivities are required for materials employed in the preparation of charged membranes[151] or in thermoelectric generators.[152] Only a few solid electrolytes are presently known to exhibit such a favorable conductance and most of them only at high temperature. From the known ion exchange properties of α-type layered compounds and particularly since they exhibit solid-solid ion exchange, it is to be expected that the counter ions can move under an applied field.

Knowledge of the ionic transport properties of acid salts is also important from a fundamental point of view, their crystalline structure being known. In particular, for α-layered acid salts, it is possible to change the distance between fixed charges of adjacent layers without appreciably changing the distribution of the fixed charges. Therefore, α-layered acid salts present a unique possibility for relating the transport properties to the arrangement and distance of fixed charges and counter-ions, as well as to the presence of water within the layers and to steric factors of the matrix.

* This section was written in collaboration with Prof. G. Alberti.

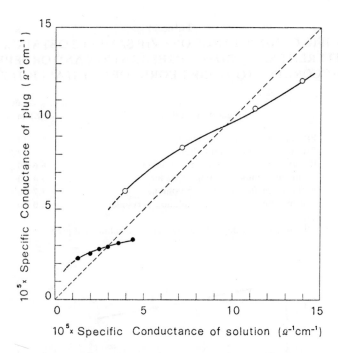

FIGURE 31. Specific conductance of two plugs of α-ZrP against specific conductance of the solutions (t = 25.0 ± 0.1°C). ● and ○ refer to sample nos. 4 and 6 of Table 11, respectively. (From Alberti, G., Casciola, M., Costantino, U., Levi, G., and Ricciardi, G., *J. Inorg. Nucl. Chem.*, 40, 533, 1978. With permission.)

A. Ionic Conductivity

In α-ZrP, the electric current is only due to the transport of counter-ions. The specific conductance, σ, can therefore be written:

$$\sigma = C F \mu \tag{26}$$

where C is the concentration of counter-ions in eq/cm³, μ is their mobility, and F is the Faraday constant. Owing to its high ion exchange capacity ($6.64 \cdot 10^{-3}$ eq/g) and high density (2.72 g/cm³), the concentration of counter-ions in α-Zr(HPO$_4$)$_2 \cdot$ H$_2$O is very high (1.8×10^{-2} eq/cm³). Thus, if the mobility of the protons in α-ZrP were as high as that in an aqueous solution of a strong acid, σ would be as high as 6.3 Ω^{-1}cm^{-1}. Owing to the lack of large crystals, the transport properties of α-ZrP have been determined using compacts of pressed microcrystals.[153,154]

For temperatures ranging from 0° to 100°C the isoconductance method[155,156] was employed. In this method the specific conductance of a plug of microcrystals is plotted against specific conductance of the interstitial solution of an electrolyte flowing through the plug itself. By gradually increasing the electrolyte concentration, a point is reached in which the specific conductance of the plug (microcrystals + solution) becomes equal to that of the solution. The isoconductance point corresponds to the specific conductance of the microcrystals and is easily found by the intersection of the plot with a line drawn at 45° to the abscissa (see Figure 31).

By using this latter method, it was found that the specific conductance of α-Zr(HPO$_4$)$_2 \cdot$ H$_2$O strongly depends on the method of preparation (see Table 11). The results seem to indicate that the conductance of α-Zr(HPO$_4$)$_2 \cdot$ H$_2$O increases with decrease in the structural order.

Table 11
SPECIFIC CONDUCTANCE OF α-ZrP SAMPLES OBTAINED BY DIFFERENT METHODS OF PREPARATION AND ORDERED ACCORDING TO THEIR DEGREE OF CRYSTALLINITY

Sample No.	Preparation method	Specific conductance $(\Omega^{-1}cm^{-1})$
1	Precipitation at r.t., amorphous[a]	$8.4 \cdot 10^{-3}$
2	Precipitation at r.t., amorphous[a]	$3.5 \cdot 10^{-3}$
3	Refluxing method (7:48), semicrystalline	$6.6 \cdot 10^{-4}$
4	Refluxing method (10:100), crystalline	$9.4 \cdot 10^{-5}$
5	Refluxing method (12:500), crystalline	$3.7 \cdot 10^{-5}$
6	Slow precipitation from HF solutions, crystalline	$3.0 \cdot 10^{-5}$

[a]   The specific conductance depends strongly on the conditions of preparation.

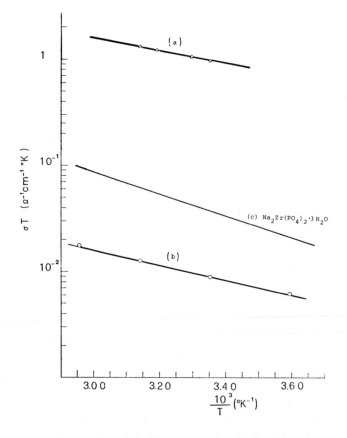

FIGURE 32.   Plot of Log σT versus $1/T$ for amorphous (A) and crystalline (B) α-ZrP, and (C) $Zr(NaPO_4)_2 \cdot 3H_2O$. Data are for samples nos. 2 and 6 of Table 11, respectively and $Zr(NaPO_4)_3 \cdot 3H_2O$ in Table 12. (From Alberti, G., Casciola, M., Costantino, U., Levi, G., and Ricciardi, G., *J. Inorg. Nucl. Chem.*, 40, 533, 1978. With permission.)

This is in agreement with the expectation that the ion transport properties of a solid should increase with increase in the number of defects in its crystalline structure. The activation energy for the conduction (evaluated by Arrhenius plots in the range 5 to

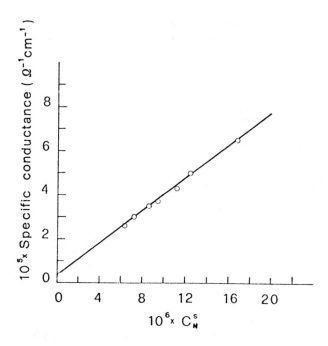

FIGURE 33. Specific conductance of α-ZrP samples having the same degree of crystallinity but different surface ion exchange capacity, C^s_H. (From Alberti, G., Casciola, M., Costantino, U., Levi, G., and Ricciardi, G., *J. Inorg. Nucl. Chem.*, 40, 533, 1978. With permission.)

70°C) apparently does not depend on the degree of crystallinity and is surprisingly low (2.6 to 3.1 kcal/mol) as seen in Figure 32.

In order to explain these results, the specific conductance of samples of α-$Zr(HPO_4)_2 \cdot H_2O$ having the same degree of crystallinity, but different specific surface areas, have been measured.[52] The surface ion exchange capacity of the samples was also measured, this quantity being proportional of their surface area.[78] It was found that the specific conductance increases linearly with increase in the surface area of the sample (see Figure 33). If the surface conductance is not negligible, we can write

$$\sigma = \sigma_i + \sigma_s + \sigma_s = CFX_i\mu_i + CFX_s\mu_s \tag{27}$$

where X is the ionic fraction of protons and the prefixes i and s refer to internal and surface protons, respectively.

Now, $C = C_i + C_s = 1.8 \cdot 10^{-2}$ eq H^+/cm^3; $X_s = C_s/C$; $X_i = 1-X_s \cong 1$.
Therefore,

$$\sigma = 1.8 \cdot 10^{-2}\ F\mu_i + F\mu_s C_s \tag{28}$$

By plotting σ as a function of C_s a straight line with slope $F\mu_s$ and intercept $1.8 \cdot 10^{-2}$ $F\mu_i$, must be obtained, as was found to be the case (see Figure 33). The mobility of protons on the surface can be evaluated from the slope and was found to be 3.9×10^{-5} cm² sec⁻¹ V⁻¹. Figure 33 also shows that the intercept of the straight line is near 0. Thus a small variation in the slope leads to a large variation in the intercept value; therefore, only very approximate values of the internal mobility of protons can be obtained by this method. It is, however, evident that the internal mobility is much lower than the surface mobility, the ratio μ_s/μ_i being higher than 10^{-4}. As a result, the

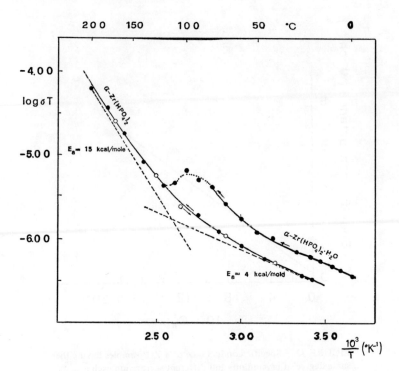

FIGURE 34.   Plot of Log σT against the reciprocal of the absolute temperature for a compact of α-ZrP initially in mono-hydrated form. ●, temperature increases; ○, temperature decreases; for dashed lines, see text. (From Alberti, G., Casciola, M., Costantino, U., and Radi, R., *Gazz. Chim. Ital.*, 109, 421, 1979. With permission.)

contribution of surface protons to the total conduction is high. It is interesting to point out that the same conclusions were derived from measurements of the electrochemical properties of membranes consisting of α-Zr(HPO$_4$)$_2 \cdot$H$_2$O microcrystals.[157] These results indicate that, before drawing definitive conclusions on the internal cationic transport of α-layered acid salts, the surface area of the samples must be determined. The low total activation energy found by the isoconductance method in the temperature range 5 to 70°C, is essentially related to surface transport.

In order to obtain the activation energy for the internal transport, the conductance of α-Zr(HPO$_4$)$_2 \cdot$H$_2$O compacts were measured in the range 0 to 190°C. In particular, the conductance was first measured in the range 0 to 120°C. The sample was then kept at 120° overnight and the anhydrous α-Zr(HPO$_4$)$_2$ so obtained was used for measurements in the range 120 to 20°C, then in the range 20 to 190°C and again in the range 190 to 20°C (to test the reversibility). The results are shown in Figure 34. The large range of temperatures explored makes it possible to distinguish between the activation energies of surface and internal protons. In other words, the experimental curve, referring to log σT = log (σ_i + σ_s)T, can be decomposed into two straight lines representing log $\sigma_i T$ and log $\sigma_s T$, separately. This is possible, assuming that at low temperature, σ_i is negligible with respect to σ_s, while the opposite occurs at high temperature. Taking into account that the intersection point of the two straight lines must lie 0.3 units below the experimental curve (note that, at the intersection point, $\sigma_s = \sigma_i = \sigma_{int.}$) therefore, log ($\sigma_s + \sigma_i$)T$_{int.}$ = log($\sigma_{int.}$ T$_{int.}$ + 0.3). The activation energy for internal surface transport, obtained from the slopes of the two straight lines are 15 ± 1 kcal/mol and 4 ± 1 kcal/mol, respectively.[154] Note that the activation energy for the surface transport of anhydrous α-Zr(HPO$_4$)$_2$ is of the same order of magnitude as that derived from measurements in aqueous solution by the isoconductance method in the range 5 to 70°C. However, the activation energy for internal transport is near to the activation energy for self-diffusion of Na$^+$ in Zr(NaPO$_4$)$_2 \cdot$ 3H$_2$O (17 kcal/mol).[49] Furthermore, a comparison of the transport properties of monohydrate and anhydrous α-ZrP in the range 0 to 100°, shows that the hydration appreciably increases the surface conduction and, very likely, also the internal one. In a further set of experiments,[154] the measurements were extended to 400°C (at higher temperatures the condensation of $\equiv$ P$-$OH groups to pyrophosphate occurs). α-Zr(HPO$_4$)$_2$ exhibits a reversible phase transition at about 200°C with a discontinuous change of the interlayer distance from 7.4 to 7.1 Å.[23,35] It was found that, in correspondence with this phase transition, there is a sharp increase of the conductance, while the activation energy for the internal transport decreases from 15 to 8.6 kcal/mole^{-1}. The specific conductance seems to be too low for practical use of α-ZrP as a solid electrolyte. However, improvements could be obtained by introducing appropriate defects in the structure or by replacing part of the P atoms with Si atoms as was done for NaZr$_2$(PO$_4$)$_3$.[145,146]

Another way of improving the conductance of α-ZrP is to use high surface area preparations. Preliminary work[146] in this direction increased the specific conductance considerably. Also γ-acid salts are expected to have better transport properties than α-compounds, because of their higher density of fixed charges in the layers and their high interlayer distance (see Chapter 2). Investigations on α-Ti(HPO$_4$)$_2 \cdot$ 2H$_2$O are now being performed in G. Alberti's laboratory and preliminary results seem to confirm this supposition.

B. Membranes

Ion exchange membranes consisting of acid salts of tetravalent metals are attractive for their potential use in some technological processes where organic membranes cannot be employed because of their degradability under drastic conditions (e.g., high temperature, high concentration of oxidizing agent, high doses of ionizing radiations, etc.). The first inorganic ion exchange membranes consisting of amorphous acid salts of tetravalent metals were prepared and studied independently by Dravnieks and Bregman[158] and Alberti.[159,160] Subsequently, these have been investigated in several laboratories and considerable improvements were made, especially in the preparation procedure.[160-166] The main defect with these membranes is their heterogeneity, being prepared from powders and suitable binders. Furthermore, their specific conductance is usually lower than that of organic ion exchange membranes. Some general aspects of inorganic ion exchange membranes, such as their preparation, the choice of the inorganic ion exchanger or binder in relation to the particular use of the membrane, as well as their potential applications, have been reviewed.[151] The electrochemical properties of membranes prepared with α-Zr(HPO$_4$)$_2 \cdot$ H$_2$O microcrystals bound by Kynar (polyvinylidene fluoride) have been investigated.[157] It is important to point out that these heterogeneous membranes behave as homogeneous porous membranes, the pores being the free spaces between adjacent microcrystals of α-Zr(HPO$_4$)$\cdot$ H$_2$O. This can easily be explained by remembering that, at room temperature, proton transport essentially occurs at the surface of the microcrystals. For this reason the concentration potential depends essentially on the nature of the counter-ions present in the surface. Thus, from e.m.f. measurements it is possible to calculate the ionic fraction, X_M, of a given cation M present in the surface. In the case of Cs$^+$, the complete surface H/Cs ion exchange isotherm has been determined by e.m.f. measurements.[156] Very good agreement with the same isotherm determined by usual ion exchange procedures has been obtained.[78]

Inorganic ion exchange membranes are still in the first stage of their development.

Table 12
CONDUCTIVITY OF SALT FORMS OF ZIRCONIUM PHOSPHATES

Phase	Interlayer spacing ($\mathring{A}$)	Ionic radius ($\mathring{A}$)	σ_{300} (ohm^{-1}cm^{-1})	E_a (kcal mol^{-1})	Ref.
α-Zr(LiPO$_4$)$_2$	7.05	0.60	3.21×10^{-6}	14.5	166
α-Zr(NaPO$_4$)$_2$	8.38	0.95	8.33×10^{-7}	15.7	166
α-Zr(NaPO$_4$)$_2$	7.60	0.95	2.14×10^{-5}	15.6±0.8	146
α-Zr(KPO$_4$)$_2$	9.02	1.33	6.58×10^{-8}	20.9	166
α-Zr(NaPO$_4$)$_2 \cdot$3H$_2$O	9.8	0.95	2.2×10^{-4}	4.6	7,52
γ-Zr(NaPO$_4$)$_2$	10.7	0.95	2.54×10^{-5}	14.7	166
α-ZrNaH(PO$_4$)$_2$	7.3		2.85×10^{-6}	18.6±1.0	146
α-ZrNa$_{0.8}$H$_{1.2}$(PO$_4$)$_2$	7.2		2.31×10^{-6}	17.1±0.09	146

Important improvements are expected, especially if it will be possible to increase the internal transport of counter-ions. In this case, inorganic ion exchange membranes could find attractive applications in fuel cells, in the chlor-alkali process, and in nuclear and several other technologies.

C. Conductivity of Salt Forms

Alberti and his co-workers[52] measured the conductance of Na$^+$ in Zr(NaPO$_4$)$_2 \cdot$3H$_2$O (see Figure 34) and found an activation energy of 4.6 kcal/mol. This result is not in keeping with the value of ~17 kcal/mol for the activation energy of self-diffusion of Na$^+$ in the same phase.[49] Apparently, the transport mechanisms in the two processes are different.

Yamanaka[165] obtained the conductivities of the anhydrous Li$^+$, Na$^+$, and K$^+$ phases of a highly crystalline α-ZrP (autoclaved in 10 M H$_3$PO$_4$ for 168 hr). The exchanged phases were heated at 350°C for 24 hr, pressed into discs and pressed between carbon electrodes at 500 atm. Some of the results are shown in Table 12. It is seen that the conductivities decrease in the order of increasing ionic radius of the conducting ion. By comparison, Clearfield and Jerus,[146] using silver electrodes, obtained conductivities two orders of magnitude greater for the sodium ion phase. However, the interlayer spacing reported by Yamanaka, 8.38 $\mathring{A}$, is that for phase F (see Table 10), while Clearfield and Jerus made their measurements on phase G. In addition, Yamanaka did not obtain a single straight line for the log σ vs. 1/T plots in the temperature range of his measurements. Rather, the data was linear only above about 220°C. In contrast Clearfield and Jerus' results gave a linear plot from 150° to 300°C.

Conductivity data for two phases containing both sodium ion and hydrogen were also determined (see Table 12). The conductivity decreased somewhat in the mixed ion phases. Calculation of Haven ratios for these phases using the diffusion coefficients from both conductivity and kinetic studies[146] yielded no simple ratios. Thus, as with the result for hydrated phases,[52] the mechanisms of the two processes must be different.

Yamanaka postulated[166] that there are three possible cation sites in α-ZrP, one in the center of the cavity M$_1$, and two above (or below) ZrO$_6$ octahedra(M$_2$). A maximum of two of the three sites can be filled so that conduction occurs by movement of ions through the unoccupied sites. Yamanaka observed that the interlayer spacings of the dehydrated half-exchanged phases are about the same or slightly less than that of α-ZrP which has a water molecule sitting in the center of each cavity. Thus, he speculated that the cations in these phases are also in the center of the cavity. The interlayer spacings of the fully exchanged phases increase with increase in ionic radius of the

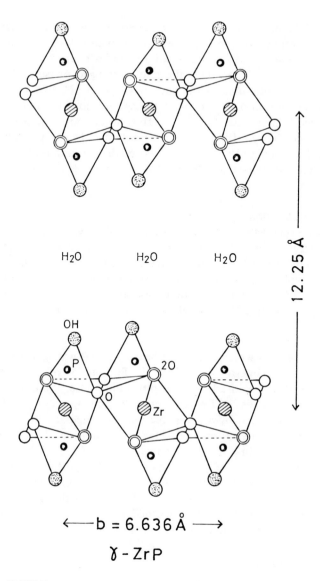

FIGURE 35. Schematic structural model for γ-ZrP according to Yamanaka. (From Yamanaka, S. and Tanaka, M., *J. Inorg. Nucl. Chem.*, 41, 45, 1979. With permission.)

cation and therefore, he proposed that they occupy M_2 type sites. However, in $Zr(NH_4PO_4)_2 \cdot H_2O$ the cations were found to be in neither the M_1 or M_2 sites, but to lie between two Zr and two P—O⁻ groups in adjacent layers.[92] In the half-exchanged phases it is likely that the cation occupies the M_1 site.

VII. γ-ZIRCONIUM PHOSPHATE

A. Preparation

γ-Zirconium phosphate, $Zr(HPO_4)_2 \cdot 2H_2O$ was first prepared[167] by refluxing a mixture 1 M in Zr(IV), 6 M in NaH_2PO_4 and 3 M in HCl. The interlayer spacing of this compound is 12.2 Å and on drying yields an anhydrous phase with interlayer spacing of 9.4 Å. Thus, γ-ZrP is not merely a more highly hydrated α-ZrP, but a new phase. This point is discussed in more detail below.

Yamanaka and Tanaka[168] carried out an extensive study of the preparative conditions. All of their preparations were carried out in an autoclave at temperatures of 180 to 230°C in the presence of high concentrations of phosphate and sodium ions. γ-ZrP was not synthesized directly. Rather, the half-exchanged phase $Zr(NaPO_4)(HPO_4)\cdot 1.5H_2O$ (phase P) was obtained in the narrow range of pH 1 to 4 (which decreased with increasing temperature). Removal of the sodium ions with acid yielded γ-ZrP. Alberti et al. recently prepared γ-TiP from HF solutions containing a high concentration of H_3PO_4 as well as by refluxing a TiP gel in 15.5 $M\,H_3PO_4$ (see Chapter 2). From this he concluded that a high PO_4/Ti ratio favored the formation of the γ-phase. Thus, it may be possible to prepare γ-ZrP without the presence of Na^+ under the proper conditions.

B. Structural Considerations

Initially it was thought that γ-ZrP consisted of α-ZrP-type layers which were shifted so as to be directly above each other rather than staggered as in α-ZrP.[167] However, unit cell dimensions (Table 1) and density data indicate a different layer arrangement. A more detailed explanation is given for γ-TiP in Chapter 2. It was suggested that the difference lies in the possibility that the phosphate groups act as both bidentate and monodentate ligans. A structural model based on this idea[168] is presented in Figure 35.

C. Thermal Behavior

The sequence of events which occurs on heating γ-ZrP was revealed by differential thermal and thermogravimetric analysis.[169-171] Two moles of water are lost below 100°C to yield β-ZrP (9.4 Å interlayer spacing). In one case,[171] an inflection in the TG curve was noted after the loss of 1 mol water, indicating a two stage dehydration. The dehydration is then followed by a reversible phase change at 270° to 300°C without weight loss. At higher temperatures a two stage condensation of monohydrogen phosphate groups occurs. The first is accompanied by loss of 2/3 of the water at $\sim$370°C and yields a crystalline phase of composition $Zr_3(HPO_4)_2(P_2O_7)_2$. The second water loss occurs between 500° and 700°C and results in the formation of ZrP_2O_7, which, however, crystallizes at a higher temperature (900°C). Although Dollimore et al.[169] indicated that the pyrophosphate which formed was not that of cubic ZrP_2O_7, the X-ray pattern they presented is similar to that of α-ZrP$_2$O$_7$.

D. Ion Exchange Properties

Much less work has been done on the ion exchange behavior of γ-ZrP as compared to α-ZrP. In general, γ-ZrP does not suffer the restrictions resulting from a small interlayer spacing and hence can exchange large cations and even complexes.[107]

1. Alkali Metal Cations

γ-ZrP exchanges alkali metal cations in two stages.[172] The initial selectivity sequence is $K^+ > Rb^+ > Cs^+ > Na^+ > Li^+$ (Eisenman's sequence IV) and the exchange took place at pH = 2 for K^+ and 2.9 for $Li+$. As exchange progressed the position of Cs^+ shifted to give Eisenman's sequence V; $K^+ > Rb^+ > Na^+ > Cs^+ > Li^+$. Each cation formed a half-exchanged phase but by two different routes. With Na^+ and Li^+ a half-exchanged phase formed at low loads and coexisted with unexchanged γ-ZrP. The titration curve was relatively flat as γ-ZrP was converted to the half-exchanged phase. For Li^+ the γ-ZrP was no longer present at 35% loading as a solid solution of Li^+ in the exchanger formed, accompanied by a steep rise in pH. The larger cations (K^+, Rb^+, Cs^+) formed a single phase almost immediately which extended to 50% loading. The interlayer spacings of the half-exchanged phases (except Li^+) are all smaller than 12.2 Å, indicating that the cation can fit in open spaces between the layers. There is some confusion concerning the exact water content of the exchanged phases. La Ginestra and Mas-succi[171] reported the composition $ZrNaH(PO_4)_2 \cdot 2.5H_2O$ whereas Dollimore et al.[169] found less than two moles of water but with the same interlayer spacing (11.6 Å).

The second stage of exchange, in which the half-exchanged phases are converted to $Zr(MPO_4)_2 \cdot xH_2O$, takes place at pH values above 7. Hydrolysis, which was negligible at lower pHs becomes more pronounced ($\sim$0.5 mmol/g PO_4^{3-} solubilized) but only for Cs^+ is it severe enough to make the titration results uncertain. The selectivity sequence without Cs^+ is $Li^+ > Na^+ > K^+ > Rb^+$ which is Eisenman's strong field sequence (IX). The interlayer distances are now larger than 12.2 Å, being 12.6 Å for Na^+, 14.3 Å for K^+ and 15.4 Å for Rb^+. It is interesting to note that at elevated temperatures both the half and fully exchanged phases yield the same products upon decomposition as the corresponding α-phases.[169-171]

2. Divalent Ions

In contrast to α-ZrP, γ-ZrP exchanges large amounts of Cu^{2+} as well as other divalent ions from either nitrate or acetate solutions at room temperature.[173] Complete exchange can probably be attained by column techniques. Even Ni(II) is taken up to a large extent. At 100°C quantitative uptake of Cu^{2+}, Ni^{2+}, Co^{2+}, Mn^{2+}, and Zn^{2+} was observed until a loading of about 3 meq. Beyond this load only Cu^{2+} was taken up quantitatively until 100% of exchange. With the other ions excess cation was required to achieve this level of exchange. The exchanged phases had the composition $ZrM(PO_4)_2 \cdot 4H_2O$.

E. Organic Derivatives

γ-ZrP intercalates amines and alcohols as does α-ZrP (see Chapter 3). However, it has recently been shown,[174,175] that ethylene oxide reacts with γ-ZrP to form a phosphate ester (see Equation 29).

$$
\begin{array}{c}
\mathrm{Zr-O} \\
\mathrm{Zr-O-P-OH} \\
\mathrm{Zr-O}
\end{array}
+ \mathrm{CH_2-CH_2} \longrightarrow
\begin{array}{c}
\mathrm{Zr-O} \\
\mathrm{Zr-O-P-OCH_2CH_2OH} \\
\mathrm{Zr-O}
\end{array}
$$

$$\gamma-\mathrm{ZrP} \qquad\qquad\qquad\qquad (29)$$

Under the proper conditions all of the OH groups can be esterfied, yielding a product with an interlayer spacing of 18.4 Å. A similar reaction with α-ZrP was not observed presumably because the oxide cannot diffuse into the crystals.

Propylene oxide reacts similarly[176] but only half the hydroxyl groups are esterified. With very concentrated solutions of propylene oxide not only were more of the P—OH groups esterfied, but polymerization ensued with formation of di- and tripropylene glycol chains. The interlayer spacing increased linearly from 21.5 Å (1 mol of ester) to greater than 30 Å for the product containing 4 mol organic. Ethylene oxide also formed polymers of this type.

The ester derivatives were found to undergo ester interchange reactions.[177-179] For example, when the phosphate esters were refluxed in phosphoric acid, the original γ-ZrP is formed. The reaction is one in which monohydrogen phosphate ions of the solution replace $HOCH_2CH_2OPO_3^{2-}$ groups in the solid. It was then found that mon-ophenyl orthophosphoric ester ($C_6H_5OPO_3H_2$)[178] and η-alkyl orthophosphoric esters[179] replace the HPO_4^{2-} groups of γ-ZrP to form derivatives of the type $Zr(ROPO_3)HPO_4 \cdot 2H_2O$. A structural model for the monophenyl compound is shown in Figure 36. The η-alkyl derivatives are able to intercalate η-alkanols.[179] These deri-

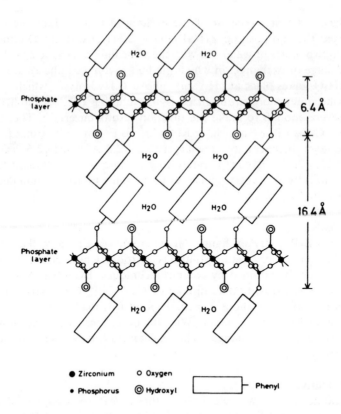

FIGURE 36. Structural model for $Zr(C_6H_5OPO_3)$ $(HPO_4) \cdot 2H_2O$ (basal spacing 16.4 Å). (From Yamanaka, S. and Hattori, M., *Chem. Lett. Jpn.*, 1073, 1979. With permission.)

vations may resemble phospholipids in structure and deserve study as model compounds of biomembranes.

Corresponding organic derivatives of α-ZrP have been prepared by direct reaction of alkylorthophosphates with soluble Zr(IV) in hydrofluoric acid solutions. These derivations are described in Chapters 2 and 3. Clearfield and co-workers[109] have esterified the surfaces of high surface area α-ZrP samples by methods similar to those described above. Partial esterification of the interior of α-ZrP was also achieved by using θ-ZrP as the starting phase.

VIII. APPLICATIONS

A. Renal Dialysis

Amorphous zirconium phosphate is used as a sorbant in portable renal dialysis systems.[180] Urea, which is the compound dialysed from the blood stream in the greatest quantity by artificial kidneys is not readily sorbed by common sorbants. Thus, in order to remove it from the dialysate, it is hydrolysed to ammonium carbonate by the enzyme urease. The dialysate is then passed over a column containing activated charcoal and ZrP. The ZrP is exchanged with sodium ion to the level where it does not remove additional Na^+ from the dialysate at the operating pH. However, either NH_4^+ is exchanged out or NH_3 is intercalated by the proton portion of the exchanger. Other organic contaminants are sorbed by the activated carbon. Cleansing of the dialysate is sufficient that it can be recirculated until the treatment is complete. The process has been commercialized.

B. Ion Exchange

Although both amorphous and crystalline forms of zirconium phosphate exhibit interesting ion exchange behavior their use in ion exchange technology has lagged. This state of affairs is due to several reasons. The solids do not lend themselves to conventional column use. They exhibit poor hydrodynamic properties and tend to bleed phosphate in alkaline solution. Many attempts have been made to obtain coarse granules by control of the process conditions. We have already mentioned the production of spherical particles (1.2 mm in diameter) by Ullrich et al.[32,33] Another approach tried was to precipitate silica gel onto the zirconium phosphate particles.[181] Clearfield took the opposite tack, precipitating ZrP onto porous silica to obtain coarse (1 to 2 mm) high surface area products.[107] Zirconium phosphate has been embedded in a polytetrafluoroethylene (fluoroplast) coating,[182] which imparts high mechanical strength and still allows for high exchange rates. To prevent phosphate from entering the process stream, hydrous zirconia may be admixed with the phosphate.[180,183] Ahrland et al. found that greater reproducibility and stability were obtained by using 6:6.[183-184] They found this exchanger suitable for the removal of corrosion products from reactor cooling water.

A large number of separations of radioisotopes have been reported.[1,9,11,24,102] As one example we may cite the complete separation of ^{137}Cs from fission products. The French Atomic Energy Commission utilizes a mixed bed exchanger consisting of ZrP and ammonium phosphotungstate in a process called ELAN.[185]

A great deal of effort has been expanded on studies devoted to the separation of actinides.[186-188] A process for the separation of plutonium from uranium may be in operation by the French. Separation of divalent ions has also received some recent attention.[189-90]

Two developments should spur the increased use of zirconium phosphates in ion exchange processes. The discovery that large cations can be readily exchanged by $\overline{NaH} \cdot 5H_2O$, θ-ZrP and amine intercalates and the use of high surface area forms. A surface area of 150 M^2/g means that ~1 meq of exchange capacity resides on the surface. Reactions at the surface are very rapid and separations based on surface exchange selectivities could be carried out rapidly. In addition, the superior resistance to temperature and high radiation field of inorganics recommends them for use in nuclear technology. The effect of high radiation doses has been reported.[191-193] Zirconium phosphates are stable to oxidizing solutions, can be used in fused salts, and resist the action of acids. However, it should be kept in mind that α-ZrP alters to a triphosphate on hydrothermal treatment in the presence of cations above about 250°C.[142,194]

C. Water Softening

Both amorphous zirconium phosphate and $ZrNaH(PO_4)_2 \cdot 5H_2O$ have a high affinity for Ca^{2+} but a less than average affinity for Mg^{2+}. Nevertheless, they are capable of removing these ions from hard water. As yet no such use has been reported, but as the price of organic resins increases the inorganic exchangers become more attractive.

A patent has been granted for the use of ZrP in detergents.[195] The exchanger removes Ca^{2+} and Mg^{2+} from the wash water efficiently in the presence of the large amounts of Na^+ introduced from the detergent builders, $Na_2SO_4 \cdot 10H_2O$ and Na_2SiO_3.

D. Chromatography

In view of the voluminous literature on zirconium phosphates it is surprising that only a few studies have examined its use for gas chromatography columns. Work has been carried out on gels[196-198] as well as crystals.[199,200] Amines were separated on columns containing a gel in the Cu^{2+}, Zn^{2+}, or Mn^{2+} form using ammonia as the mobile gas phase.[197,198] Chlorohydrocarbons and mercaptans were effectively separated on crystalline potassium zirconium phosphate.[199] Recently, Maya[201] examined the use of alkyl phosphate derivatives of α-ZrP as solid supports in reverse phase liquid chromatography. His preparations of the ZrP derivatives were carried out in HNO_3 rather than HF. Separations of aromatic hydrocarbons were effected on small columns at relatively low pressures.

Interesting separations of mixtures of ions have been demonstrated both by paper chromatography,[202-204] and thin layer chromatography.[205,206] All of these chromatography studies must be considered as preliminary and additional; more systematic studies are required. The use of high surface area materials will undoubtedly improve the separation factors. Also, the use of γ-ZrP phosphate esters for the separation of straight chain from branched-chain polar molecules is indicated.[179]

E. Catalysis

Any systematic determination of the catalytic properties of zirconium phosphates must take into account the great variety of forms of this material (P-Zr ratio, crystallinity, phase(s) present under reaction conditions, etc.) and their influence on the nature of the catalytic sites. Only a few studies have been carried out along these lines as detailed below.

1. Surface Acidity and Alcohol Dehydration

Since zirconium phosphates are solid acids, one of the fundamental properties to be determined in relation to catalytic behavior is the nature of the acidic surface sites. This was done[207,208] for α-ZrP by titration with butylamine in iso-octane using various indicators with different pKa (Benesi method). The results are shown in Figure 37. It is seen that the total number of acid sites (6.2 meq/g) is very close to the exchange capacity of the solid and remains constant (except for 0.5:48) irrespective of crystallinity and heat treatment. X-ray powder patterns taken on the solid after titration are identical to those of the almost completely intercalated exchanger.[209,210] Thus, the titration is a measure of the interaction of the amine with the P—OH groups of the exchanger. A portion of these sites, lying between Ho -3.3 and -5.6, may be considered as strong acid sites. Their number increases with heat treatment and increased surface area. However, the number of such strong acid sites is always much larger than the number of P—OH groups on the surface. For example, exchanger 4.5:48 (S.A. = 34.6 M^2/g, Table 3) has 0.24 meq of P—OH groups on the surface. This is 0.77 to 0.24 times the number of strong acid sites. The ratios are much smaller for the more crystalline samples 12:336[208] and 10:48.[207] X-ray patterns of the solids, to which the amount of amine added corresponds to the number of strong acid groups, reveal the presence of α-ZrP + a 10.5 Å intercalate. This latter phase contains amine between and parallel to the layers.[210] Thus, the strong acid groups must be those on the surface and in the interior layers close to the surface. Hattori et al.[207] considered the weak acid sites to be P—OH groups interacting with zeolitic water, whereas the strong acid groups are the free P—OH groups. When the exchangers are heated above 450°C, the phosphate groups condense and the number of strong and weak acid groups decreases correspondingly, as seen for 0.5:48 heated to 400°C.

The dehydration of cyclohexanol to cyclohexene using α-zirconium phosphate as catalyst was found to follow first order kinetics.[208] A plot of the logarithm of the rate constant versus the logarithm of the number of surface protons, in meq/g, for catalysts of increasing surface area was linear (see Figure 38).[209] Furthermore, when the surface protons were exchanged out by Cs^+, a drastic reduction in rate was observed. Quinoline poisoning produced similar results. All of this points to Bronsted acid sites as being responsible for catalytic activity. However, the calcined gel (0.5:48), which exhibited almost no Bronsted acidity (see Figure 37), was mildly active in the dehydration reac-

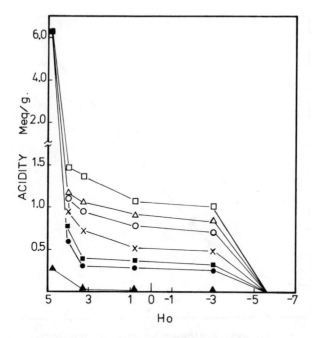

FIGURE 37. Acid-strength distribution of hydroxyl groups in α-ZrP samples heated at various temperatures. ZrP(12:336): 110°C, ●; 320°C, X; 400°C, O; ZrP(4.5:48): 110°C, ■; 320°C, △; 400°C, □; ZrP(0.5:48): 400°C, ▲. (From Clearfield, A. and Thakur, D. S., *J. Catal.*, 65, 185, 1980. With permission.)

tion. Even the Cs^+ and quinoline-poisoned samples exhibited some residual activity. Thus, a second type of site, probably of the Lewis acid type, may also be involved. This second site is also thought to be responsible for the deviation of the low surface area catalysts from the straight line plot of Figure 38.

A number of other studies of alcohol dehydration have been carried out. A gel with a reported surface area of 335 M^2/g was found to yield 93 to 94% conversions of C_2-C_4 alcohols to olefins.[211-213] Significant amounts of methylcyclopentanes was obtained in the dehydration of cyclohexanol.[214] This stands in contrast to the relative inactivity observed for 0.5:48 in the study of Clearfield and Thakur.[208] Nozaki et al.[215] examined the dehydration of 2-propanols. The rate was found to be zero order with an activation energy of 22 kcal/mol at 170 to 230°C and 9.1 kcal/mol at temperatures greater than 230°C. Lewis acid sites formed by water split out were considered to be the origin of the catalytic activity.

In contrast to the reported studies with gels, Clearfield et al.[107] found an almost total lack of 1- and 3- pentanol dehydration activity at 300°C for the amorphous ZrP (0.5:48). We shall return to this point later.

2. Synthesis of Methyl Isobutyl Ketone

Methyl isobutyl ketone is an important industrial solvent which is produced in low yields from acetone by a three-step process. Recently a one-step synthesis was developed which uses a ZrP gel containing about 0.5% Pd.[216,217] The ZrP apparently dehydrates the acetone to $(CH_3)_2C=CHCOCH_3$ which is then hydrogenated by H_2 with the Pd acting as catalyst. A puzzling aspect of this reaction and the vapor phase hydrolysis of chlorobenzene[218] discussed in Section VII.E.3 above is the high dehydration activity of the gel. The catalyst is heated to 450°C before use and at this temperature almost all of the P—OH groups have split out water to form P—O—P type links. This point bears further study.

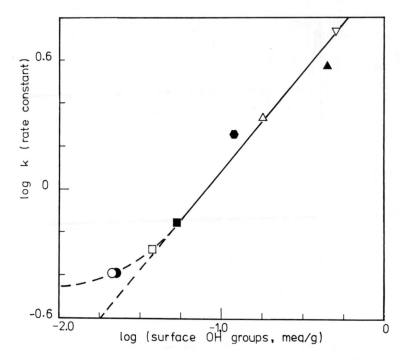

FIGURE 38.   Cyclohexanol dehydration activity of ZrP samples of varying crystallinity plotted as the logarithm of the first order rate constant, k, versus the logarithm of the number of surface hydroxyl groups. ZrP samples are 12:336 - O, 12:100 - ●, 12:50 - ■, 9:48 - □, 6.48   , 4.5:48 - △, 3.5:48 - ▲, 2.5:48 - ▽. (From Clearfield, A. and Thakur, D. S., *J. Catal.*, in press. With permission.)

3. Miscellaneous Reactions

A copper(II)-containing ZrP gel was found to effectively catalyse the vapor phase hydrolysis of chlorobenzene to phenol at 450°C.[218] Interestingly, gels precipitated at pH = 4 showed the highest activity while the activity fell off sharply for gels prepared at higher or lower pH values. The reasons for this behavior are obscure and require further study. The activity decreases with time due to the loss of Cu(II), probably as $CuCl_2$. However, when $CuCl_2$ was supplied in the gas stream the activity was maintained for long periods (~600 hr) of time.

Austerweil employed ZrP as a catalyst for the Pechmann condensation of malic acid with phenol into cumarin.[219] The polymerization of olefins[220] and ethylene oxide[221,222] has been reported as has the hydration of ethylene to ethyl alcohol.[223] A number of catalysed oxidations have been reported including butane to maleic acid,[224] CO to CO_2,[225] and oxidative waste water treatment.[226]

4. Metals Supported on Zirconium Phosphate

During an examination of the oxidative dehydration of cyclohexene by $ZrCu(PO_4)_2$ it was found that a portion of the Cu(II) was reduced to Cu°.[227] The metal spontaneously reoxidized to Cu(II) on exposure to air, even at room temperature. However, CuO was not formed but rather the copper ions diffused back into the zirconium phosphate to reform $ZrCu(PO_4)_2$. Similar results were obtained upon hydrogen reduction of $ZrCu(PO_4)_2$ in the temperature range 220 to 450°C.[227,228] Cu(I) was found to be present when the reduction was carried out under mild conditions.

A study of the kinetics of reduction of the Cu(II) containing α-ZrP has been carried out.[229] It was found that complete reduction to Cu(I) at temperatures of 200 to 300°C occurs if the hydrogen pressure is below ~150 torr. Above this pressure only copper

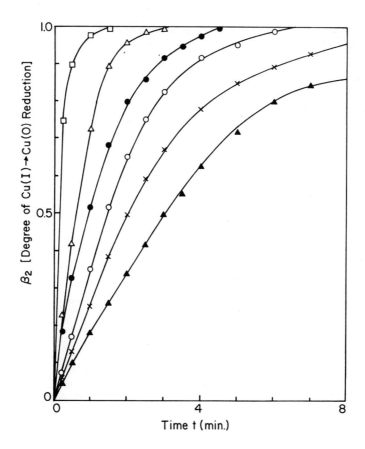

FIGURE 39. Rate of hydrogen reduction of $ZrCuH(PO_4)_2$ to copper metal as a function of temperature and initial H_2 pressure. Conditions are 200°C and 182 torr - ▲, 240°C and 182 torr - X, 275° and 182 torr - ○, 303° and 182 torr - ●; 303°C and 229 torr -△, 303°C and 447 torr - □.

metal is obtained. The reaction rates are strongly dependent upon hydrogen pressure and temperature as shown in Figure 39. The pressure dependence is of the order of P_{H2} 1.8 for each reduction step. Thus, at 1 atm of pressure the reaction proceeds at temperatures below 100°C.

A plausible explanation for the oxidative dehydrogenation of cyclohexene can be given based upon the hydrogen reduction studies. Hydrogen is abstracted from the hydrocarbon by reducing Cu(II). The oxygen then reoxidizes both Cu(I) and Cu° to Cu(II) which can then participate in abstracting hydrogen from the cyclohexene again.[227] Objection was raised to this mechanism[230] on the grounds that dehydrogenation of ethylbenzene was found to be catalysed by zirconium phosphate without Cu(II) being present. However, it was pointed out[231] that their reaction required temperatures in excess of 400°C whereas when Cu(II) is present, oxidative dehydrogenation can take place at 300°C.

In very recent studies[232] it has been found that cation-containing zirconium phosphates catalyse a wide variety of hydrogen reductions, hydroformylations and oxidation reactions at gas pressures of 200 to 600 psi. In fact, unexchanged ZrP was able to hydrogenate olefins but at a much lower rate than when cations are present.

F. Membranes and Solid Electrolytes

Inorganic membranes are attractive from the standpoint of stability towards acids, temperature, and high radiation fields. Considering the whole family of acid salts as discussed in this and succeeding chapters they also present an opportunity of relating their electrochemical and osmotic properties to the known arrangement of the fixed charges and counter-ions or steric factors.[7] Problems of cohesiveness and flexibility of the membranes are yet to be solved, but it seems clear that further increases in conductivity are possible.

The transformation of zirconium phosphates into three-dimensional triphosphates or silicophosphates by hydrothermal and high temperature reactions indicates that they may well play a role in solid electrolyte technology.

REFERENCES

1. **Kraus, K. A. and Phillips, H. O.**, Adsorption on inorganic materials. I. Cation exchange properties of zirconium phosphate, *J. Am. Chem. Soc.*, 78, 644, 1956.
2. **Amphlett, C. B., McDonald, L. A., and Redman, M. J.**, Cation exchange properties of zirconium phosphate, *Chem. Ind. (London)*, 1314, 1956.
3. **Russell, E. R., Adamson, A. W., Shubert, J., and Boyd, G. E.**, Decontamination of product by adsorption on tailor-made inorganic adsorbents, *U.S. A. E. C.*, Rep. CN-508, 1943, (declassified 1957).
4. **Clearfield, A. and Stynes, J. A.**, The preparation of crystalline zirconium phosphate and some observations on its ion exchange behavior, *J. Inorg. Nucl. Chem.*, 26, 117, 1964.
5. **Clearfield, A.**, Crystalline Titanium Phosphate, Research Report, Titanium Alloy Mfg. Div., NL Industries, Niagara Falls, N.Y., 1964.
6. **Alberti, G. and Costantino, U.**, Recent progress in the field of synthetic inorganic exchangers having a layered or fiberous structure, *J. Chromatogr.*, 102, 5, 1974.
7. **Alberti, G.**, Synthesis, crystalline structure, and ion exchange properties of insoluble acid salts of tetravalent metals and their salt forms, *Acc. Chem. Res.*, 11, 163, 1978.
8. **Winkler, A. and Thilo, E.**, Concerning a series of acid compounds, HX (IV) P_2O_8 and $H_2X(IV)P_2O_8$ with layered structures, *Z. Anorg. Allg. Chem.*, 346, 92, 1966.
9. **Clearfield, A., Nancollas, G. H., and Blessing, R. H.**, New inorganic ion exchangers, in *Ion Exchange and Solvent Extraction*, Marinsky, J. A. and Marcus, Y., Eds., Marcel Dekker, New York, 1973, chap. 1.
10. **Clearfield, A., Oskarsson, Å., and Oskarsson, C.**, On the mechanism of ion exchange in crystalline zirconium phosphates. VI. The effect of crystallinity of the exchanger on Na^+-H^+ exchange, *Ion Exch. Membr.*, 1, 9, 1972.
11. **Vesely, V. and Pekarek, V.**, Synthetic inorganic ion exchangers. I. Hydrous oxides and acidic salts of polyvalent metals, *Talanta*, 19, 219, 1972.
12. **Clearfield, A. and Smith, G. D.**, The crystallography and structure of zirconium bis(monohydrogen orthophosphate) monohydrate, *Inorg. Chem.*, 8, 431, 1969.
13. **Alberti, G. and Torracca, E.**, Crystalline insoluble salts of polybasic metals. II. Synthesis of crystalline zirconium or titanium phosphate by direct precipitation, *J. Inorg. Nucl. Chem.*, 30, 317, 1968.
14. **Troup, J. M. and Clearfield, A.**, On the mechanism of ion exchange in zirconium phosphates. 20. Refinement of the crystal structure of α-zirconium phosphate, *Inorg. Chem.*, 16, 3311, 1977.
15. **Ahrland, S. and Albertsson, J.**, Inorganic ion exchangers. VI. The unit-cell dimensions of crystalline zirconium phosphate, *Acta Chem. Scand.*, 23, 1446, 1969.
16. **Dushin, R. B. and Krylov, V. N.**, Structure of crystalline titanium (IV) hydrogen phosphate, *Akad. Nauk SSSR, Neorg. Mat. Izvest.*, 14, 288, 1978.
17. **Greis, O. and Clearfield, A.**, Unit Cell Dimensions of α-Zirconium Phosphate by the Guinier-Jagodzinski Method, Internal Rep., Texas A&M University, College Station, 1979.
18. **Albertsson, J., Oskarsson, Å., Tellgren, R., and Thomas, J. O.**, Inorganic ion exchangers. 10. A neutron powder diffraction study of the hydrogen bond geometry in α-$Zr(HPO_4)_2 \cdot H_2O$. A model for the ion exchange, *J. Phys. Chem.*, 81, 1574, 1977.
19. **Clearfield, A., Kullberg, L., and Oskarsson, Å.**, On the mechanism of ion exchange in crystalline zirconium phosphates. XI. The variation in unit cell dimensions and Na^+/H^+ exchange behavior in highly crystalline α-zirconium phosphates, *J. Phys. Chem.*, 78, 1150, 1974.

20. Clearfield, A., Duax, W. L., Medina, A. S., Smith, G. D., and Thomas, J. R., On the mechanism of ion exchange in crystalline zirconium phosphate. I. Sodium ion exchange on α-zirconium phosphate, *J. Phys. Chem.*, 73, 3424, 1969.

21. Horsley, S. E., Nowell, D. V., and Stewart, D. T., The infrared and Raman spectra of α-zirconium phosphate, *Spectrochim. Acta*, 30A, 535, 1974.

22. Dushin, R. B., Krylov, V. N., Larina, K. P., and Nikolskii, B. P., IR spectroscopic study of the mechanism of ion exchange on amorphous hafnium phosphate, *Bull. Acad. Sci. USSR*, 3, 469, 1977.

23. Clearfield, A. and Pack, S. P., Factors determining ion exchange selectivity. I. High temperature phases of α-zirconium phosphate and its sodium and potassium exchanged forms, *J. Inorg. Nucl. Chem.*, 37, 1283, 1975.

24. Amplett, C. B., *Inorganic Ion Exchangers*, Elsevier, Amsterdam, 1964.

25. Szirtes, L., Zsinka, L., Zaborenko, K. B., and Iofa, B. Z., Synthetic inorganic ion exchangers, *Acta Chim. Acad. Sci. Hung.*, 54, 215, 1967.

26. Tikavyi, V. F. and Komorov, V. D., Hydrolysis of zirconium phosphate, *Izv. Akad. Nauk SSSR, Neorg. Mater.*, 5, 180, 1969.

27. Ahrland, S., Albertsson, J., Johansson, L., Nihlgard, B., and Nilsson, L., Inorganic ion exchangers. I. Acidity, hydrolysis and resistance to acids of some inorganic ion exchangers, especially zirconium phophate, *Acta Chem. Scand.*, 18, 707, 1964.

28. Baetsle, L. and Pelsmaekers, J., Ion exchange properties of zirconyl phosphates. I. Contribution to the structure of zirconyl phosphates, *J. Inorg. Nucl. Chem.*, 21, 124, 1961.

29. Ahrland, S., Albertsson, J., Johansson, L., Nihlgard, B., and Nilsson, L., Inorganic ion exchangers. II. Sorption rate and dehydration studies on zirconium phosphate and tungstate gels, *Acta Chem. Scand.*, 18, 1346 1357, 1964.

30. Alberti, G., Torracca, E., and Conte, A., Stoichiometry of ion exchange materials containing zirconium and phosphate, *J. Inorg. Nucl. Chem.*, 28, 607, 1966.

31. Ahrland, S., Albertsson, J., Alnas, Å., Hemmingsson, S., and Kullberg, L., Inorganic ion exchangers. V. The influence of the water content on the sorption of zirconium phosphate gel of different crystallinity, *Acta Chem. Scand.*, 21, 195, 1967.

32. Ullrich, J., Tympl, V., Pekarek, V., and Vesely, V., Preparation and sorption properties of zirconium phosphate spherical particles, *J. Radioanal. Chem.*, 24, 361, 1975.

33. Caletka, R. and Tympl, M., Sorption properties of zirconium phosphate prepared by the sol-gel method, *J. Inorg. Nucl. Chem.*, 39, 669, 1977.

34. Ahrland, S., Albertsson, J., Oskarsson, Å., and Niklasson, Å., Inorganic ion exchangers. VII. The sorption of first-row transition metal ions on a zirconium phosphate gel of low crystallinity, and a study of the reproducibility of the gel, *J. Inorg. Nucl. Chem.*, 32, 2069, 1970.

35. La Ginestra, A., Massucci, M. A., Ferragino, C., and Tomassini, N., Thermal behavior of some synthetic ion exchangers: insoluble acid phosphates and arsenates of tetravalent metals, *Thermal Analysis, Proc. 4th I.C.T.A., Budapest, 1974*, Vol. 1, Heyden, London, 1975, 631.

36. Horsley, S. E. and Nowell, D. V., Thermal decomposition of zirconium phosphate, *Thermal Analysis, Proc. 3rd I.C.T.A., Davos*, Vol. 2, Birkhauser Verlag, Basel, 1971, 611.

37. Torracca, E., Crystalline insoluble salts of polyvalent metals and polybasic acids. VII. Ion exchange behavior of Li⁺, Na⁺ and K⁺ forms of crystalline zirconium phosphate, *J. Inorg. Nucl. Chem.*, 31, 1189, 1969.

38. Horsley, S. E. and Nowell, D. V., The preparation and characterization of crystalline α-zirconium phosphate, *J. Appl. Chem. Biotechnol.*, 23, 215, 1973.

39. Herbell, J. D., Specht, S., and Born, H. J., DTA, ETA and TG investigations of zirconium phosphates of different crystallinity, *Thermochim. Acta*, 20, 87, 1977.

40. Chernorukov, N. G., Korshunov, I. A., and Zhuk, M. I., Polymorphic transformations in titanium, zirconium and hafnium hydrogen phosphates, (transl.), *Zhur. Neorg. Khim.*, 22, 2065, 1977; *Russ. J. Phys. Chem.*, 51, 1223, 1977.

41. Inoue, Y. and Yamada, Y., The Synthesis of crystalline zirconium phosphate with large particle size by the direct-precipitation method, *Bull. Chem. Soc. Jpn.*, 52, 3528, 1979.

42. Albertsson, J., Inorganic ion exchangers. IV. The sorption on crystalline zirconium phosphate and its dependence upon crystallinity, *Acta Chem. Scand.*, 20, 1689, 1966.

43. Prospert, J., Some Properties of Zirconium Phosphate, Rappt. CEA-R 2835, Commissariat A L'Energie Atomique, Paris, 1966.

44. Alberti, G., Conte, A., and Torracca, E., Influence of thermal treatment on the rate of ion exchange of zirconium phosphate, *J. Inorg. Nucl. Chem.*, 28, 225, 1966.

45. Karaseva, T. A., Skripnik, Z. D., and Strelko, V. V., Study of the mechanism of zirconium phosphate dehydration, *Ukr. Khim. Zh.*, 42, 479, 1976.

46. Allulli, S., Massucci, M. A., and Tomassini, N., The standard enthalpy of formation of anhydrous, nonohydrated and dihydrated zirconium bis(monohydrogen phosphate), *J. Chem. Thermodyn.*, 11, 613, 1979.

47. **Fillippova, N. M. and Chemodanov, O. I.**, Thermodynamic characteristics of certain zirconium phosphates, *Zh. Fiz. Chim.*, 49, 266, 1975.
48. **Warren, B. E.**, *X-ray Diffraction*, Addison-Wesley, Reading, Mass., 1969, chap. 13.
49. **Costantino, U., Naszodi, L., Szirtes, L., and Zsinka, L.**, On the mechanism of diffusion in crystalline insoluble acid salts of tetravalent metals. II. Self diffusion of Na⁺ and K⁺ on microcrystals of Zr(NaPO₄)₂·3H₂O, *J. Inorg. Nucl. Chem.*, 40, 901, 1978.
50. **Alberti, G., Costantino, U., and Giulietti, R.**, Preparation of large crystals of α-Zr(HPO₄)₂·H₂O, *J. Inorg. Nucl. Chem.*, 42, 1062, 1980.
51. **Alberti, G., Bertrami, R., Costantino, U., and Gupta, J. P.**, Crystalline insoluble acid salts of tetravalent metals. XXVI. Ammonium and ammonia uptake on different ionic forms of crystalline zirconium phosphate, *J. Inorg. Nucl. Chem.*, 39, 1057, 1977.
52. **Alberti, G., Casciola, M., Costantino, U., Levi, G., and Ricciardi, G.**, On the mechanism of diffusion and ionic transport in crystalline insoluble acid salts of tetravalent metals. I. Electrical conductance of zirconium bis(monohydrogen orthophosphate)monohydrate with a layered structure, *J. Inorg. Nucl. Chem.*, 40, 533, 1978.
53. **Clearfield, A. and Djuric, Z.**, On the mechanism of ion exchange in zirconium phosphates. XXV. Exchange of surface protons with ammonium ion, *J. Inorg. Nucl. Chem.*, 41, 903, 1979.
54. **Clearfield, A. and Berman, J. R.**, On the mechanism of ion exchange in zirconium phosphates. XXXIV. Determination of surface areas from surface exchange, *J. Inorg. Nucl. Chem.*, in press.
55. **Clearfield, A. and Medina, A. S.**, On the mechanism of ion exchange in crystalline zirconium phosphate. V. Thermodynamic treatment of the hydrogen ion-sodium ion exchange of α-zirconium phosphate, *J. Phys. Chem.*, 75, 3750, 1971.
56. **Torracca, E., Alberti, G., Platania, R., Salala, P., and Galli, P.**, Preparation and properties in inorganic exchangers of the zirconium phosphate type, in *Ion Exchange in the Process Industries*, Society of Chemical Industry, London, 1970, 315.
57. **Alberti, G., Costantino, U., and Gill, J. S.**, Crystalline insoluble acid salts of tetravalent metals. XXIII. Preparation and main ion exchange properties of highly hydrated zirconium bis(monohydrogen orthophosphates), *J. Inorg. Nucl. Chem.*, 38, 1783, 1976.
58. **Chernorukov, N. G. and Prokof'eva, T. V.**, Thermodynamics of ion exchange of some doubly charged cations on amorphous zirconium phosphate, *Zh. Fiz. Khim.*, 53, 791, 1979.
59. **Chernorukov, N. G., Korshunov, I. A., and Prokof'eva, T. V.**, Thermodynamics of the exchange of alkali metals ions on amorphous zirconium phosphate, *Zh. Fiz. Khim.*, 50, 3091, 1976.
60. **Strelko, V. V., Karaseva, T. A., Struzhko, V. L., and Skrepnik, Z. O.**, Sorption properties of salt forms of amorphous zirconium phosphate, *Teor. Ekso. Khim.*, 12, 846, 1976.
61. **Laskorin, B. N., Karaseva, T. A., and Stelko, V. V.**, Reasons for the selective sorption of heavy alkali metal cations by zirconium phosphate-type ion exchangers, *Dokl. Akad. Nauk SSSR*, 229, 910, 1976.
62. **Chernorukov, N. G. and Prokof'eva, T. V.**, Thermodynamics of the exchange of transition element ions on amorphous zirconium phosphate, *Zh. Fiz. Khim.*, 52, 1839, 1978.
63. **Ragoisha, A. A., Soldatov, V. S., and Tikavyi, V. F.**, Thermodynamics of the ionic exchange of alkali metal cations on zirconium phosphate, *Tezisy Dokl.-Vses. Simp. Termodin Ionnogo Obmena*, 75, 46, 1975.
64. **Clearfield, A. and Oskarsson, Å.**, On the mechanism of ion exchange in crystalline zirconium phosphates. IX. The effect of crystallinity on Cs⁺-H⁺ exchange of α-zirconium phosphate, *Ion Exch. Membr.*, 1, 205, 1974.
65. **Clearfield, A. and Tuhtar, D. A.**, On the mechanism of ion exchange in crystalline zirconium phosphates. 15. The effect of crystallinity of the exchanger on Li⁺-H⁺ exchange of α-zirconium phosphates, *J. Phys. Chem.*, 80, 1296, 1976.
66. **Kullberg, L. and Clearfield, A.**, On the mechanism of ion exchange in zirconium phosphates. 28. Calorimetric determination of heats of Rb⁺-H⁺ exchange on α-ZrP, *J. Phys. Chem.*, 84, 165, 1980.
67. **Clearfield, A., Day, G. A., Ruvarac, A., and Milonjic, S.**, On the mechanism of ion exchange in zirconium phosphates. 29. The effect of crystallinity on the exchange of K⁺-H⁺ exchange of α-ZrP, *J. Inorg. Nucl. Chem.*, 43, 165, 1981.
68. **Kullberg, L. and Clearfield, A.**, On the mechanism of ion exchange in zirconium phosphates. 31. Thermodynamics of alkali metal ion exchange on amorphous ZrP, *J. Phys. Chem.*, 85, 1578, 1981.
69. **Eisenman, G.**, Cation selective glass electrodes and their mode of operation, *Biophys. J.*, 2, 259, 1962.
70. **Clearfield, A. and Kullberg, L.**, On the mechanism of ion exchange in crystalline zirconium phosphates. X. Calorimetric determination of heats of Na⁺-H⁺ exchange, *J. Phys. Chem.*, 78, 152, 1974.
71. **Clearfield, A., Nancollas, G. H., and Blessing, R. A.**, in *Ion Exchange and Solvent Extraction*, Marinsky, J. A. and Marcus, V., Eds., Marcel Dekker, New York, 1973, 34.
72. **Lewis, G. N. and Randall, M.**, *Thermodynamics*, 2nd ed., revised by Pitzer, K. S. and Brewer, L., McGraw-Hill, New York, 1961.

73. **Kullberg, L. and Clearfield, A.**, On the mechanism of ion exchange in zirconium phosphates. 32. Thermodynamics of alkali metal ion exchange on crystalline α-ZrP, *J. Phys. Chem.*, 85, 1585, 1981.

74. **Alberti, G., Costantino, U., Allulli, S., and Massucci, M. A.**, Crystalline insoluble acid salts of tetravalent metals. XX. Forward and reverse Cs^+/H^+ and Rb^+/H^+ ion exchange on crystalline zirconium phosphates, *J. Inorg. Nucl. Chem.*, 37, 1779, 1975.

75. **Ruvarac, A., Milonjic, S., Clearfield, A., and Garces, J. M.**, On the mechanism of ion exchange in zirconium phosphates. XVIII. The effect of crystallinity upon K^+-H^+ exchange of α-Zirconium phosphate, *J. Inorg. Nucl. Chem.*, 40, 79, 1978.

76. **Bernasconi, M. G., Casciola, M., and Costantino, U.**, Crystalline insoluble acid salts of tetravalent metals. XXXI. Effect of particle-size on the H^+/K^+ ion-exchange in α-zirconium phosphate, *J. Inorg. Nucl. Chem.*, 41, 1047, 1979.

77. **Kullberg, L. and Clearfield, A.**, On the mechanism of ion exchange in zirconium phosphates. 33. An equilibrium study of Na^+-K^+-H^+ exchange on crystalline α-zirconium phosphate, *J. Inorg. Nucl. Chem.*, in press.

78. **Alberti, G., Bernasconi, M. G., Casciola, M., and Costantino, U.**, Ion exchange processes on the surface of micro-crystals of zirconium bis(monohydrogen orthophosphate)monohydrate, *Ann. Chim. (Italy)*, 68, 265, 1978.

79. **Clearfield, A. and Smith, G. D.**, Exchange of alkaline earth cations on zirconium phosphate, *J. Inorg. Nucl. Chem.*, 30, 3613, 1968.

80. **Alberti, G., Costantino, U., and Pelliccioni, M.**, Crystalline insoluble acid salts of tetravalent metals. XIII. Ion exchange of crystalline zirconium phosphate with alkaline earth metal ions, *J. Inorg. Nucl. Chem.*, 35, 1327, 1973.

81. **Alberti, G., Costantino, U., Allulli, S., Massucci, M. A., and Pelliccioni, M.**, Crystalline insoluble acid salts of tetravalent metals. XV. The influence of preparation methods on the ion-exchange behavior of crystalline zirconium phosphate, *J. Inorg. Nucl. Chem.*, 35, 1347, 1973.

82. **Clearfield, A. and Djuric, Z.**, On the mechanism of ion exchange in zirconium phosphates. XXVI. Irreversible exchange of alkaline earth cations, *J. Inorg. Nucl. Chem.*, 41, 885, 1979.

83. **Harvie, S. J. and Nancollas, G. H.**, Ion exchange properties of crystalline zirconium phosphate, *J. Inorg. Nucl. Chem.*, 32, 3923, 1970.

84. **Dyer, A., Leigh, D., and Ocon, F. T.**, Studies on crystalline zirconium phosphate. I. Ion-exchanged forms of α-zirconium phosphate, *J. Inorg. Nucl. Chem.*, 33, 3141, 1971.

85. **Clearfield, A. and Hagiwara, H.**, On the mechanism of ion exchange in zirconium phosphates. XIX. Exchange of alkaline earth cations using acetate salts, *J. Inorg. Nucl. Chem.*, 40, 907, 1978.

86. **Clearfield, A. and Kalnins, J. M.**, On the mechanism of ion exchange in zirconium phosphates. XIII. Exchange of some divalent transition metal ions on α-zirconium phosphate, *J. Inorg. Nucl. Chem.*, 38, 849, 1976.

87. **Allulli, S., Ferragina, C., La Ginestra, A., Massucci, M. A., Tomassini, N., and Tomlinson, A. G.**, Characterization and electronic properties of some inorganic ion exchangers of the zirconium phosphate type containing transition-metal ions, *J. Chem. Soc. Dalton Trans.*, 2115, 1976.

88. **Clearfield, A. and Hunter, R. A.**, On the mechanism of ion exchange in zirconium phosphates. XIV. The effect of crystallinity on NH_4^+/H^+ exchange of α-zirconium phosphate, *J. Inorg. Nucl. Chem.*, 38, 1085, 1976.

89. **Gupta, J. P., Manning, N. J., and Nowell, D. V.**, Synthesis and ammonium ion exchange of α-zirconium phosphate prepared from zirconia, *J. Inorg. Nucl. Chem.*, 40, 91, 1978.

90. **Hasegawa, Y. and Kuwayama, M.**, Studies on the ammonium form of crystalline zirconium phosphate. IV. Ammonium hydrogen ion exchange on α-zirconium phosphate prepared by the direct precipitation method, *Bull. Chem. Soc. Jpn.*, 51, 3485, 1978.

91. **Hasegawa, Y. and Aoki, H.**, The ion-exchange behavior of the ammonium ion on crystalline zirconium phosphate, *Bull. Chem. Soc. Jpn.*, 16, 836, 1973.

92. **Clearfield, A. and Troup, J. M.**, On the mechanism of ion exchange in crystalline zirconium phosphates. VII. The crystal structure of α-zirconium bis(ammonium orthophosphate) monohydrate, *J. Phys. Chem.*, 77, 243, 1973.

93. **Nancollas, G. H.**, *Interactions in Electrolyte Solutions*, Elsevier, New York, 1966, 123.

94. **Clearfield, A. and Cheng, S.**, On the mechanism of ion exchange in zirconium phosphates. XXX. Exchange of silver ion on α-zirconium phosphate, *J. Inorg. Nucl. Chem.*, 42, 1341, 1980.

95. **Bernasconi, M. G., Casciola, M., Costantino, U., and Giovagnotti, M. L.**, Crystalline insoluble acid salts of tetravalent metals. XXIX. Ion-exchange of silver ion on $ZrHNa(PO_4)_2 \cdot 5H_2O$, *Ann. Chim. (Italy)*, 69, 9, 1979.

96. **Alberti, G., Costantino, U., and Gupta, J. P.**, Crystalline insoluble acid salts of tetravalent metals. XVIII. Ion exchange properties of crystalline $ZrNaH(PO_4)_2 \cdot 5H_2O$ towards alkali metal ions, *J. Inorg. Nucl. Chem.*, 36, 2103, 1974.

97. **Alberti, G., Costantino, U., and Gupta, J. P.,** Crystalline insoluble acid salts of tetravalent metals. XIX. Na^+-catalysed H^+-Mg^{2+} and H^+-Cs^+ ion exchanges on α-zirconium phosphate, *J. Inorg. Nucl. Chem.*, 36, 2109, 1974.

98. **Alberti, G., Bertrami, R., Casciola, M., Costantino, U., and Gupta, J. P.,** Crystalline insoluble acid salts of tetravalent metals. XXI. Ion exchange mechanism of alkaline earth metal ions on crystalline $ZrHNa(PO_4)_2 \cdot 5H_2O$, *J. Inorg. Nucl. Chem.*, 38, 843, 1976.

99. **Allulli, S., La Ginestra, A., Massucci, M. A., Pelliccioni, M., and Tomassini, N.,** Uptake of transition metal ions by crystalline zirconium phosphate, *Inorg. Nucl. Chem. Lett.*, 10, 337, 1974.

100. **Allulli, S., Ferragina, C., La Ginestra, A., Massucci, M. A., and Tomassini N.,** Ion-exchange mechanism of some bivalent transition-metal ions on half-converted sodium and lithium forms of crystalline zirconium phosphate, *J. Chem. Soc. Dalton Trans.*, 1880, 1977.

101. **Eigen, M.,** Fast elementary steps in chemical reaction mechanisms, *Pure Appl. Chem.*, 6, 105, 1963.

102. **Baestle, L. and Huys, H.,** Ion exchange equilibriums of zirconyl phosphate, *J. Inorg. Nucl. Chem.*, 21, 133, 1961; 25, 271, 1963.

103. **Alberti, G., Bernasconi, M. G., Costantino, U., and Gill, J. S.,** Crystalline insoluble salts of tetravalent metals. XXVII. Ion exchange of trivalent cations on ionic forms of crystalline zirconium phosphate with larger interlayer distances, *J. Chromatogr.*, 132, 477, 1977.

104. **Massucci, M. A., La Ginestra, A., and Ferragina, C.,** Oxocations in Layered Ion-Exchangers, Laboratorio Metadologie Avanzate Inorganiche, Centro Nacional de Richerche, Rome, Italy, 1980, 181.

105. **Torracca, E., Galli, P., and Fabiani, G. M.,** Ion exchange behavior of zirconium phosphate with mercury(II) solutions, *J. Inorg. Nucl. Chem.*, 40, 91, 1978.

106. **Clearfield, A. and Tindwa, R. M.,** Exchange of Large cations and charged complexes with amine intercalates of zirconium phosphates, *Inorg. Nucl. Chem. Lett.*, 15, 251, 1979.

107. **Clearfield, A.,** unpublished work.

108. **Hasegawa, Y. and Kizaki, S.,** Hexaamminecobalt(III)-hydrogen ion-exchange on crystalline zirconium phosphate, *Chem. Lett. Jpn.*, 241, 1980.

109. **Clearfield, A. and Medina, A. S.,** On the mechanism of ion exchange in crystalline zirconium phosphates. VIII. Na^+/K^+ exchange on α-zirconium phosphate, *J. Inorg. Nucl. Chem.*, 35, 2985, 1973.

110. **Alberti, G., Costantino, U., Allulli, S., and Massucci, M. A.,** Crystalline insoluble acid salts of tetravalent metals. XIV. Forward and reverse sodium-potassium ion exchange isotherms on crystalline zirconium phosphate, *J. Inorg. Nucl. Chem.*, 35, 1339, 1973.

111. **Torracca, E.,** Crystalline insoluble salts of polyvalent metals and polybasic acids. VII. Ion exchange behavior of Li^+, Na^+, K^+ forms of crystalline zirconium phosphate, *J. Inorg. Nucl. Chem.*, 31, 1189, 1969.

112. **Allulli, S., Massucci, M. A., Costantino, U., and Bertrami, R.,** Crystalline insoluble acid salts of tetravalent metals. XXV. The influence of temperature on Li/K ion-exchange isotherms of crystalline zirconium phosphate in aqueous medium, *J. Inorg. Nucl. Chem.*, 39, 659, 1977.

113. **Hasegawa, Y.,** Studies on the ammonium form of crystalline zirconium phosphate. I. Ammonium-sodium ion exchange isotherms, *J. Inorg. Nucl. Chem.*, 38, 319, 1976.

114. **Hasegawa, Y. and Komiyama, Y.,** Studies on the ammonium form of crystalline zirconium phosphate. II. Ammonium-lithium ion-exchange isotherms, *Bull. Chem. Soc. Jpn.*, 51, 2302, 1978.

115. **Costantino, U.,** Crystalline insoluble acid salts of tetravalent metals. XXX. Forward and reverse Li^+/Cs^+, Na^+/Cs^+ and K^+/Cs^+ ion exchange isotherms on α-zirconium phosphate, *J. Inorg. Nucl. Chem.*, 41, 1041, 1979.

116. **Alberti, G., Allulli, S., and Cardini, G.,** Ion exchange in fused salts. IV. Ion-exchange properties of crystalline zirconium phosphate in molten $NaNO_3$-KNO_3 at 450°, *J. Chromatogr.*, 45, 298, 1969.

117. **Allulli, S. and Cardini, G.,** Ion exchange in fused salts. V. The influence of temperature on the ion-exchange behavior of crystalline zirconium phosphate in molten $NaNO_3$-KNO_3 mixtures, *J. Inorg. Nucl. Chem.*, 34, 339, 1972.

118. **Allulli, S., La Ginestra, A., and Tomassini, N.,** Ion exchange in fused salts. VI. A new phase of the crystalline dilithium form of the zirconium phosphate and its influence of Li/K and Li/Na ion exchange isotherms in molten (Li-K)NO_3 and (Li-NA)NO_3 mixtures at 300°C, *J. Inorg. Nucl. Chem.*, 36, 3839, 1974.

119. **Allulli, S., Tomassini, N., and Massucci, M. A.,** Ion exchange in fused salts. VII. Ion-exchange isotherms for Thallium(I)-Potassium and Rubidium-Potassium on crystalline zirconium phosphate in molten thallium nitrate-potassium nitrate and rubidium nitrate-potassium nitrate mixtures at 360°C, *J. Chem. Soc. Dalton Trans.*, 1816, 1976.

120. **Clearfield, A. and Troup, J. M.,** On the mechanism of ion exchange in crystalline zirconium phosphate. II. Lithium ion exchange of α-zirconium phosphate, *J. Phys. Chem.*, 74, 314, 1970.

121. **Alberti, G., Bernansconi, M. G., Casciola, M., and Costantino, U.,** Ion exchange of some divalent and trivalent cations on the surface of zirconium acid phosphate micro-crystals, *J. Chromatogr.*, 160, 109, 1978.

122. Harvie, S. J. and Nancollas, G. H., The kinetics of ion exchange on crystalline zirconium phosphate, *J. Inorg. Nucl. Chem.*, 30, 273, 1968.

123. Boyd, G. E., Adamson, A. W., and Myers, L. S., The exchange adsorption of ions from aqueous solutions by organic zeolites. III. Kinetics, *J. Am. Chem. Soc.*, 69, 2836, 1947.

124. Olson, D. H. and Sherry, H. S., An X-ray study of strontium-sodium ion exchange in Linde-. X. An example of a two-phase zeolite system, *J. Phys. Chem.*, 72, 4095, 1968.

125. Dyer, A. and Ocon, F. T., Studies on crystalline zirconium phosphate. II. Self-diffusion of cations, *J. Inorg. Nucl. Chem.*, 33, 3153, 1971.

126. Dyer, A. and Gill, J. S., Studies on crystalline zirconium phosphate. IV. Self-diffusion of La(III) and Ce(III) ions, *J. Inorg. Nucl. Chem.*, 40, 97, 1978.

127. Dyer, A. and Gill, J. A., Studies on crystalline zirconium phosphate. III. Self-diffusion of sodium ion into mono-sodium forms of crystalline zirconium phosphate, *J. Inorg. Nucl. Chem.*, 39, 665, 1977.

128. Dyer, A. and Yusof, A. M., The mechanism of ion-exchange in some crystalline sodium and caesium zirconium phosphates, *J. Inorg. Nucl. Chem.*, 41, 1479, 1979.

129. Clearfield, A. and Troup, J. M., Ion exchange between solids, *J. Phys. Chem.*, 74, 314, 1970.

130. Clearfield, A., Saldarriaga-Molina, C. H., and Buckley, R. H., Solid-Solid ion exchange. II. Zeolites, in *Proc. 3rd Int. Conf. on Molecular Sieves*, Uytterhoeven, J. B., Ed., University of Leuven Press, Leuven, Belgium, 1973, 241.

131. Jerus, P. and Clearfield, A., Kinetics of gas-solid reactions in α-zirconium phosphate. H$^+$/Na$^+$ mixed diffusion coefficients, *J. Inorg. Nucl. Chem.*, 43, 2117, 1981.

132. Crank, J., *The Mathematics of Diffusion*, 2nd ed., Clarendon Press, Oxford, 1975, 94.

133. Inoue, Y. and Yamada, Y., Sodium isotopic exchange rate between crystalline zirconium phosphate and molten NaNO$_3$, *Chem. Lett. Jpn.*, 1293, 1975.

134. Clearfield, A. and Frianeza, T. N., On the mechanism of ion exchange in zirconium phosphates. XXII. Mixed zirconium titanium phosphates, *J. Inorg. Nucl. Chem.*, 40, 1925, 1978.

135. Yazawa, Y., Eguchi, T., Takaguchi, K., and Tomita, J., Sodium ion exchange on crystalline zirconium titanium phosphate, *Bull. Chem. Soc. Jpn.*, 52, 2923, 1979.

136. Zsinka, L., Szirtes, L., Poko, Z., and Fodor, M., Thermoanalytical investigations of crystalline zirconium phosphate in various forms, *Thermal Analysis, Proc. 4th I.C.T.A., Budapest, 1974*, Vol. 1, Heyden, London, 1975, 663.

137. Clearfield, A. and Medina, A. S., On the mechanism of ion exchange in crystalline zirconium phosphates. The dehydration behavior of sodium ion exchanged phases of α-zirconium phosphate, *J. Inorg. Nucl. Chem.*, 32, 2775, 1970.

138. Clearfield, A., Duax, W. L., Garces, J. M., and Medina, A. S., On the mechanism of ion exchange in crystalline zirconium phosphates. IV. Potassium ion exchange of α-zirconium phosphate, *J. Inorg. Nucl. Chem.*, 34, 329, 1972.

139. Clearfield, A., Pack, S. P., and Troup, J. M., On the mechanism of ion exchange in zirconium phosphates. XVII. Dehydration behavior of lithium ion exchanged phases, *J. Inorg. Nucl. Chem.*, 39, 1437, 1977.

140. Hasegawa, Y., Thermal decomposition studies of the ammonium forms of the crystalline zirconium phosphate ion exchanger, *Bull. Chem. Soc. Jpn.*, 46, 3296, 1973.

141. Clearfield, A. and Pack, S. P., unpublished data.

142. Clearfield, A., Jerus, P., Cotman, R. N., and Pack, S. P., Synthesis of sodium dizirconium triphosphate from α-zirconium phosphate, *Mater. Res. Bull.*, 15, 1603, 1980.

143. Hagman, L. and Kierkegaard, P., The crystal structure of NaMe$_2^{IV}$(PO$_4$)$_3$; Me^{IV} = Ge, Ti, Zr, *Acta Chem. Scand.*, 22, 1822, 1968.

144. La Ginestra, A., Ferragina, C., and Patrono, P., Ag-zirconium phosphate system: Characterization of the phases obtained at different temperatures, *Mater. Res. Bull.*, 14, 1099, 1979.

145. Goodenough, J. B., Hong, H. Y-P., and Kafalas, J. A., Fast Na$^+$ ion-transport in skeleton structures, *Mater. Res. Bull.*, 11, 203, 1976.

146. Clearfield, A. and Jerus, P., unpublished results.

147. Clearfield, A. and Pack, S. P., On the mechanism of ion exchange in zirconium phosphates. XXVII. Dehydration behavior of Cu(II) ion exchanged phases, *J. Inorg. Nucl. Chem.*, 42, 771, 1980.

148. Ferragina, C., La Ginestra, A., and Tomlinson, A. A. G., Partially Converted Synthetic Inorganic Exchangers with Transition Metal Ions. Structural Changes Caused by Heating, Laboratorio Metodologie Avanzate Inorgische, Centro National de Richerche, Rome, Italy, 1980, 177.

149. Horsely, S. E. and Nowell, D. V., The particle characteristics of cation exchanged α-zirconium phosphate, *J. Colloid Interface Sci.*, 49, 394, 1974.

150. Pizzini, S. and Bianchi, G., Solid state electrochemistry. II. Devices and electrochemical processes, *Chim. Ind. (Milan)*, 55, 966, 1973.

151. **Alberti, G.**, Inorganic ion exchange membranes, in *Study Week on Membranes*, Passino, R., Ed., Pontificiae Academiae Scientiarum Scripta Varia, Rome, 1976, 629.

152. **Kummer, J. T. and Weber, N.**, U.S. Patent 3,455,233, 1968.

153. **Hamlen, R. P.**, Ionic conductivity of amorphous ZrP, *J. Electrochem. Soc.*, 109, 746, 1962.

154. **Alberti, G., Casciola, M., Costantino, U., and Radi, R.**, The mechanism of proton transport in powder compacts of acid salts with α-layered structure, *Gazz. Chim. Ital.*, 109, 421, 1979.

155. **Sauer, M. C., Southwick, P. F., Spiegler, K. S., and Wyllie, M. B. J.**, Electrical conductance of porous plugs. Ion-exchange resin-solution systems, *Ind. Eng. Chem.*, 47, 2187, 1955.

156. **Alberti, G. and Torracca, E.**, Electrical conductance of amorphous zirconium phosphate in various salt forms, *J. Inorg. Nucl. Chem.*, 30, 1093, 1968.

157. **Alberti, G., Casciola, M., Costantino, U., and Levi, G.**, Inorganic ion exchange membranes consisting of micro-crystals of zirconium phosphate supported by Kynar, *J. Membr. Sci.*, 3, 179, 1978.

158. **Dravnieks, A. and Bregman, J . I.**, Inorganic membrane works in fuel cells; polymeric $ZrO(H_2PO_4)_2$ may lead to more efficient fuel cells, allow high temperature operation, *Chem. Eng. News*, 39, 40, 1961.

159. **Alberti, G.**, Perm-selectivity of inorganic ion exchange membranes consisting of amorphou ZrP supported on glass wool fibers, *Atti Accad. Naz. Lincei, Cl. Sci. Fis. Mat. Nat. Rend.*, 31, 427, 1961.

160. **Alberti, G., Conte, A., and Torracca, E.**, Preparation and electrochemical properties of inorganic ion-exchange membranes, *Atti. Accad. Naz. Lincei, Cl. Sci. Fix. Mat. Nat. Rend.*, 35, 548, 1963.

161. **Materova, E. A. and Skabichevskii, P. A.**, Electrochemical properties of zirconyl phosphate, *Zh. Fiz. Khim.*, 38, 676, 1964.

162. **Bregman, J. I. and Braman, R. S.**, Inorganic ion exchange membranes, *J. Colloid Sci.*, 20, 913, 1965.

163. **Guther, A. and Bishop, J.**, Report SM-46229, 1965, and Report SM-46229-F, Astropower Laboratory, OSW, Contract 14-01-01-613, McDonald Douglas Aircraft Corporation, Newport Beach, Calif., 1967.

164. **Rajan, K. S., Boies, D. B., Casolo, A. J., and Bregman, J. I.**, Inorganic ion-exchange membranes and their application to electro-dialysis, *Desalination*, 1, 231, 1966.

165. **Rajan, K. S., Boies, D. B., Casolo, A. J., and Bregman, J. I.**, Electrodialytic demineralization of brackish waters by using inorgani ion-exchange membranes, *Desalination*, 5, 371, 1968.

166. **Yamanaka, S.**, Ionic conductivity in anhydrous zirconium phosphates, $Zr(HPO_4)_2$ (M = Li, Na, K), with layered structures, *J. Inorg. Nucl. Chem.*, 42, 717, 1980.

167. **Clearfield, A., Blessing, R. H., and Stynes, J. A.**, New crystalline phases of zirconium phosphate, *J. Inorg. Nucl. Chem.*, 30, 2249, 1968.

168. **Yamanaka, S. and Tanaka, M.**, Formation region and structural model of γ-zirconium phosphate, *J. Inorg. Nucl. Chem.*, 41, 45, 1979.

169. **Dollimore, D., Horsley, S. E., Manning, N. J., and Nowell, D. V.**, The thermal decomposition of zirconium phosphates. II. γ-zirconium phosphate, *Thermal Analysis Proc. 4th I.C.T.A.*, Budapest, *1974*, Vol. 1, Heyden, London, 1975, 647.

170. **Dollimore, D., Manning, N. J., and Nowell, D. V.**, The thermal decomposition of zirconium phosphates. III. γ-zirconium phosphate and its alkali metal ion-exchange forms, *Thermochim. Acta*, 19, 37, 1977.

171. **La Ginestra, A. and Massucci, M. A.**, Titanium and zirconium acid phosphate dihydrates: Thermal behavior and phase changes of their hydrogen, sodium and strontium forms, *Thermochim. Acta*, 32, 241, 1979.

172. **Clearfield, A. and Garces, J. M.**, On the mechanism of ion exchange in zirconium phosphates. XXIV. Exchange of Alkali metal cations on γ-zirconium phosphate, *J. Inorg. Nucl. Chem.*, 41, 879, 1979.

173. **Clearfield, A. and Kalnins, J.**, On the mechanism of ion exchange in zirconium phosphates. XXIII. Exchange of first row divalent transition elements on γ-zirconium phosphate, *J. Inorg. Nucl. Chem.*, 40, 1933, 1978.

174. **Yamanaka, S. and Koizumi, M.**, Structural consideration of zirconium phosphate and its organic complexes, *Clays Clay Miner.*, 23, 477, 1975.

175. **Yamanaka, S.**, Synthesis and characterization of the organic derivatives of zirconium phosphate, *Inorg. Chem.*, 15, 2811, 1976.

176. **Yamanaka, S., Tsujimoto, M., and Tanaka, M.**, Synthesis of the organic derivatives of γ-zirconium phosphate by the reaction with propylene oxide, *J. Inorg. Nucl. Chem.*, 41, 605, 1979.

177. **Yamanaka, S., Maeda, H., and Tanaka, M.**, Exchange reaction of phosphoric ester ions with phosphate ions in a heterogeneous system containing the organic derivative of γ-zirconium phosphate, *J. Inorg. Nucl. Chem.*, 41, 1187, 1979.

178. **Yamanaka, S. and Hattori, M.**, Exchange between HPO_4^{2-} and $C_6H_5OPO_3^{2-}$ in a heterogeneous system with γ-zirconium phosphate, $Zr(HPO_4)_2 \cdot 2H_2$, *Chem. Lett. Jpn.*, 1073, 1979.

179. **Yamanaka, S., Matsunaga, M., and Hattori, M.,** Preparation and structure of *n*-alkyl ester derivatives of zirconium bis(monohydrogen orthophosphate) dihydrate with a layer structure, *J. Inorg. Nucl. Chem.,* in press.

180. **Gordon, A., Betler, O. S., Greenbaum, M., Marantz, L., Gral, T., and Maxwell, M. H.,** Clinical maintenance hemodialysis with a sorbent based, low-volume dialysate regeneration system, *Trans. Am. Soc. Artif. Int. Organs,* 17, 253, 1971.

181. **Koenig, K. H., Schaefer, H., Hoyer, F., and Rassl, G.,** coarse-grained inorganic ion exchangers with an inactive matrix, *Radiochim. Acta,* 1, 213, 1963.

182. **Moskvin, L. N., Miroshnokov, V. S., and Slutskii, G. K.,** U.S.S.R. Patent 347, 306, 1972.

183. **Ahrland, S. and Carleson, G.,** Inorganic ion exchangers. VIII. The purification of water at elevated temperatures by a combination of zirconium phosphate and zirconium hydroxide gels, *J. Inorg. Nucl. Chem.,* 33, 2229, 1971.

184. **Ahrland, S., Bjork, N., Blessing, R. H., and Herman, R. G.,** Inorganic ion exchangers. IX. The sorption of divalent transition metal ions on semicrystalline zirconium phosphate, *J. Inorg. Nucl. Chem.,* 36, 2377, 1974.

185. **Raggenbass, A., Courouble, J. M., Lefebvre, J., Fradin, J., and Perebaskine, C.,** ELAN: Installation for the recovery and packaging cesium-137 in France, AEC Accession No. 39319, Rep. DP-1066, Vol. 2, Paris, 1966.

186. **Souka, N., Shabana, R., and Farah, K.,** Adsorption behavior of some actinides on zirconium phosphate: stability constant determinations, *J. Radioanal. Chem.,* 33, 315, 1976.

187. **Akatsu, E., Ono, R., Tsukuechi, K., and Uchiyama, H.,** Radiochemical study of adsorption behavior of inorganic ions on Zr phosphate, SiO_2 gel, and charcoal, *J. Nucl. Sci. Tech.,* 2, 141, 1965.

188. **Chernorukov, N. G., Korshunov, I. A., Prokof'eva, T. V., Zhuk, M. I., and Moskvichev, E. P.,** Use of titanium and zirconium acid phosphates in the separation of neptunium and plutonium in different valence states, *Ref. Dokl. Soobshch. Mendeleevsk. S'ezd. Obshch. Prikl. Khim. 11th,* 1, 270, 1975.

189. **Sanchez Batanero, P. and Crespo Garcia, R.,** Study of the effect of dielectric constant on the fixation and chromatographic separation of different bivalent cations on zirconium phosphate in semiaqueous iodide media. II. Ethylene-glycol-water and dioxane-water, *Quim. Anal.,* 30, 136, 1976.

190. **Palmer, B. R. and Fuerstenau, M. C.,** Ion-exchange separation of copper from iron and aluminum with zirconium phosphate gel, *Proc. Int. Mineral Process Congr.,* 10th, Institute of Mining and Metallurgy, London, 1973, 1123.

191. **Born, E. and Paul, G.,** Alterung Na-beladener und γ-bestrahlter zirconium phosphate, *Z. Kristallogr.,* 146, 29, 1977.

192. **Born, E. and Paul, G.,** Strahlungsinduzierte und ionenaustauschbedingte kristalldefekte in zirconium phosphate, *Z. Kristallogr.,* 146, 19, 1977.

193. **Zsinka, L., Szirtes, L., Mink, J., and Kalman, A.,** Effect of γ-radiation on various synthetic inorganic ion exchangers, *J. Inorg. Nucl. Chem.,* 36, 1147, 1974.

194. **Tikavyi, V. F. and Korpus, V. A.,** Influence of hydrothermal treatments on ion exchange and physicochemical properties of zirconium phosphate, *Zhur. Neorg. Khim.,* 22, 1193, 1977.

195. **Kto, K., Kawada, Y., Kunube, K., and Dahchi, K.,** (to Kagaku Kogyo, Inc.), Japan Patent 73 17, 810, 1973.

196. **Urbach, G.,** Thin layer chromatography of aliphatic 2,4 dinitrophenylhydrazones, *Anal. Chem.,* 36, 2262, 1964.

197. **Fujimura, K. and Ando, T.,** Ligand-exchange chromatography, *J. Chromatogr.,* 114, 15, 175.

198. **Fujimura, K. and Ando, T.,** Ligand-exchange gas chromatographic separation of pyridine bases, *Anal. Chem.,* 49, 1179, 1977.

199. **Allulli, S., Tomassini, N., Bertoni, G., and Bruner, F.,** Synthetic inorganic ion exchangers as adsorbents for gas chromatography, *Anal. Chem.,* 48, 1259, 1976.

200. **Dyer, A., Leigh, D., and Sharples, W. E.,** Gas adsorption studies on ion-exchanged forms of crystalline zirconium phosphate, *J. Chromatogr.,* 118, 319, 1976.

201. **Maya, L.,** Structure and chromatographic applications of crystalline $Zr(OPO_3R)_2$; R = butyl, lauryl and octylphenyl, *Inorg. Nucl. Chem. Lett.,* 15, 207, 1979.

202. **Alberti, G. and Grassini-Strassa, G.,** Chromatography on paper impregnated with Zr phosphate, *J. Chromatogr.,* 4, 83, 1960.

203. **Alberti, G.,** Chromatographic separations on paper impregnated with inorganic ion exchangers, *Chromatogr. Rev.,* 8, 246, 1969.

204. **Tuhtar, D.,** Ion Exchange Studies on Zirconium Phosphates. I. Lithium/Hydrogen Ion Exchange of α-ZrP. II. Chromatography of Metal Ions on Paper Impregnated with ZrP. III. Sorption of First Row Transition Metal Ions on ZrP's, Ph.D. Thesis, Ohio University, Athens, 1975.

205. **Zabin, B. A. and Rollins, C. B.,** Inorganic ion exchangers for thin layer chromatography, *J. Chromatogr.,* 14, 534, 1964.

206. Shimomura, K. S. and Walton, H. F., Thin-layer chromatography of amines by ligand exchange, *Sep. Sci.,* 3, 493, 1968.
207. Hattori, T., Ishiguro, A., and Murakami, Y., Acidity of crystalline zirconium phosphate, *J. Inorg. Nucl. Chem.,* 40, 1107, 1978.
208. Clearfield, A. and Thakur, D. S., The acidity of zirconium phosphates in relation to their activity in the dehydration of cyclohexanol, *J. Catal.,* 65, 185, 1980.
209. Clearfield, A. and Thakur, D. S., Cyclohexanol dehydration over zirconium phosphates of varying crystallinity, *J. Catal.,* 69, 230, 1981.
210. Clearfield, A. and Tindwa, R. M., On the mechanism of ion exchange in zirconium phosphates. XXI. Intercalation of amines by α-zirconium phosphate, *J. Inorg. Nucl. Chem.,* 41, 871, 1979.
211. Balandin, A. A., Catalytic properties of zirconium phosphate, *Vestn. Mosk. Univ.,* 4, 137, 1957.
212. Balandin, A. A., Kukina, A. I., Malenberg, N. E., and Ermilova, M. M., Catalytic properties of zirconium phosphate, *Dokl. Akad. Nauk SSSR,* 161, 851, 1965.
213. Malenberg, N. E., Kukina, A. I., and Fadieva, T. N., Catalytic properties of metal - zirconium phosphate catalysts, *Vestn. Mosk. Univ. Ser. II Khim.,* 21, 107, 1966.
214. Sharf, V. Z., Nekrasov, A. S., Nemkova, L. P., and Friedlin, L. Kh., Investigation of the dehydration of pentanol-1 and cyclohexanol in the presence of zirconium phosphate, *Izvest. Akad. Nauk SSSR, Ser. Khim.,* 1, 46, 1967.
215. Nozaki, F., Itoh, T., and Ueda, S., Metal phosphate catalyst. I. Catalytic activity of zirconium phosphate for dehydration of 2-propanol, *Nippon Kagaku Zasshi,* 674, 1973.
216. Watanabe, Y., Matsumura, Y., Izumi, Y., and Mizutani, Y., Synthesis of methyl isobutyl ketone from acetone and hydrogen catalysed by palladium supported on zirconium phosphate, *Bull. Chem. Soc. Jpn.,* 47, 2922, 1974.
217. Onoue, Y., Mizutani, Y., Akiyama, S., Izumi, Y., and Watanabe, Y., Why not do it in one step. The case of MlBK, *Chemtech,* 36, Jan. 1977.
218. Izumi, Y. and Mizutani, Y., Vapor-phase hydrolysis of chlorobenzene catalyzed by copper(II) ion exchanged zirconium phosphate, *Bull. Chem. Soc. Jpn.,* 52, 3065, 1979.
219. Austerweil, G. V., Acid resistant, thermally stable cation exchangers as cylization catalysts, *C. R. Acad. Sci.,* 248, 1810, 1959.
220. Kagiya, T., Shimizu, T., Sano, T., and Fukui, K., Polymerization of olefins by catalysts of metal phosphate, *Kogyo Kagaku Zasshi,* 66, 841, 1963.
221. Kagiya, T., Sano, T., Shimizu, T., and Fukui, K., Polymerization of ethylene oxide with metal phosphate catalysts, *Kogyo Kagaku Zasshi,* 66, 1893, 1963; 66, 1896, 1963.
222. Kagiya, T., Shimizu, T., Sano, T., Hatta, M., and Fukui, K., Polymerization of ethylene oxide. I. Polymerization of ethylene oxide by metal phosphate catalysts, *Kyoto Daigaku Nippon Kagaku Seni Kenkyusho Koenshu,* 20, 19, 1963; 20, 25, 1963; 20, 30, 1963.
223. Todd, M. J. (to BP Chemicals Int., Ltd.) British Patent 1, 351, 492 1974.
224. Burress, G. T. (to Mobil Oil Corp.), German Offenbach 2, 516, 229, 1976.
225. Kalman, T., Dudukovic, M., and Clearfield, A., Copper-substituted zirconium phosphate, a new oxidation catalyst, *Proc. Int. Symp. Chem. Reac. Eng., Adv. Chem. Ser.,* 133, 65, 1974.
226. Mizutani, K. and Inoue, H. (to Tao Gosei Chem. Ind. Co., Ltd.), Japan Kokai 76 06, 359, 1976.
227. Clearfield, A. and Pack, S. P., Reversible reduction of copper-exchanged zirconium phosphate, *J. Catal.,* 51, 431, 1978.
228. LaGinestra, A., Ferrigina, C., Massucci, M. A., Tomassini, N., and Tomlinson, A. G., Redox behavior of transition metal ions in zirconium phosphate. The reversibility of copper reduction, in *Thermal Analysis,* Chihara, H., Ed., Heyden, London, 1977, 424.
229. Clearfield, A., Thakur, D. S., and Cheung, H. C., Hydrogen reduction of copper(II) exchanged α-zirconium phosphate, *J. Phys. Chem.,* submitted.
230. Hattori, T., Hanai, H., and Murakami, Y., Catalytic sites of α-zirconium phosphate in oxidative dehydrogenation, *J. Catal.,* 56, 295, 1979.
231. Clearfield, A., Cu(II)-exchanged α-zirconium phosphate as an oxidative dehydrogenation catalyst, *J. Catal.,* 56, 296, 1979.
232. Clearfield, A. and Pittman, C. U., unpublished studies.
233. Clearfield, A. and Jirustithipong, P., in *Fast Ion Transport in Solids,* Vashista, P., Mundy, J. M., and Shenoy, G. K., Elsevier North Holland, New York, 1979, 153.

Chapter 2

OTHER GROUP(IV) ACID SALTS

Giulio Alberti

TABLE OF CONTENTS

I. INTRODUCTION

Most investigations concerned with the insoluble acid salts of tetravalent metals have been carried out on α-zirconium monohydrogen phosphate (α-ZrP) and its salt forms (see Chapter 1). However, several other insoluble acid salts have been prepared and studied although not so thoroughly as α-ZrP. It was of interest to examine the properties of these materials and to attempt a preliminary rationalization of their properties according to the crystalline structure of the insoluble acid salts. In particular, where possible, analogies and differences with α-ZrP will be reported and discussed. For our purpose, the acid salts of tetravalent metals will be subdivided according to their crystalline structure as:

1. Acid salts with layered structure of α-type
2. Acid salts with layered structure of γ-type
3. Acid salts with fibrous structure
4. Acid salts with three-dimensional structure
5. Acid salts having an as yet unknown structure

II. ACID SALTS WITH LAYERED STRUCTURE OF THE α-TYPE

By α-layered materials we mean the acid salts of tetravalent metals having the layered structure of α-zirconium phosphate and the general formula $M(HXO_4)_2 \cdot nH_2O$ (where M = tetravalent metal; X = P, As, Sb). There is usually one water molecule of hydration in these compounds but polyhydrated acid salts can be also obtained. The α-layered materials have been generally prepared by refluxing the amorphous materials in concentrated phosphoric acid (10 to 14 M) for a few days.[1-4] As in the case of α-ZrP (see Chapter 1), the degree of crystallinity increases with increase of the refluxing time and of the concentration of phosphoric acid. The α-layered materials can also be obtained by the direct precipitation method in the presence of hydrofluoric acid[5,6] and larger crystals,[5,7] and a better degree of crystallinity[8] is usually obtained with this method.

The most important α-layered materials investigated to date are reported in Table 1. Since the replacement of a tetravalent atom by a different tetravalent atom does not appreciably modify the strength of the anionic field of the phosphate or arsenate groups, the α-layered materials usually exhibit ion exchange properties similar to those of α-ZrP, but there are marked differences, especially as regards properties dependent upon the steric hindrance to the diffusion of the counter-ions. In particular, on the basis of the known ion exchange properties of α-ZrP, the following analogies are expected:

1. Dependence of the interlayer distance of the salt forms on the radius and hydration of the counter-ion involved.
2. Occurrence of discontinuous changes in the interlayer distance during the replacement of counter-ions and, hence, of ion exchange at fixed composition of the solution.
3. Ion exchange irreversibility and consequently, hysteresis loops between the forward and reverse process.
4. Possibility of obtaining salt forms containing large cations by exchange of the Na⁺ of the polyhydrated monosodium form.
5. Initial decrease of the pH with increasing metal-hydroxide addition, especially when this addition is made rapidly and when the salt form obtained exhibits an interlayer distance larger than that of the original hydrogen form.

Table 1
SOME IMPORTANT ACID SALTS OF TETRAVALENT METALS WITH LAYERED STRUCTURE OF THE α-TYPE

Compound	Formula	Interlayer distance (Å)	Ion exchange capacity (meq/g)
Titanium phosphate	$Ti(HPO_4)_2 \cdot H_2O$	7.56	7.76
Zirconium phosphate	$Zr(HPO_4)_2 \cdot H_2O$	7.56	6.64
Hafnium phosphate	$Hf(HPO_4)_2 \cdot H_2O$	7.56	4.17
Germanium(IV) phosphate	$Ge(HPO_4)_2 \cdot H_2O$	7.6	7.08
Tin(IV) phosphate	$Sn(HPO_4)_2 \cdot H_2O$	7.76	6.08
Lead(IV) phosphate	$Pb(HPO_4)_2 \cdot H_2O$	7.8	4.79
Titanium arsenate	$Ti(HAsO_4)_2 \cdot H_2O$	7.77	5.78
Zirconium arsenate	$Zr(HAsO_4)_2 \cdot H_2O$	7.78	5.14
Tin(IV) arsenate	$Sn(HAsO_4)_2 \cdot H_2O$	7.8	4.80

The differences between the ion exchange properties of α-layered exchangers seem to arise essentially from the different dimensions of the unit cell. In fact, the smaller are these dimensions, the smaller are the dimensions of the windows connecting the cavities, and the higher is the steric hindrance to jumps of counter-ions from one cavity to another. In order to better understand the effect of the dimensions of the windows connecting the cavities in α-layered materials, it seems useful to briefly discuss the ion exchange mechanism that probably occurs in such materials.

In order to replace the original protons, the cation present in the external solution must diffuse within the layers and, therefore, they must cross the openings connecting the cavities. If the size of the openings is smaller than the diameter of the hydrated counter-ions, a part or all of the water of their hydration shell must be lost in order to allow the cation to pass through the openings. Since the dehydration process requires energy, the rate of the ion exchange process becomes very low if sufficient energy is not supplied (i.e., by increasing the temperature or the pH of the external solution). In fact, as the pH of the external solution is increased, the tendency of the counter-ions to cross the openings becomes progressively higher until, at a certain pH value, sufficient energy for total or partial dehydration is supplied and the rate of the ion exchange process appreciably increases. Note that cations having a diameter larger than the size of the openings should not cross these openings even when completely anhydrous; therefore, their ion exchange should not be possible. However, the layered structure is not as rigid as that in zeolites and, as the pH is increased, the tendency to replace the internal protons becomes so high that the large cations can force the openings and enter inside the cavities.

The pH value at which the exchange occurs must increase as the dimensions of the openings connecting the cavities decrease. Furthermore, the pH is also dependent upon the dehydration energy which, in turn, depends upon the size and charge of the cation examined. Once within the cavities, the cations tend to rehydrate; however, this is possible only if there is enough room in the cavities, or if the energy of their rehydration is sufficient to overcome the forces holding the layers so that the layers can be spread apart to a new interlayer distance. In this connection, we underline that the forces holding the layers of the salt forms are essentially due to the coulombic attraction between the negative fixed charges of adjacent planar macroanions and the counter-ions placed among them. Thus it is likely that these forces become higher as the density of the fixed charges of the layers increases, or, in other words, as the product of the parameters (a × b) of the unit cell becomes smaller. Now, the stronger the forces holding the layers, the more energy is required to separate them. Thus, the smaller is the product (a × b), the more do the α-layered exchangers tend to behave as materials having a rigid structure. In such cases the steric hindrance to diffusion of the large counter-ions becomes very large and ion-sieve effects can be obtained. In addition it must be pointed out that, if energy sufficient to enlarge the layers of the external part of the crystal is supplied, the openings connecting the cavities near the interphase are also enlarged. Therefore, once started, the exchange may take place at lower energy and a minimum in the titration curve is usually obtained.[9] On the basis of these considerations, many properties of α-layered material can be understood and predicted. The main ion exchange properties of some α-layered materials will now be examined and discussed.

A. α-Titanium Phosphate

After α-zirconium phosphate, α-titanium phosphate (α-TiP) is the most investigated α-material. It has been obtained independently in various laboratories by refluxing the amorphous titanium phosphate in 10 to 14 M H_3PO_4 for a few days.[10-13] α-titanium phosphate has been also obtained by direct precipitation in the presence of hydrofluoric acid.[5] A typical preparation is the following: $TiCl_4$ (11.8 g) is dissolved in 125 mℓ of 3 M HF, then 6.3 M H_3PO_4 (500 mℓ) is added. The solution is heated at 60°C in a 1000 mℓ plastic beaker and HF is allowed to evaporate. The volumes of the solution must be maintained constant by addition of distilled water. When the concentration of HF is decreased to a certain value, microcrystals of α-TiP begin to precipitate. The precipitation is allowed to continue for some time, then the precipitate is washed and air dried. Since the length of the Ti—O bond is shorter than that of the Zr—O bond, the distance between fixed charges in the planar macroanion $[Ti(PO_4)_2]_n^{2n-}$ is shorter than in $[Zr(PO_4)_2]_n^{2n-}$. The unit cell dimensions[3,14] are a = 8.631 ± 0.001 Å; b = 5.002 ± 0.001 Å; c = 16.176 ± 0.002 Å; and β = 110.20 ± 0.01°.

Owing to its smaller unit cell, the dimensions of the windows connecting the cavities in α-TiP are correspondingly smaller, and the density of the fixed charges higher, than in α-ZrP. Thus, following arguments presented above, the steric hindrance to the diffusion of large cations is expected to be higher in α-TiP than in α-ZrP and the ion exchange rate is slower. Rb^+ and Cs^+ ions are not appreciably exchanged at pH values below 7. It is not possible to study their exchange at higher pH values since, unfortunately, α-TiP is not stable in alkaline medium, being strongly hydrolyzed. Thus, the Rb- and Cs-forms of α-TiP are not obtained by direct titration of α-TiP. However, as for α-ZrP, the salt forms containing large cations can be obtained by replacing the Na^+ of the monosodium form[15] (interlayer distance 10.4 Å). The titration curve of α-TiP with 0.1 M (NaOH + NaCl) solution (batch procedure, at 25°) is shown in Figure 1. This curve is similar to that obtained by Clearfield and Frianeza[16] and is very different from the corresponding curve of α-ZrP.

In order to understand the reasons for this different behavior, the H^+/Na^+ ion exchange process of α-TiP has been studied in detail.[15] Alberti et al. found that:

1.   If the titration is carried out at temperatures $\leqslant 15°C$ and if the volume of 0.1 M NaOH solution necessary to reach a given percentage of Na-loading is added to the α-TiP sample in a single addition (as in the case of the batch procedure), a certain amount of disodium phase is formed before all the original α-Ti(HPO_4)_2·H_2O phase has been completely transformed into the monosodium form; three phases, α-Ti(HPO_4)_2·H_2O, α-TiHNa(PO_4)_2·4H_2O, and α-Ti(NaPO_4)_2·3H_2O, are thus found to coexist in the solid sample. A ready explanation for the presence of the disodium phase is forthcoming from the model of the coexisting phases in a single crystal.[4] In fact, the ion exchange in layered materials proceeds from the surface to the center of the crystals. If the exchange process is slow, the phase α-TiHNa(PO_4)_2·4H_2O, initially formed on the surface of the crystals, according to the process

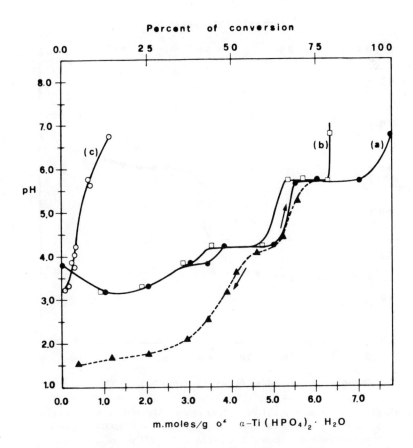

FIGURE 1. α-Ti(HPO$_4$)$_2 \cdot$ H$_2$O titrated with 0.1 M (NaOH + NaCl) solutions by the "batch" procedure (t = 25 ± 1°C). Curves a, b, and c refer to NaOH added, Na$^+$ taken up by the exchanger, and phosphate released to the solution, respectively. Dashed curve refers to the reverse titration of the sodium form of α-TiP with 0.100 M (NaCl + HCl) solution. (From Alberti, G., Costantino, U., and Luciani Giovagnotti, M. L., *Gazz. Chim. It.*, 110, 61, 1980. With permission.)

$$\alpha-Ti(HPO_4)_2 \cdot H_2O + Na^+ + 4H_2O \xrightarrow{\text{pH3.5}} \alpha-TiHNa(PO_4)_2 \cdot 4H_2O + H_3O^+ \tag{1}$$
$$(7.56\ \text{Å}) \qquad\qquad\qquad\qquad (10.4\ \text{Å})$$

remains in contact, for a certain time, with a solution at pH 8. A certain percentage of the disodium form is thus produced, according to the process

$$\alpha-TiHNa(PO_4)_2 \cdot 4H_2O + Na^+ \xrightarrow{\text{pH6.5}} \alpha-Ti(NaPO_4)_2 \cdot 3H_2O + H_3O^+ \tag{2}$$
$$(10.4\ \text{Å}) \qquad\qquad\qquad (9.9\ \text{Å})$$

before all the α-Ti(HPO$_4$)$_2 \cdot$ H$_2$O is entirely transformed into α-TiHNa(PO$_4$)$_2 \cdot$ 4H$_2$O phase, according to Process 1. As the ion exchange proceeds, NaOH is consumed and the pH of the supernatant solution decreases. When the pH is decreased below 6.5, the reverse conversion of Ti(NaPO$_4$)$_2 \cdot$ 3H$_2$O into TiHNa(PO$_4$)$_2 \cdot$ 4H$_2$O should occur. However, as in the case of α-ZrP, the reverse process occurs at pH values considerably lower than in the forward process (dashed curve in Figure 1). Therefore, the Ti(NaPO$_4$)$_2 \cdot$ 3H$_2$O phase, once formed, can coexist with TiHNa(PO$_4$)$_2 \cdot$ 4H$_2$O and Ti(HPO$_4$)$_2 \cdot$ H$_2$O phases.

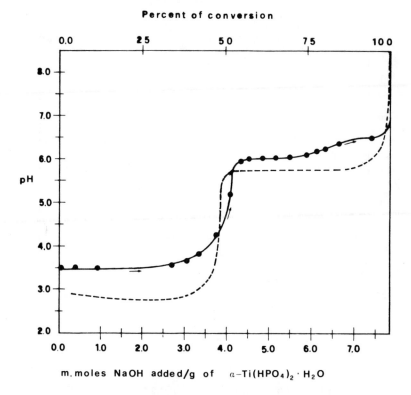

Percent of conversion

FIGURE 2.   Titration of α-Ti(PO$_4$)$_2 \cdot$ H$_2$O with 0.1 M(NaOH + NaCl) solution (slow titration at 15 ± 1°C). Full curve. Batch procedure with NaOH addition performed with an automatic titrimeter operating in the "pH stat mode". The Na$^+$-uptake curve of α-Zr(HPO$_4$)$_2 \cdot$ H$_2$O is also reported as a comparison (dashed curve). In this case, the pH values are plotted against the percent of conversion. (From Alberti, G., Costantino, U., and Luciani Giovagnotti, M. L., *Gazz. Chim. It.,* 110, 61, 1980. Wtih permission.)

2.   The process is even more complicated at temperatures higher than 18 to 20°C because of the formation of a certain percentage of less-hydrated phases such as TiHNa(PO$_4$)$_2 \cdot$ H$_2$O, and Ti(NaPO$_4$)$_2 \cdot$ H$_2$O which coexist with TiHNa(PO$_4$)$_2 \cdot$ 4H$_2$O and Ti(NaPO$_4$)$_2 \cdot$ 3H$_2$O phases.[15,16] Hysteresis phenomena, or very low rates of hydration (or dehydration) could explain, the coexistence of differently hydrated phases of the same salt form at a given relative humidity and temperature.

These results indicate that, in order to obtain a good titration curve of α-TiP, it is necessary to operate at temperatures lower than 20°C and to avoid the formation of the disodium form in the range 0 to 50% of Na$^+$ exchange. The latter condition can be easily accomplished by gradually adding very small volumes of NaOH solution (in order not to exceed pH 4 to 5) by means of an automatic titrimeter operating in the pH-statmode. The titration curve obtained using these precautions is shown in Figure 2. As expected on the basis of their similar crystalline structure, the titration curve of α-TiP is very similar to that of α-ZrP, although the second step does not exibit a well-defined plateau as in α-ZrP. This seems to be due to the fact that the TiHNa(PO$_4$)$_2 \cdot$ 4H$_2$O phase can accommodate an appreciable amount of Na$^+$ without giving rise to the discontinuous change of the interlayer distance from 10.4 to 9.9 Å. X-ray analyses of samples at various Na-loading showed that a large part of this dis-

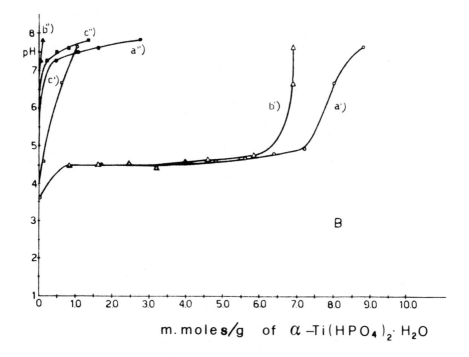

FIGURE 3. Titration curves of α-Ti(HPO$_4$)$_2 \cdot$H$_2$O with 0.1 M(LiC1-LiOH) or 0.1 M(CsC1 + CsOH) solutions. Curves a′, b′, and c′ refer to LiOH added, Li taken up by the exchanger, and phosphates released to the solution, respectively. Curves a″, b″, and c″ refer to CsOH added, Cs⁺ taken up by the exchanger, and phosphate released to the solutions, respectively. (From Alberti, G., Cardini-Galli, P., and Torracca, E. *J. Inorg. Nucl. Chem.*, 29, 571, 1967. With permission.)

continuous change of the interlayer distance takes place in the range 80 to 95% of Na⁺-exchange.

The titration curves of α-TiP with 0.1 M solution of LiOH, KOH, and CsOH, in the presence of 0.1 M added salt, are shown in Figures 3 and 4. In agreement with expectations based on the unit cell of α-TiP, the first proton is exchanged by K⁺ at pH considerably higher than that of α-ZrP (6.5 against 2.3). It can also be seen that the titration curve with LiOH exhibits a single plateau (pH 4.6) in the approximate range 0 to 75% of Li-conversion. X-ray analyses of the solids at the various stages of the conversion showed that the original interlayer distance of 7.6 Å does not appreciably change during the H⁺/Li⁺ ion exchange. This behavior also seems to be due to the higher density of the fixed charges. As for α-ZrP, a polyhydrate hydrogen form, Ti(HPO$_4$)$_2 \cdot$4-5H$_2$O (interlayer distance 9.2 Å), is obtained by backtitrating the mono-sodium form of α-TiP with dilute HCl.[15]

Owing to its high density of fixed charges, α-TiP tends to behave as a rigid layered exchanger and therefore it possesses more marked ion-sieve properties than does α-ZrP. The ion-sieve properties of α-TiP have been used[17] to effect separations of Cs⁺ and K⁺ ions from Na⁺. Ion exchange equilibrium between α-TiP and NaCl-KCl aqueous solution has been recently also investigated by Kobayashi[18] who also considered the possibility of separating Na⁺ and K⁺ ions.

Finally, the thermal behavior of α-TiP has been investigated by thermogravimetric and differential thermal analyses.[19,20]

It was found that the dehydration process is

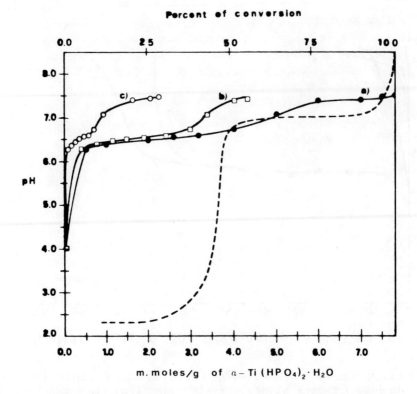

FIGURE 4. α-Ti(HPO$_4$)$_2 \cdot$ H$_2$O titrated with 0.1 M(KCl + KOH) solution by the "batch procedure" (t = 25 ± 1°C). Curves a, b, and c refer to KOH added, K$^+$ taken up by the exchanger, and phosphate released to the solution, respectively. Dashed curve refers to K$^+$-uptake curve of α-Zr(HPO$_4$)$_2 \cdot$ H$_2$O. (From Alberti, G., Costantino, U., and Luciani Giovagnotti, M. L., *Gazz. Chim. It.*, 110, 61, 1980. With permission.)

$$\alpha-\text{Ti(HPO}_4)_2 \cdot \text{H}_2\text{O} \xrightarrow[-\text{H}_2\text{O}]{100-250°} \alpha-\text{Ti(HPO}_4)_2 \underset{390°}{\overset{260-390°}{\rightleftharpoons}} \alpha-\text{Ti(HPO}_4)_2 \xrightarrow{380-500°}$$

$$\qquad (7.56 \text{ Å}) \qquad\qquad\qquad (7.33 \text{ Å}) \qquad\qquad\qquad (7.10 \text{ Å})$$

$$\alpha'-\text{TiP}_2\text{O}_7 \xrightarrow{730°} \text{TiP}_2\text{O}_7 \qquad\qquad\qquad\qquad\qquad (3)$$

It is likely that the layered structure is still preserved in α'-TiP$_2$O$_7$ (with $\equiv$P$-$O$-$P$\equiv$ groups binding adjacent layers), while at 730°C there is rearrangement to a cubic three-dimensional structure. The loss of the first moles of water requires 12 kcal/mol, while the reversible phase transition at 260-290° requires 2 kcal/mol.[21] The dehydration process of the Li-form[20] is

$$\text{Ti(LiPO}_4)_2 \cdot 2\text{H}_2\text{O} \xrightarrow[-\text{H}_2\text{O}]{80-200°} \text{Ti(LiPO}_4)_2 \cdot \text{H}_2\text{O} \xrightarrow[-\text{H}_2\text{O}; \; -\text{Li}_3\text{PO}_4]{310-400°} \text{LiTi}_2(\text{PO}_4)_3 \qquad (4)$$

B. α-Zirconium Arsenate

This compound can be prepared by refluxing amorphous zirconium arsenate in arsenic acid.[22,23] The structural relations to α-ZrP have already been mentioned in the previous chapter. The titration curves with hydroxides of alkali metal ions, Tl$^+$, Ba^{2+}, and NH$^+_4$ have been determined.[22-24] The forward and reverse Na$^+$/K$^+$ ion-exchange isotherms in aqueous solution and in molten $NaNO_3$ - KNO_3 mixtures at 400°C have been investigated by Allulli et al.[25] The thermal behavior of α-ZrAs has been studied by La Ginestra et al.[19] Although the windows connecting the cavities in α-$Zr(HAsO_4)_2 \cdot H_2O$ (α-ZrAs) are about the same size as in α-ZrP,[26] it seems that steric hindrance to the diffusion of large cations is less in α-ZrAs than in α-ZrP. Thus, the ion-exchange properties of α-ZrAs and α-ZrP are similar but with some small differences concerning the sieving properties (i.e., Ba^{2+} is exchanged by α-ZrAs but not by α-ZrP).[22]

C. α-Titanium Arsenate

Although obtained by the refluxing procedure as long ago as 1968,[27] this compound has been scarcely investigated to date. α-TiAs is less stable than α-TiP and is strongly hydrolyzed, even in neutral medium. Ion exchange experiments in aqueous solution are thus restricted to acid media (pH 5) where only one proton of α-$Ti(HAsO_4)_2 \cdot H_2O$ is replaced by Li^+, Na^+, or K^+ ion. Therefore, from a practical point of view, α-TiAs is considered a poor inorganic ion-exchanger although ion exchange towards multivalent ions has not yet been investigated. However, the ion exchange properties of α-TiAs are expected to be between those of α-ZrAs and α-TiP.

D. α-Hafnium Phosphate

α-$Hf(HPO_4)_2 \cdot H_2O$ has been prepared by Clearfield.[28] The ion exchange properties of α-HfP have been little investigated but are expected to be similar to those of α-ZrP. Owing to the strong similarity in the chemical properties of Zr and Hf, it is also expected that other acid salts of Hf(IV), such as α-HfAs and α-HfP, with properties similar to those of corresponding acid salts of Zr(IV), may be obtained.

E. α-Tin Phosphate and Arsenate

α-$Sn(HPO_4)_2 \cdot H_2O$ has been obtained by heating amorphous tin phosphate in phosphoric acid.[12,29-31] Costantino and Gasperoni[30] also prepared α-$Sn(HAsO_4)_2 \cdot H_2O$. The ion exchange properties of α-SnP and α-SnAs towards alkali metal ion have been investigated.[30]

These materials are also strongly hydrolyzed in alkaline medium. They are therefore poor exchangers, unless specific applications in acid solution and in nonaqueous media, or separations of trace elements, are required. We recall that Sn(IV) may be reduced to Sn(II) when contacted with solutions containing reducing substances. This is an additional disavantageous property of α-tin phosphate and arsenate, although it may be exploited for some particular application.

F. Organic-Inorganic α-Layered Exchangers

Recently, several compounds having a general formula $Zr(R\text{-}PO_3)_2$ and $Zr(R\text{-}OPO_3)_2$ (R = organic radical) and a layered structure of the α-type have been synthesized.[32] Such compounds can be considered as organic derivatives of α-ZrP in which the $\equiv$P$-$OH tetrahedral groups are replaced by $\equiv$P$-$R or $\equiv$P$-$OR groups. Apart from the interest in their fundamental aspects, these compounds constitute a new class of solid supports for gas or thin layer chromatography[33] and can be used as intercalating agents for polar molecules.[32] If an ionogenic group, such as $-SO_3H$, $-COOH$, N$-(CH_3)_3OH$ etc., is present in the organic radical, the compound obtained can be considered as an organic-inorganic ion exchanger in which the ionogenic group of organic nature is bonded to an insoluble crystalline inorganic matrix. One organic-inorganic exchanger containing carboxyl groups, zirconium bis(carboxymethanphosphonate), $Zr(HOOCCH_2PO_3)_2$, has recently been obtained.[34] A typical preparation is as follows: a clear solution 0.4 M in a zirconyl salt, 2.4 M in HF, 1 M in HCl, and 4 M in

$(CH_3O)_2P(O)CH_2CO_2CH_3$ is warmed at 60°C in order to decompose the zirconium fluoro-complex and to hydrolyze the ester group. The material begins to precipitate within 4 days and the precipitation is usually complete after 10 days. The acid protons of $Zr(HOOC-CH_2PO_3)_2$ can be replaced by Na^+. The exchange occurs in a single step at pH = 7 with change of the interlayer distance, according to the process

$$Zr(HOOCCH_2PO_3)_2 + 2Na^+ + 2OH^- + 2H_2O \longrightarrow Zr(NaOOCCH_2PO_3)_2 \cdot 4H_2O \qquad (5)$$
$$(d = 11.1 \text{ Å}) \qquad\qquad\qquad\qquad (d = 14.4 \text{ Å})$$

Attempts to convert $Zr(HOOCCH_2PO_3)_2$ into the lithium or potassium forms led to highly hydrolyzed products.

The surface ion exchange properties towards Mg^{2+}, Ca^{2+}, Ba^{2+}, and La^{3+} were also investigated. The surface ion exchange capacity was 13.4 µeq/g and S-shaped isotherms were found.[34] It is very probable that with a suitable choice of different phosphonic acids (or esters) and also by replacing the zirconium with other tetravalent metals, several other inorganic-organic ion exchangers can be prepared in the near future.

G. Other α-Layered Materials

During a systematic investigation on the acid salts of tetravalent metals[29] Winkler and Thilo were able to obtain α-Pb(HPO$_4$)$_2 \cdot$H$_2$O, α-Ge(HPO$_4$)$_2 \cdot$H$_2$O and α-Si(HPO$_4$)$_2$ (as well as α-ZrP, α-TiP, and α-SnP). It is difficult to consider these compounds as ion exchange materials since they are solubilized or decomposed in aqueous medium. The determination of the cation mobility in these materials may be of interest. Finally, mixed acid salts, such as zirconium-titanium phosphate have been prepared and studied. It has been reported[16] that zirconium and titanium phosphates form extensive solid solutions with each other. In many respects, those high in zirconium behave as α-ZrP while those high in titanium behave as α-TiP. It would be of interest to determine the ion-sieve and the electrochemical properties of these mixed α-materials.

III. ACID SALTS WITH LAYERED STRUCTURE OF γ TYPE

The insoluble acid salts of tetravalent metals can be obtained with a different layered structure, usually known as γ-structure. After γ-Zr(HPO$_4$)$_2 \cdot$2H$_2$O, first obtained by Clearfield[35] (see Chapter 1), another compound, with formula Ti(HPO$_4$)$_2 \cdot$2H$_2$O and showing marked analogies with γ-ZrP, was prepared by Allulli et al.[36] It is probable that other γ-insoluble acid salts* may be obtained in the near future.

It is very difficult to obtain crystals large enough for the determination of the crystal structure of γ-materials by X-ray procedures; therefore their crystalline structure is as yet unknown. Clearfield postulated that γ-ZrP has the same type of layers as ZrP, i.e., within a single layer the structure is the same, but the layers of γ-ZrP and α-ZrP are packed in a different manner, so giving different interlayer distances and different ion exchange properties.[35] By way of contrast, recent investigations performed on γ-ZrP by Yamanaka and Tanaka[37] and on γ-TiP in the author's laboratory[38] showed that α- and γ-materials have layers of different structure (see later).

---

* This nomenclature derives from the fact that the compound Zr(HPO$_4$)$_2 \cdot$2H$_2$O was named γ-ZrP by Clearfield. Recall that Clearfield[35] assigned the name β-ZrP to the product obtained by dehydrating γ-ZrP. Since the structure of the layers does not appreciably change with the nature and amount of the polar molecules and/or with the nature of the counter-ions placed between the layers themselves (see later), we prefer to use the prefix γ to indicate the class of exchangers having a layered structure similar to that of Zr(HPO$_4$)$_2 \cdot$2H$_2$O, independently of the counter-ions and amount of polar molecules placed between the layers.

A. γ-Titanium Phosphate

1. Three Methods for Preparing γ-Ti(HPO₄)₂·2H₂O

1. By digesting the amorphous titanium phosphate in 10 M H_3PO_4 in a hydrothermal bomb at 300°C for two days.[36]
2. By refluxing amorphous titanium phosphate in 15 to 16 M phosphoric acid.[38] A high concentration of phosphoric acid is essential since, if this concentration is lower than 15 M, α-TiP is obtained instead.
3. By the direct precipitation method in the presence of hydrofluoric acid.[38]

A typical preparation is the following: a solution 0.1 M in Ti(IV) salt, 0.5 M in HF and 8 M in H_3PO_4 is placed in a plastic beaker and the HF is slowly eliminated by evaporation at 60° to 80°C for a few days. Also in this case, if the H_3PO_4 concentration is less than 7 M, α-type titanium phosphate is obtained.

Note that the hemihydrate material $Ti(HPO_4)_2 \cdot 0.5H_2O$ (interlayer distance 9.21 Å) obtained by Kobayashi[38,40] by the reflux procedure and washing of the product with acetone also has a γ-structure.[38]

2. Some Consideration on the Formation and Structure of γ-TiP

In order to obtain other γ-insoluble acid salts, it is important to highlight those factors which favor the formation of the γ-structure. A study of the synthesis of γ-TiP has shown that the γ-structure if favored by high concentration of $H_2PO_4^-$ and/or HPO_4^{2-} anions.[38] This seems to indicate that M(IV) complexes with these anions are involved in the formation of the γ-phase. Although the γ-structure is as yet unknown, some indirect information has been obtained[38] as follows: both γ-ZrP and γ-TiP are able to take up stoichiometric amounts of several polar organic molecules (see Chapter 3) and the first d-values of these γ-materials increase with increase in the length of these molecules. Furthermore, there is a discontinuous change of the first d-value during the dehydration of γ-$Zr(HPO_4)_2 \cdot 2H_2O$ (from 12.2 to 9.4 Å) and of γ-$Ti(HPO_4)_2 \cdot 2H_2O$ (from 11.6 to 9.2 Å). These properties provide strong evidence that the γ-structure, like that of α-materials, is built up to polymeric macroanions $[M(IV)(XO_4)_2]_n^{2n-}$, with negative charges neutralized by protons, while the hydration water, or other polar molecules, can be accommodated between adjacent layers. Now, in a layered compound, the number of formula weights, n, contained in 1 cm² of a layer can be easily calculated[32] by the relationship

$$n = \frac{\rho d}{M} \tag{6}$$

where ϱ is the density (g/cm³), d the inter-layer distance and M is the formula weight of the layered exchanger. The n value of a given layered exchanger does not depend upon the nature of the counter-ions and/or upon the polar molecules placed between adjacent layers. Furthermore, the n-value is independent of the manner in which the macroanions are packed. It essentially depends upon the structure of the planar macroanions and, in the absence of other structural information, it can be usefully used to recognize if the structure of a given planar macroanion is of α or γ-type.

The n-values for some hydrated and anhydrous salt forms of α and γ-layered compounds are reported in Table 2.

It is evident that the γ-macroanions contain a larger number of tetravalent metal atoms per cm² of layer than the corresponding α-macroanions. This also indicates that the planar density of the fixed charges is higher in the γ than in the α-macroanions. Recently, Yamanaka and Tanaka[37] have established (by using electron and X-ray diffraction methods) that γ-ZrP crystallizes in the monoclinic system and that the param-

Table 2
DENSITY, INTERLAYER DISTANCE, AND VALUES OF n FOR SOME α AND γ-LAYERED COMPOUNDS

α-Compound	Density (g/cm³)	Interlayer distance (cm × 10⁹)	n (mol cm⁻² × 10¹⁰)	γ-Compound	Density (g/cm³)	Interlayer distance (cm × 10⁸)	n (mol cm⁻² × 10⁸)
α-Zr(HAsO₄)₂·H₂O	3.39	7.78	6.8	—	—	—	—
αZr(HPO₄)₂	2.62	7.41	6.8	γ-Zr(HPO₄)₂	2.79	9.40	9.3
αZr(HPO₄)₂·H₂O	2.72	7.56	6.8	γ-Zr(HPO₄)₂·2H₂O	2.43	12.20	9.3
α-Zr(KPO₄)₂·3H₂O	2.61	10.70	6.8	—	—	—	—
α-Ti(HPO₄)₂	2.44	7.43	7.6	γ-Ti(HPO₄)₂	2.60	9.10	9.9
α-Ti(HPO₄)₂·H₂O	2.61	7.56	7.7	γ-Ti(HPO₄)₂·2H₂O	2.37	11.60	9.9
α-Ti(HAsO₄)₂·H₂O	3.34	7.77	7.5	γ-Ti(NH₄PO₄)₂·H₂O	2.16	13.4	9.9
α-Sn(HPO₄)₂·H₂O	3.12	7.76	7.4	—	—	—	—

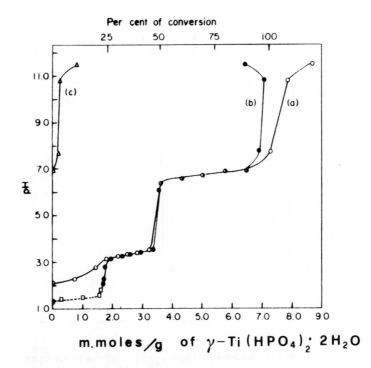

FIGURE 5. γ-Ti(HPO$_4$)$_2$·2H$_2$O titrated with 0.1 M (NaOH + NaCl) solutions by the "batch procedure" (t = 20°C), Curves a, b, and c refer to
NaOH added, Na$^+$ taken up by the exchanger, and phosphates released to
the solution, respectively. Dashed curve; titrant 0.1 M (NaCl + HCl) solutions. (From Allulli, S., Ferragina, C., LaGinestra, A., Massucci, M. A.,
and Tomassini, N., *J. Inorg. Nucl. Chem.*, 39, 1043, 1977. With permission.)

eters of the unit cell are a = 5.376 ± 0.002 Å; b = 6.636 ± 0.004 Å; c = 24.56 ± 0.01
Å; and β = 93.94 ± 0.05 Å. Assuming that the ratio a/b and β are equal for γ-ZrP
and γ-TiP and calculating the product a × b from the relationship:[32]

$$a \times b = \frac{2M}{N \rho d} = \frac{2}{M n} \tag{7}$$

where N is the Avogadro's number, it can be derived that the dimensions of the unit
cell of γ-TiP are a = 5.2 Å; b = 6.4 Å; and c = 2d/sin β = 23.2 Å.

At present, only suggestions on the arrangement of the phosphate groups in the γ-
structure can be put forward. Taking into account that the formation of the γ-structure
is favored by the presence of HPO$^{2-}_4$ anions, one possibility is the following: while in
the α-layers each tetravalent metal atom is octahedrally coordinated to six oxygens of
six different XO$_4$ groups, in the γ-layers six coordination is instead obtained with only
four XO$_4$ groups. In other words, two XO$_4$ groups could be bonded to the tetravalent
metal via two oxygens. Whatever the case, the planar density of the fixed negative
charges of the γ-macroanions is higher than that of the α-macroanions. Therefore, the
distance between adjacent fixed charges in a layer of γ-TiP is expected to be shorter
than that in the correspondent α-material. Thus, steric hindrance, due to the closeness
of fixed charges, could arise in α-TiP, especially if large counter-ions are involved in
the ion exchange processes.

3. Ion-Exchange Properties

The ion exchange capacity of γ-Ti(HPO$_4$)$_2$·2H$_2$O is 7.25 meq/g. The titration and

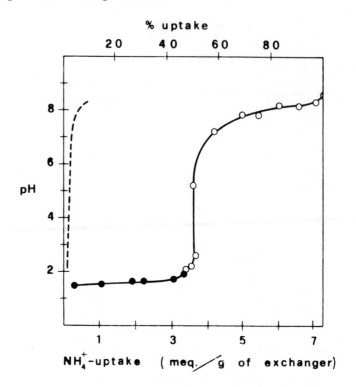

FIGURE 6. NH_4^+-uptake curve of γ-Ti(HPO$_4$)$_2 \cdot$ 2H$_2$O obtained from the batch titration curve. Full and open circles refer to samples equilibrated with 0.100 M (NH$_4$Cl + HCl) and 0.100 M (NH$_3$ + NH$_4$Cl) solutions, respectively. The dashed curve shows the mmol of phosphates per gram of exchanger released to the supernatant solution. (From Alberti, G., Bernasconi, M. G., Casciola, M., and Costantino, U., *J. Inorg. Nucl. Chem.* 42, 1637, 1980. With permission.)

uptake curves for the H$^+$/Na$^+$ process are shown in Figure 5, together with the amount of the phosphate released by the exchanger at the various pH values. A comparison with the analogous curves of α-TiP (Figure 2) shows that Na$^+$ is taken up by γ-TiP at pHs considerably lower than in the case of α-TiP.

The H$^+$/Na$^+$ ion exchange process can be roughly divided into the following three steps, each occurring with a discontinuous change in the interlayer distance:

$$\text{Ti(HPO}_4)_2 \cdot 2\text{H}_2\text{O} + 0.5\,\text{Na}^+\text{(aq)} \longrightarrow \text{TiNa}_{0.5}\text{H}_{1.5}(\text{PO}_4)_2 \cdot \text{H}_2\text{O}$$
$$(11.6\ \text{Å}) \qquad\qquad\qquad\qquad (11.0\ \text{Å})$$

$$\xrightarrow{\ \frac{1}{2}\,\text{Na}^+\ } \text{TiHNa(PO}_4)_2 \cdot 3\text{H}_2\text{O} \xrightarrow{\ \text{Na}^+\ } \text{Ti(NaPO}_4)_2 \cdot 2\text{H}_2\text{O}$$
$$(13.2\ \text{Å}) \qquad\qquad\qquad (12.8\ \text{Å}) \qquad\qquad (8)$$

The H$^+$/NH$_4^+$ exchange has also been investigated.[41] The exchange occurs in two steps (see Figure 6). The first proton is completely replaced by NH$_4^+$ at pH 2 and the replacement occurs with a discontinuous change of the interlayer distance from 11.6 to 11.2 Å, while the second proton is exchanged (or ammonia is protonated) at pH 7. Between 50 and 80% of NH$_4^+$ exchange, increased loading takes place without appreciable change in the interlayer distance while, for higher NH$_4^+$ loading, there is a discontinuous change from 11.2 to 13.6 Å.

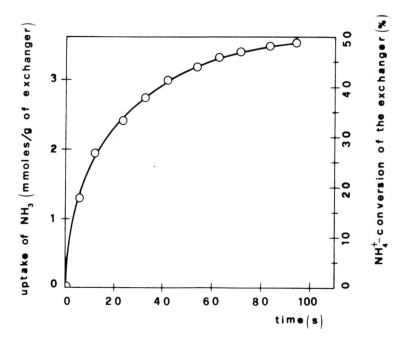

FIGURE 7. Uptake of NH₃ on γ-Ti(HPO₄)₂·2H₂O as a function of time. Experimental conditions: 0.5 g of exchanger, equilibrated under moderate stirring at 20°C, with 100 mℓ of an aqueous solution containing 3.63 mmol of ammonia. (From Alberti, G., Bernasconi, M. G., Casciola, M., and Costantino, U., *J. Inorg. Nucl. Chem.*, 42, 1637, 1980. With permission.)

It was also found that NH₃ is taken up by γ-Ti(HPO₄)₂·2H₂O at an appreciable rate (see Figure 7) according to the schematic protonation reaction

$$\gamma-\text{Ti(HPO}_4)_2 \cdot 2\text{H}_2\text{O} + \text{NH}_3 \longrightarrow \text{TiHPO}_4 \cdot \text{NH}_4\text{PO}_4 \cdot \text{H}_2\text{O} + \text{H}_2\text{O} \tag{9}$$

When the first proton has been completely saturated, the rate of uptake becomes considerably slower. Steric hindrance, very probably due to the closeness of fixed charges in the planar macroanions, may be responsible for the slow diffusion of NH₃ in TiHPO₄·NH₄PO₄·H₂O.

The large interlayer distance of γ-TiP also permits fast H⁺/Ca²⁺ and H⁺/Sr²⁺ ion exchange processes.[36,42] The Ca-uptake as a function of the pH is shown in Figure 8. Since Ca²⁺ and Sr²⁺ are taken up by γ-TiP very selectively, a significant amount of exchange takes place before the addition of the corresponding hydroxide.

Kobayashi[43] has carried out extensive ion exchange studies in aqueous solution with Ti(HPO₄)₂·0.5H₂O. It was subsequently demonstrated, in the author's laboratory,[38] that this phase has a γ-structure and that it can be obtained by dehydration of γ-Ti(HPO₄)₂·2H₂O. Owing to the loss of the water, the interlayer distance of γ-TiP decreases from 11.6 to 9.2 Å. It is therefore expected that the steric hindrance for the exchange of large cations is larger in the hemihydrate than in di-hydrate γ-TiP. However, it is now known that the anhydrous γ-TiP rehydrates completely in water.[38,44] Thus, the ion exchange processes investigated by Kobayashi with the hemihydrate γ-TiP probably occurred simultaneously with the hydration process. Before definitive conclusions can be reached, the same processes as investigated by Kobayashi should also be studied using γ-Ti(HPO₄)₂·2H₂O. In any case, Kobayashi[43] found that γ-Ti(HPO₄)₂·0.5H₂O is able to take up Cs⁺ from aqueous solution; furthermore the value of K_d for K⁺ was about 4 times that for Na⁺. Thus Na⁺/K⁺ separations are expected.

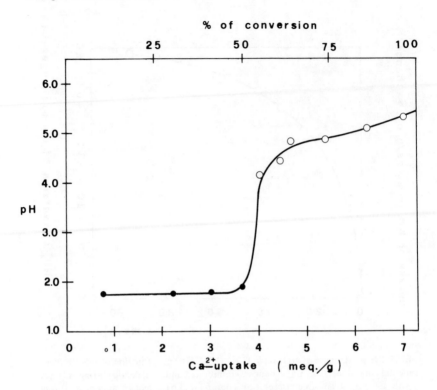

FIGURE 8.   Ca^{2+} -uptake curve of γ-Ti(HPO$_4$)$_2$·2H$_2$O, obtained from the batch titration curve. Full and open circles refer to samples equilibrated with 0.100 *N* (CaCl$_2$ + HCl) solutions and 0.100 *N*(CaCl$_2$ + Ca(OH)$_2$) solutions, respectively. (From Alberti, G. and Costantino, U., unpublished data, 1980.)

In Table 3 are listed the interlayer distances of some anhydrous and hydrated salt forms of γ-TiP. Other salt forms are now being prepared and investigated in the writer's laboratory in order to study the variation of the interlayer distance at a function of diameter and hydration of counter-ions. However, the few data reported in Table 2 and 3 already clearly indicate that the difference between the interlayer distance of the anhydrous di-hydrogen form and that of a given salt form, is higher in γ- than in α-materials. This means that, in γ-materials, the counter-ions are less dipped between adjacent fixed charges of a same layer, in agreement with the higher density of fixed charges of γ-layers.

B. Other γ-Materials

To date, no γ-materials other than γ-ZrP and γ-TiP have been reported in the literature. It is however probable that the structure of Ce(HAsO$_4$)$_2$·2H$_2$O is of γ-type[45] (see later) and that other γ-materials will be obtained in the near future. The ion-exchange properties of new γ-materials are not expected to be better than those of γ-ZrP and γ-TiP, but their preparation should allow the conditions which favor the formation of the γ-structure to be understood.

IV. ACID SALTS WITH FIBROUS STRUCTURE

The first fibrous acid salt of a tetravalent metal to be prepared was cerium (IV) phosphate.[46,47] Subsequently, fibrous thorium phosphate was obtained.[48,49] Fibrous titanium arsenate and titanium phosphate were also recently synthesized[50] and it is very likely that other fibrous acid salts will be obtained in the near future. An electron

Table 3
INTERLAYER DISTANCE OF SOME ANHYDROUS AND HYDRATED SALT FORMS OF γ-TiP

γ-Compound	Interlayer distance (Å)	Ref.	γ-Compound	Interlayer distance (Å)	Ref.
$Ti(HPO_4)_2$	9.1	39	$Ti(NaPO_4)_2$	10.5	44
$Ti(HPO_4)_2 \cdot H_2O$	11.4	44	$TiHK(PO_4)_2$	10.8	42
$Ti(HPO_4)_2 \cdot 2H_2O$	11.6	36	$Ti(KPO_4)_2$	12.1	42
$TiHLi(PO_4)_2$	9.6	42	$TiHNH_4(PO_4)_2 \cdot yH_2O$	11.2	42
$Ti(LiPO_4)_2$	9.9	42	$Ti(NH_4PO_4)_2 \cdot H_2O$	13.4	42
$TiH_{1.5}Na_{0.5}(PO_4)_2 \cdot H_2O$	11.0	36	$TiHMg_{0.5}(PO_4)_2$	9.8	42
$TiHNa(PO_4)_2 \cdot 3H_2O$	13.2	36	$TiHCa_{0.5}(PO_4)_2 \cdot 3H_2O$	13.4	42
$TiHNa(PO_4)_2 \cdot 2H_2O$	12.6	44	$TiHCa_{0.5}(PO_4)_2$	10.3	42
$TiHNa(PO_4)_2 \cdot H_2O$	10.2	44	$TiHSr_{0.5}(PO_4)_2 \cdot 3H_2O$	13.4	36
$TiHNa(PO_4)_2$	10.1	44	$TiHSr_{0.5}(PO_4)_2 \cdot H_2O$	11.0	44
$Ti(NaPO_4)_2 \cdot 2H_2O$	12.8	36	$TiHSr_{0.5}(PO_4)_2$	10.7	44
$Ti(NaPO_4)_2 \cdot H_2O$	11.5	44			

micrograph of a sample of cerium(IV) phosphate showing its fibrous structure is given in Figure 9.

Fibrous acid salts are very interesting from a practical point of view because they can be employed to prepare inorganic ion exchange papers, or thin layers, suitable for fast separations of cations.[51] Furthermore, by pressing these papers, inorganic ion exchange membranes[52,53] with good electrochemical behavior,[54,55] can be obtained. Unfortunately, single fibers of suitable size for working out the structure by X-ray diffraction methods have not yet been obtained. Their structure is therefore unknown and it is difficult to give a good systematization to their ion-exchange properties. Some important ion exchange feature of fibrous ion exchange materials are now examined.

A. Fibrous Cerium(IV) Phosphate

Fibrous cerium(IV) phosphate (CeP_f) was first obtained by adding dropwise (3 mℓ/min), one volume of 0.05 M $Ce(SO_4)_2 \cdot 4H_2O$ solution in 0.5 M H_2SO_4 to one volume of a well-stirred solution of 6 M H_3PO_4, previously heated at 95°C. After a digestion of a few hours at this temperature, the precipitate was washed, until free of sulfate ions, and air dried. Flexible sheets similar to cellulose papers can be easily obtained by dispersing the fibrous precipitate in a large volume of water, then filtering the slurry in a large buchner funnel. Fibrous cerium(IV) phosphate has been also obtained by Herman and Clearfield[56] during a systematic investigation of the Ce(IV) phosphoric acid system.

The chemical formula of CeP_f is not yet known with certainty. However, some information has been derived from chemical and thermal analyses, ion-exchange properties, X-ray powder diffraction patterns and infrared spectroscopy.[2,57] The chemical composition is $CeO_2 \cdot P_2O_5 \cdot 4H_2O$ and its thermal behavior can be summarized as:

$$CeO_2 \cdot P_2O_5 \cdot 4H_2O \xrightarrow[\text{(P_2O_5)}]{-2H_2O} CeO_2 \cdot P_2O_5 \cdot 2H_2O \xrightarrow[120-180°C]{-H_2O} Ce(HPO_4)_2 \xrightarrow{-H_2O} CeP_2O_7$$

$$(10)$$

The loss of two water molecules over P_2O_5 seems not to cause significant changes in the mechanical properties and in the X-ray powder pattern while, when the third water molecule is lost at 180°, the material becomes friable and the first d-value of the X-ray powder pattern decreases from 10.9 to 7.9 Å. For $CeO_2 \cdot P_2O_5 \cdot 2H_2O$, two possible formulas, $CeO(H_2PO_4)_2$ and $Ce(HPO_4)_2 \cdot H_2O$, can be written. Infrared spectroscopy

FIGURE 9.   Electron micrograph of a sample of CeP$_f$. (Magnification × 10,000.) (From Alberti, G. and Costantino, U., *J. Chromatogr.*, 102, 5, 1974. With permission.)

seems to give more support to the formula $Ce(HPO_4)_2 \cdot H_2O$ and the theoretical ion exchange capacity of 2 mol of counter-ions per formula weight of material is in good agreement with the experimental ion exchange capacity (5 meq/g) especially if the phosphate groups lost by hydrolysis are taken into account. The ion exchange properties towards monovalent and divalent metal ions have been investigated.[46,58]

The titration and the uptake curves of alkali metal ions are shown in Figures 10 and 11 while the uptake of alkaline earth metal ions are reported in Figure 12.

From the shape of the uptake curves the following conclusions can be drawn:

1.   In contrast to the corresponding uptake curves of α- and γ-layered exchangers, where there is usually a definite plateau for each phase transition, the uptake curves of CeP$_f$ show that the exchangeable protons display a wide range of acidities, similar to that of amorphous or semicrystalline ion exchangers.

2.   The nature of the counter-ions strongly affects the shape of the titration curve. At low metal ion loading (25% of conversion) the sequences of decreasing preference for alkali and alkaline earth metal ions are those of the lyotropic series: $Cs^+ > K^+ > Na^+ > Li^+$ and $Ba^{2+} > Sr^{2+} > Ca^{2+} > Mg^{2+}$ while several inversions, probably due to steric hindrance, occur at higher loading.

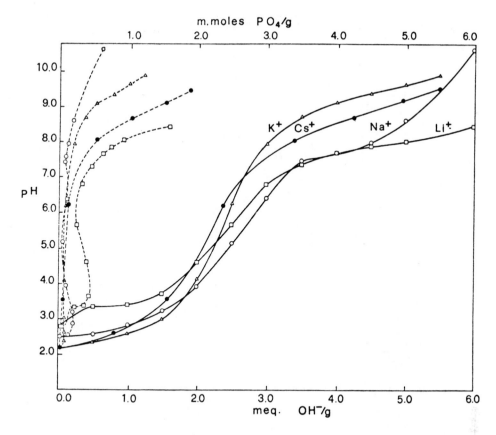

FIGURE 10. Titration curves of CeP$_f$ with 0.1 M(MOH + MCl) solutions (M = alkali metal ions). The dashed curves show the mmol of phosphate per gram of exchanger released to the solution. (From Alberti, G., Casciola, M., Costantino, U., and Luciani Giovagnotti, M. L., *J. Chromatogr.*, 128, 289, 1976. With permission.)

3. Conversions higher than 50% were not obtained with large monovalent cations such as K$^+$ and Cs$^+$ since in alkaline medium, where full conversion can probably be obtained, the material is strongly hydrolyzed. It is not clear if the steric hindrance is due to the presence of narrow openings in the structure or to the closeness of adjacent fixed charges.

The X-ray powder patterns exhibit only a few lines, the first being much more intense than the others. As shown in Table 4, its value (d = 11.2 Å) increases only very slightly with increase of the ionic radius of the counter-ions and does not appreciably depend on the percentage of exchange and the water content. Thus, either CeP$_f$ has a rigid structure or it forms a continuous solid solution over the entire range of uptake.

Another important difference between CeP$_f$ and α-layered materials is that the ion exchange processes occurring in CeP$_f$, in contrast with those of α-layered materials, apparently exhibit reversibility.[58]

Inorganic ion exchange papers or thin layers obtained by CeP$_f$ have been used successfully for the chromatographic separation of inorganic ions and R$_f$ values of several ions have been determined.[51] A very high selectivity for certain cations, such as Pb^{2+}, Ag$^+$, Tl$^+$, and K$^+$, was found. The separation factors and K$_d$ for some inorganic ions were also determined.[58,59] Some data are reported in Tables 5 and 6. The H$^+$/Pb^{2+} exchange has been studied over the entire range of uptake. The ion exchange isotherm (Figure 13) shows that lead is strongly preferred in the range 0 to 50% of loading.

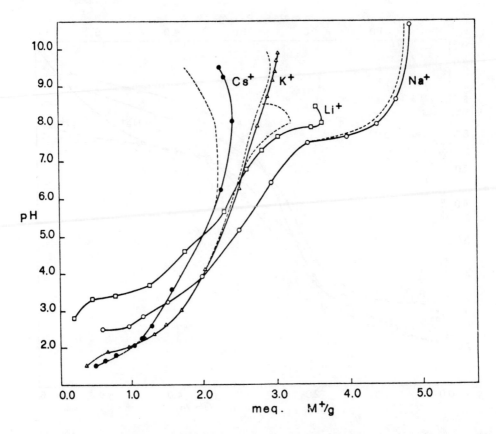

FIGURE 11.   Comparison between experimental (full lines) and calculated (dashed lines) uptake curves of alkali metal ions, obtained from titration curves (see Figure 10). The dotted lines refer to M^+-uptake values obtained in the presence of added $KClO_4$. (From Alberti, G., Casciola, M., Costantino, U., and Luciani Giovagnotti, M. L., *J. Chromatogr.*, 128, 289, 1976. With permission.)

Batch experiments for $Ca^{2+}-Pb^{2+}$ separation at low pH values and different $Pb^{2+}-Ca^{2+}$ compositions (Table 7) showed that Pb^{2+} is taken up selectively by CeP_f even in the presence of high Ca^{2+} concentrations.

It has been mentioned above that CeP_f, for its fibrous nature, may be employed to prepare inorganic ion exchange membranes. To date, only some preliminary investigations on the cationic transport of CeP_f and on the electrochemical behavior of CeP_f membranes have been performed.[54,55] Some data of specific electric conductance of amorphous and fibrous CeP materials are reported in Table 8.

B. Fibrous Thorium Phosphate

Fibrous thorium phosphate (ThP_f) may be obtained[48,49] by a procedure similar to that used for CeP_f. Its chemical composition is $ThO_2 \cdot P_2O_5 \cdot 4H_2O$ and its X-ray powder diffraction pattern is similar to that of CeP_f.

Inorganic papers of ThP_f can be easily prepared and these papers compare favorably with those of CeP_f as regards stability to strong reducing agents. This property may be important in chromatographic separations where reducing agents are often used as eluents or spot-test reagents. Furthermore, CeP_f decomposes at temperatures higher than 500°C (because of the reduction of Ce(IV) to Ce(III)) while this does not occur for fibrous ThP. On the other hand, ThP_f papers are less flexible than CeP_f papers and should be used with caution because of the presence of thorium.

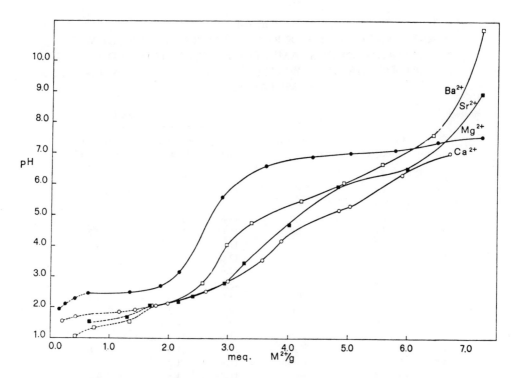

FIGURE 12. Uptake curves of alkaline earth metal ions on CeP$_f$. Dotted lines refer to uptake values obtained in presence of added KClO$_4$. (From Alberti, G., Casciola, M., Costantino, U., and Luciani-Giov-agnotti, M. L., *J. Chromatogr.*, 128, 289, 1976. With permission.)

C. Fibrous Titanium Arsenate and Phosphate

Efforts have continued to obtain fibrous materials containing nonreducible or non-radioactive tetravalent metals. Very recently, fibrous titanium arsenate was obtained and inorganic papers of this material were prepared.[50] Also in this case some caution is necessary because the toxicity of the arsenic. Therefore, several experiments were carried out in order to obtain fibrous titanium phosphate and fibrous zirconium phosphate. Fibrous titanium phosphate has finally been obtained by a hydrothermal method[50] and it is very likley that fibrous zirconium phosphate will also be obtained in the near future. The ion exchange properties of fibrous titanium arsenate and phosphate are now under investigation in the writer's laboratory.

V. ACID SALTS WITH THREE-DIMENSIONAL STRUCTURE

A. Compounds with General Formula HM$_2$(IV)(XO$_4$)$_3$ (M(IV) = Zr, Ti, Ge; X = P, As)

These can be prepared,[60] in Na-form, by heating a mixture of sodium metaphosphate (12.5 g) and metal dioxide (1.2 g ZrO$_2$ or 0.75 g TiO$_2$ or 1.0 g GeO$_2$) for 24 hr at 1200°C. Good crystals can be obtained after tempering in a platinum crucible for several weeks at 1100°C. or by crystallization from a boric acid melt. They can be also prepared, in Li$^+$ form, by melting M(IV)O$_2$, Li$_2$CO$_3$, and (NH$_4$)$_2$HPO$_4$ at 1200°C.[61] It is interesting to note that the salt forms of three-dimensional acid salts,

$$M_{\frac{1}{z}}' M_2 (IV) (XO_4)_3$$

(where M$'$ is the counter-ion of charge z), can be also obtained by thermal decompo-

Table 4
FIRST D-VALUE IN THE X-RAY POWDER PATTERNS OF WET
AND ANHYDROUS SAMPLES OF CeP$_f$ EXCHANGED AT
VARIOUS LOADINGS WITH SOME MONO AND DIVALENT
METAL IONS

| | | | | d Value, in Å of a sample | |
Cation	Conversion (meq/g)	Water content (mol H$_2$O/F.W.)	Wet	Dried over P$_4$O$_{10}$	Anhydrous (dried at 180°C)
H$^+$	—	3.0	11.2	10.9	7.9
Na$^+$	1.2	3.3	11.9	—	9.7
	4.8	3.4	11.9	—	10.1
K$^+$	1.3	3.0	11.6	10.1	9.9
	3.0	2.8	11.6	10.6	10.2
Cs$^+$	1.6	2.5	11.9	10.8	10.1
Mg^{2+}	1.3	4.7	12.6	12.1	9.7
	5.1	5.4	12.6	11.3	9.7
Ca^{2+}	2.6	3.5	13.0	11.6	9.8
	4.9	3.8	13.0	12.4	9.7
Sr^{2+}	2.4	3.6	12.4	11.3	—
	4.0	3.7	12.8	—	9.7
Ba^{2+}	1.9	3.1	11.9	11.2	—
	4.9	3.2	11.9	11.4	9.8
Pb^{2+}	2.2	—	11.4	11.2	—
	3.6	—	11.9	11.8	—

Table 5
SEPARATION FACTOR, α_N^M, OF SOME
CATIONS ON CeP$_f$, AT DIFFERENT
CONCENTRATIONS AND pH VALUES[a]

| | $\alpha_N^M \cdot 10^3$ | | |
Cation	C = 10^{-3} N pH = 3.0	C = 10^{-1} N pH = 3.0	C = 10^{-1} N pH = 1.5
Li$^+$	24	0.6	—
Na$^+$	62	3.7	—
NH$^+_4$	110	4.2	—
(CH$_3$)$_4$N$^+$	125	2.2	—
K$^+$	150	5.5	27
Cs$^+$	680	4.1	40
Tl$^+$	—	7.8	150
Mg^{2+}	—	6.7	7
Ca^{2+}	690	15	14
Sr^{2+}	870	17	60
Ba^{2+}	950	12	140
Pb^{2+}	—	500	920

a
$$\alpha_H^M = \frac{\overline{X}_M}{\overline{X}_H} \times \frac{X_H}{X_M}$$

sition of salt forms of α-layered,[62,63] or γ-layered acid salts.[61] For example, by heating a sample of α-Zr(LiPO$_4$)$_2$ (about 4 hr at 750°), the following decomposition takes place:[62]

Table 6
DISTRIBUTION COEFFICIENTS
OF SOME CATIONS ON CeP$_f$

Experimental conditions: 0.5 g of
exchanger equilibrated with 100 mℓ
of $10^{-3}N$ solutions

Cation	K_d (meq/g: meq/mℓ)
Li$^+$	11
Ni^{2+}	50
Co^{2+}	$1.0.10^2$
Na$^+$	$1.2.10^2$
Ag$^+$	$5.5.10^2$
Cu^{2+}	$1.3.10^3$
K$^+$	$3.5.10^3$
Pb^{2+}	$>5.10^4$

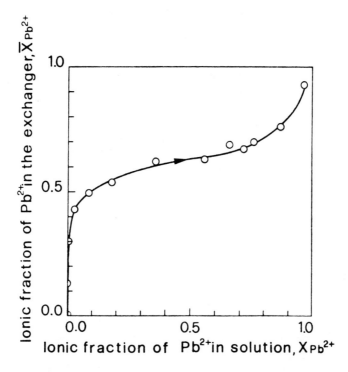

FIGURE 13. H$^+$/Pb^{2+} ion exchange isotherm on CeP$_f$. Concentration, 0.1 N; temperature, 25°C. (From Alberti, G., Casciola, M., Costantino, U., and Luciani-Giavagnotti, M. L., *J. Chromatogr.*, 128, 289, 1976. With permission.)

$$2\,\alpha-Zr(LiPO_4)_2 \xrightarrow{750°} LiZr_2(PO_4)_3 + Li_3PO_4 \qquad (11)$$

Similar decomposition occurs for α-Zr(LiAsO$_4$)$_2$ and Ti(LiPO$_4$)$_2$[20] (see also Equation 4). The structures have been worked out by Hagman, Kierkegaard, and Goodenough et al.[65] These structures may be described in terms of PO$_4$ tetrahedra and M(IV)O$_6$ octahedra which are linked by corners to form a three-dimensional network. The ar-

Table 7
BATCH EXPERIMENTS FOR $Ca^{2+} - Pb^{2+}$ SEPARATION ON CeP_f

Conditions: 1 g of $Ce(HPO_4)_2 \cdot 3H_2O$ equilibrated with solutions
at initial pH 0.95

Composition of initial solution (meq/ml)		Volume of solution (ml)	Uptake (meq/g)		$\dfrac{\overline{Pb^{2+}}}{\overline{Ca^{2+}}} \cdot \dfrac{[Ca^{2+}]e}{[Pb^{2+}]e}$ [a]
Pb^{2+}	Ca^{2+}		$\overline{Pb^{2+}}$	$\overline{Ca^{2+}}$	
$1.00 \cdot 10^{-1}$	$2.05 \cdot 0^{-1}$	200	2.6	9.10^{-2}	68
$1.0 \cdot 10^{-2}$	$2.0 \cdot 10^{-2}$	400	2.2	8.10^{-2}	$1.2 \cdot 10^2$
$1.0 \cdot 10^{-2}$	$2.05 \cdot 10^{-1}$	200	1.6	$1.1 \cdot 10^{-1}$	$1.5 \cdot 10^3$

[a] $[]_e$ = concentration at the equilibrium, in meq/ml.

Table 8
SPECIFIC ELECTRICAL CONDUCTANCE OF SOME CeP_f MATERIALS AT 20 ± 0.1°C

Material	Specific conductance ($\omega^{-1}\,cm^{-1}$)
Amorphous CeP	
Hydrogen form[a]	$1.5 - 2.5 \cdot 10^{-3}$
Fibrous CeP	
Hydrogen form[a]	$0.5 - 1.5 \cdot 10^{-3}$
Na-form 5%	$2.5 \cdot 10^{-3}$
Na-form 10%	$3.3 \cdot 10^{-3}$
Na-form 50%	$3.2 \cdot 10^{-3}$
Li-form 75%	$3.6 \cdot 10^{-3}$

[a]   The specific conductance depends strongly on the conditions of preparation.

rangement is such that empty cavities are formed, where the counter-ions are placed. The dimensions of the hexagonal unit cells are[60]

$NaZr_2(PO_4)_3$	a = 8.80 ± 2 Å	c = 22.76 ± 9 Å
$NaTi_2(PO_4)_3$	a = 8.5 ± 5 Å	c = 21.78 ± 15 Å
$NaGe_2(PO_4)_3$	a = 8.11 ± 4 Å	c = 21.51 ± 11 Å

It was found by Allulli et al.[62] that the hydrogen forms, $HZr_2(XO_4)_3$, are easily obtained by washing with acid solutions (e.g., 0.2 M HCl) the lithium form, $LiZr_2(XO_4)_3$ [previously obtained from thermal decomposition of the α-$Zr(LiPO_4)_2$]. The ion exchange properties of $HZr_2(PO_4)_3$ (ion-exchange capacity 2.14 meq/g; density 1.4 ± 0.1 g/cm^3) are very interesting since this compound behaves as a very narrow ionic sieve. Only the small counter-ions H^+, Li^+, Na^+, and Ag^+ can be interexchanged; therefore, this material can be used to carry out several interesting separations of small counter-ions from large ones (e.g., silver ion is easily separated from (Tl(I), Pb(II), Al(III), Cu(II), Zn(II), Hg(II), and Fe(III) while Na^+ can be quantitatively separated by K^+ and NH^+_4). Owing to its smaller unit cell, it is likely that $HTi_2(PO_4)_3$ behaves as an even narrower ion-sieve than $HZr_2(PO_4)_3$. Additional research on the ion exchange properties of these materials would be of interest.

Acid salts with three-dimensional structures are also very interesting because they have high ionic conductance, especially if SiO_2 is added during their preparation. In this case, some of the phosphorous atoms are replaced by silicon atoms and compounds with formula $Na_{1+x}M_2(IV)P_{3-x}Si_xO_{12}$ are obtained.[65] For example, the resistivity, at 300°, of pressed microcrystals of $Na_3Zr_2PSi_2O_{12}$ is 5 ohm-cm, while the activation energy for the Na^+ transport is 0.29 eV.[65] The transport properties of $Na_3Zr_2PSi_2O_{12}$, at 300°C, are thus equivalent to those of β''-alumina. Therefore these materials are very promising for several application where solid electrolytes are required (see also Chapter 1).

B. Zirconium Molybdate

By refluxing zirconium molybdate gels in 1 to 4 M HCl, Clearfield and Blessing[66] obtained a microcrystalline compound of formula $ZrMo_2O_7$ $(OH)_2(H_2O)_2$. Large single crystals were also grown under hydrothermal conditions and the crystal structure was worked out.[66] The structure consists of a three-dimensional network of cross-linked chains built up of quite regular $[ZrO_3(OH)_2O_2]$ pentagonal bipyramids and distorted $[cis\text{-}MoO_4(OH)(H_2O)]$ -octahedra. Crystal data are tetragonal space group $I4_1cd(No110)$; $a = 11.45 \pm 0.01$ Å; and $c = 12.49 \pm 0.01$ Å.

In contrast to the promising ion exchange properties reported by Kraus et al.[67] for amorphous zirconium molybdate, it was found that the crystalline compound was strongly hydrolyzed during the titration with 0.1 N(NaCl + NaOH) according to the process

$$ZrMo_2O_7(OH)_2(H_2O)_2 + 4OH^- + (x+y-5)H_2O \longrightarrow ZrO_{2-x}(OH)_{2x}(H_2O)_y + 2MoO_4^{2-} \qquad (12)$$

Thus, the exchange of the protons causes a total collapse of the crystal structure via hydrolysis of the molybdate group and hydroxylation of Zr(IV). At present, it appears that crystalline zirconium molybdate is not a useful inorganic ion exchanger, although ion exchange experiments with small multivalent cations and determination of the protonic transport have not yet been performed.

VI. ACID SALTS WITH UNKNOWN STRUCTURE

Several crystalline acid salts of tetravalent metals which have been prepared for potential use as ion exchangers have as yet unknown crystalline structures. Some of these materials exhibit very interesting properties. Unfortunately, the lack of information on their crystalline structure renders impossible any explanation and correlation of these properties. Therefore, investigations on the preparation of large crystals for structural determinations are highly desirable.

A. Thorium Arsenate

This has been prepared by prolonged refluxing of a solution containing a thorium salt and arsenic acid.[68,69] The best results have been obtained using solutions 0.5 M in thorium nitrate, 2 to 4 M in arsenic acid and 1 M in nitric acid. A microcrystalline product begins to precipitate after 2 to 4 days of refluxing. The crystals are needle-shaped, with an average length of 25 μm. The solubility in common mineral acids is very low and arsenate groups are not appreciably released at pH 12. Chemical and thermal analyses, as well as ion exchange experiments, showed that thorium arsenate can be represented by the formula $Th(HAsO_4)_2 \cdot H_2O$ (ion exchange capacity 3.75 meq/g). The following processes occur when thorium arsenate is heated to 500°C

$$Th(HAsO_4)_2 \cdot H_2O \xrightarrow[-H_2O]{125°-240°C} Th(HAsO_4)_2 \xrightarrow[-H_2O]{280°-450°C} ThAs_2O_7 \qquad (13)$$

The anhydrous $Th(HAsO_4)_2$ does not again take up its hydration water even when dispersed for long periods of time in aqueous solutions. Thorium arsenate is an inorganic-ion exchanger which behaves as a very narrow ion-sieve. In fact, the protons of the $\equiv As-OH$ groups can be easily replaced by Li^+ ions (in a single step at pH 9.4) but not by other, larger, counter-ions. Therefore, the exchange is highly specific for lithium. This interesting property has already been employed for carrying out good separations of Li^+ from other cations, even when the latter are present in high concentrations, and practical application in the recovery of Li^+ from natural and from dilute solutions can be expected. At present, owing to the lack of structural information, the reason for this marked ion-sieve property is unknown; some possibilities are discussed below.

The X-ray powder pattern of thorium arsenate shows a first diffraction maximum at 7.05 Å, the position and intensity of which does not appreciably change when the protons are replaced by lithium ions or when the material loses its hydration water. Thus, thorium arsenate has either an (unknown) three-dimensional lattice or a rather rigid layered structure with an interlayer distance of 7.05 Å. In the author's opinion, the latter possibility is the more likely. In fact, using the relationship $n = \varrho d/m$ (previously discussed) it can be calculated (as $\varrho = 4.759$ g/cm^3; $d = 7.05 \cdot 10^{-8}$ cm, and M $= 529.88$) that n is $6.3 \cdot 10^{-10}$ mol/cm^2. The fact that this value is very near to that of α-$Zr(HPO_4)_2 \cdot H_2O$ (n $= 6.8 \cdot 10^{-10}$ mol/cm^2) supports the layered structure of α-type for thorium arsenate.

Now, for a layered material of α-type, the product of the parameters a and b of the unit cell can be obtained from the relationship (7). Thus, a $\times$ b $= 52.22$ Å^2 and the dimensions of the unit cell can be estimated by assuming that $\sin \beta = 0.93$ and $a/b = 1.713$, as found[3] for α-$Zr(HPO_4)_2 \cdot H_2O$. These estimated dimensions of the unit cell of $Th(HAsO_4)_2 \cdot H_2O$, for a supposed α-layered structure should be: a $= 9.46$ Å, b $= 5.52$ Å, and c $= 15.41$ Å. The dimensions of the parameters a and b are thus slightly larger than in α-ZrP, as expected, given the larger size of Th compared to that of zirconium atom. Consequently, the distance between adjacent OH groups in the same layer is larger in α-$Th(HAsO_4)_2 \cdot H_2O$ than in α-$Zr(HPO_4)_2 \cdot H_2O$. Thus, it can be expected that the tetrahedral $\equiv AsOH$ groups of adjacent layers are more interpenetrated in $Th(HAsO_4)_2$ than the $\equiv P-OH$ groups in α-$Zr(HPO_4)_2 \cdot H_2O$ and the shorter interlayer distance of $Th(HAsO_4)_2 \cdot H_2O$ (7.05 against 7.56 Å) is in agreement with the supposed α-structure of the layers.

Owing to the shorter interlayer distance, the openings connecting the zeolitic-type cavities are also expected to be smaller in size in $Th(HAsO_4)_2 \cdot H_2O$ than in α-$Zr(HPO_4)_2 \cdot H_2O$. Thus, the marked ion-sieve properties of ThAs can also be explained assuming an α-structure with interlayer distance 7.05 A. It remains to explain why the interlayer distance does not increase when the protons are exchanged by Li^+ ions. In our opinion, this occurs because either the energy for the hydration of the lithium counter-ions is not sufficient to overcome the forces holding the layers, or the water molecules cannot diffuse within the layers because the openings connecting the cavities are too small. It was experimentally observed[68] that when the exchange in aqueous solution is carried out with $Th(HAsO_4)_2 \cdot H_2O$, the monohydrate $Th(LiAsO_4)_2 \cdot H_2O$ is obtained, while when anhydrous $Th(HAsO_4)_2$ is used, the anhydrous $Th(LiAsO_4)_2$ is obtained instead. This seems to support the second hypothesis. On the other hand, the exchange of Li-ions in a single step without change of the interlayer distance and of the water content of the exchanger has already been observed (as discussed before) for α-$Ti(HPO_4)_2 \cdot H_2O$. Finally, we note that thorium arsenate tetrahydrate, $Th(HAsO_4)_2 \cdot 4H_2O$ (first X-diffraction maximum at 8.2 Å) has been obtained by Sarpal.[70] It would be very interesting to see if this material exhibits ion-sieve properties and if anhydrous $Th(HAsO_4)_2$(7.05 Å) is obtained when it is dehydrated. These exper-

Table 9
ION EXCHANGE CAPACITIES AND PROPOSED FORMULAE OF SEVEN CRYSTALLINE CERIUM (IV) PHOSPHATES

Compound	Proposed formula	Theoretical[a]			Experimental	
		NH_4^+	$H^+(1)$	$H^+(2)$	Acid pH	Basic pH
A	$Ce(OH)_{1.62}(NH_4HPO_4)_{0.35}(H_2PO_4)_{0.68}(PO_4)_{0.45} \cdot 0.6H_2O$	1.07	5.24	4.96	0.8	4.3[b]
B	$Ce(OH)_{0.7}(PO_4)_{1.1} \cdot 0.5H_2O$	—	—	2.64	0.7	~2
C	$Ce(OH)_{0.27}(PO_4)_{0.27}(HPO_4)_{1.46} \cdot 0.55H_2O$	—	4.56	0.84	1.4	2.8—3.4[b]
D	$Ce(OH)_{0.45}(PO_4)_{0.45}(HPO_4)_{1.1} \cdot 0.33H_2O$	—	3.64	1.49	—	~2.9
E	$Ce(NH_4PO_4)_{0.44}(HPO_4)_{1.56}$	1.30	4.59	—	0	>6
F	$Ce(OH)_{0.375}(PO_4)_{0.375}[(NH_4)_{0.09}H_{1.16}(PO_4)_{1.25}] \cdot 0.25H_2O$	0.29	3.76	1.22	—	~3
G	$CeO_{0.21}(PO_4)(NH_4HPO_4)_{0.45}(H_2PO_4)_{0.13}$	1.49	2.34	—	-	~0.8

[a] $H^+(1) = H^+$ from monohydrogen and dihydrogen orthophosphate groups, $H^+(2) =$ from hydroxyl groups.

[b] For Li^+ from progressive titration.

From Herman, R. G. and Clearfield, A., *J. Inorg. Nucl. Chem.*, 38, 853, 1976. With permission.

iments would provide a definitive demonstration that $Th(HAsO_4)_2 \cdot H_2O$ has, indeed, an α-layered structure.

B. Cerium(IV) Phosphates

When a solution containing a Ce(IV) salt is mixed with a solution of phosphoric acid, various precipitates exhibiting ion exchange properties can be obtained. The composition, the structure and the degree of crystallinity of these precipitates is strongly dependent on the experimental conditions such as rate and order of mixing of the solutions, $PO_4/Ce(IV)$ ratio in the final solution, stirring, temperature, digestion time, etc.[46] Therefore, cerium(IV) phosphates constitute a very complicated class of inorganic ion exchangers. Other than fibrous CeP, already examined in the section on fibrous materials, a microcrystalline CeP with composition $CeO_2 \cdot P_2O_5 \cdot 2.33H_2O$, to which the formula $Ce(HPO_4)_2 \cdot 1.33H_2O$ or $Ce(OH)_{0.33}(HPO_4)_{1.67}(H_2PO_4)_{0.33} \cdot H_2O$ could be assigned, has been obtained in the author's laboratory.[71]

In a systematic study on the cerium(IV)-phosphoric acid system, Clearfield and Herman[72,73] have obtained seven crystalline cerium phosphates with P:Ce ratios ranging from 1 to 2. The proposed formulae of these compounds and their ion-exchange capacities, are reported in Table 9. Five of these belong to a series whose general formula is $Ce(OH)_x(HPO_4)_{2-x}yH_2O$. The phases having low P:Ce ratio can be converted into those of higher P:Ce ratio by suitable treatment with phosphoric acid. Thus, $Ce(HPO_4)_2 \cdot yH_2O$ materials are the end members of this series, with $X = O$. Two CeP materials (named A and G in Table 9) appear to contain both orthophosphate and dihydrogen phosphate groups. Two microcrystalline cerium phosphates with P:Ce M ratios of 1.15 and 1.55 were obtained by Konig et al.[74-76] and in the author's laboratory.[46] When CeP materials are prepared in the presence of sulfuric acid, the resultant solids contain significant amounts of sulfate ions.[76]

The complexity of the cerium phosphate materials is probably due to the fact that Ce(IV) tends to give polymeric compounds having a different type and degree of polymerization. Furthermore, phosphate groups are easily lost by hydrolysis, and significant amounts of Ce−OH groups are therefore present in CeP compounds. It can also be pointed out that a partial hydrolysis of $\equiv P-OH$ tetrahedral groups bonded with

three oxygens to Ce atoms could lead to $\begin{array}{c} -O \\ \diagdown \\ / \\ -O \end{array} P \begin{array}{c} OH \\ \diagup \\ \diagdown \\ OH \end{array}$ groups bonded to the Ce(IV)

atoms only via two oxygens. Thus, some cerium phosphate materials may contain a multiplicity of functional exchange groups. Owing to the differences in their acidities, the protons of these different groups are expected to be titrated at different pH values. Furthermore, the closeness of adjacent fixed charges, and/or steric hindrance due to the presence of small cavities, could lead to an increase in the pH with increase of the M^{z+}−loading of the exchanger, even during the titration of the same functional group. Thus, the titration curves of cerium phosphate materials do not have distinct plateaus, as in the case of layered materials, but sloping curves, with some inflexion, are usually obtained as in the amorphous inorganic ion exchangers. The cerium phosphate materials are usually rather stable in neutral solution or in solutions containing noncomplexing or reducing acids, while they are severely hydrolyzed in alkaline medium. The property of oxidizing exchanged cations may be of interest in some cases. Some aspects of the ion exchange behavior of some CeP materials are now examined.

1. Crystalline Cerium Phosphate with Composition $CeO_2 \cdot P_2O_5 \cdot 2.33 H_2O$

This has been obtained[71] by dissolving, under stirring, about 100 g of $Ce(SO_4)_2 \cdot 4H_2O$ in 400 mℓ of 10 $M H_3PO_4$, at the boiling temperature. The temperature is then decreased to about 80°C. The product begins to precipitate after a few hours

Table 10
FIRST DIFFRACTION MAXIMUM (Å)
IN THE X-RAY PATTERNS OF
$CeO_2P_2O_5 \cdot 2.33H_2O$, AND ITS SALT
FORMS, AT ROOM TEMPERATURE
$(P/P_o = 0.75)$ AND AT 150°C

	First diffraction maximum	
Counter-ion	Room temperature	150°
H	15.9	13.1
Li (75%)	15.4	13.9
Na (50%)	15.0	14.1
K (25%)	14.3	13.6

and it is left to digest for about 4 days at 80°C. The precipitate must be washed first with hot water, (at 80°C, to avoid the precipitation of undesirable amorphous CeP from the residual mother liquor) and then with cold water, to pH~4. When conditioned at 75% of relative humidity, the product contains 2.33 mol of water per formula weight which are lost in three steps

$$CeO_2 \cdot P_2O_5 \cdot 2.33H_2O \xrightarrow[-H_2O]{P_2O_5} CeO_2 \cdot P_2O_5 \cdot 1.33H_2O \xrightarrow[-0.33H_2O]{150°}$$

$$(15.9 \text{ Å}) \qquad\qquad (14.3 \text{ Å})$$

$$Ce(HPO_4)_2 \xrightarrow[-H_2O]{>400°} CeP_2O_7 \qquad\qquad (14)$$

$$(13.1 \text{ Å})$$

(numbers in parenthesis are the first reflections in the X-ray patterns).

These materials are strongly hydrolyzed at pH > 7. Ion exchange experiments with alkali metal ions showed that, except at low degrees of loading, the exchanger prefers cations with a smaller crystalline radius. This behavior is characteristic of a material with rigid three-dimensional structure in which small cavities are present and/or small openings connecting these cavities, or of a layered material in which the fixed charges are very close to each other. The hypothesis of a rigid three-dimensional structure seems to be in contrast with the fact that the anhydrous and hydrated salt forms exhibit different values of the first diffraction reflections (see Table 10). On the other hand, no discontinuous change of the first X-ray diffraction reflection has been observed during the replacement of protons with other counter-ions. This fact appears to be in disagreement with the hypothesis of a layered structure.

Additional investigations are necessary in order to understand the reasons for this behavior. At present, we think that $CeO_2 \cdot P_2O_5 \cdot 2.33H_2O$ derives from $Ce(HPO_4)_2 \cdot yH_2O$ partially hydrolyzed to $Ce(OH)_{0.33}(H_2PO_4)_{0.33}(HPO_4)_{1.67} \cdot H_2O$. The loss of 0.33 moles of water at 150°C with formation of $Ce(HPO_4)_2$ and the shape of the titration curves with alkali metal ions agrees with the supposition that different functional groups are present in $CeO_2 \cdot P_2O_5 \cdot 1.33H_2O$. No discontinuous change in the interlayer distance during ion exchange process could be detected experimentally in a layered material in which different functional groups are present. It is likely that a solid solution, stable over a large range of counter-ion composition, or several phases having very close interlayer distance, may be formed during the gradual replacement of the protons. Thus, the hypothesis of a layered structure cannot be completely excluded.

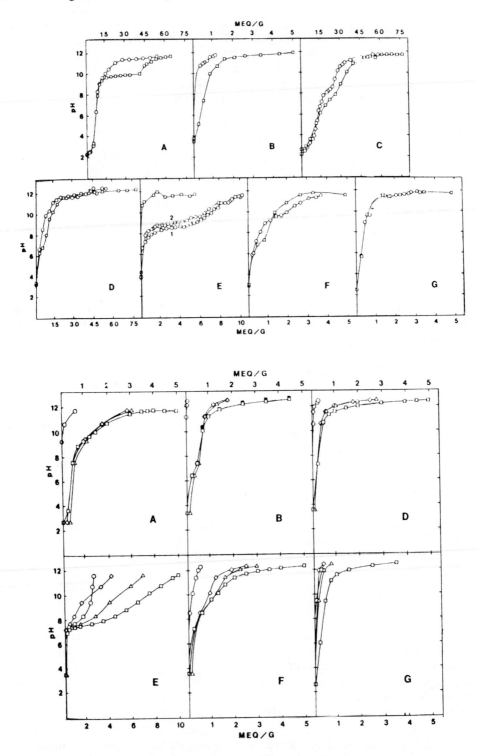

FIGURE 14.   Potentiometric and batch ion exchange titration curves for crystalline cerium (IV) phosphates reported in Table 9. Upper curves (potentiometric curves): Li$^+$, $\square$; Na$^+$, $\bigcirc$ · Lower curves (batch curves): hydroxide added, $\square$; sodium ion uptake, $\triangle$; hydrogen ion release,   ; phosphate release, $\bigcirc$. (From Herman, R. G. and Clearfield, A., *J. Inorg. Nucl. Chem.*, 38, 853, 1976. With permission.)

It is interesting to calculate the n value and the a × b product which $Ce(HPO_4)_2$ would have if it is assumed to have a layered structure with interlayer distance 13.1 Å (its first diffraction reflection). Given its density value (3.42 g/cm³) and using Equations 6 and 7, we have n = $13.5 \cdot 10^{-10}$ and a × b = 24.5 Å². Thus, the structure of the assumed planar macroanions results in an even more compact one than the structure expected for a planar macroanion of the γ-type. Note that such a compact structure for the macroanion could account for the preference for cations with small crystalline radius, but the interlayer distance of 13.1 Å for $Ce(HPO_4)_2$ seems to be too large (even assuming that no interpenetration of tetrahedral ≡P—OH groups of adjacent layers is possible owing to the compact structure of the macroanion). Hence, if the structure of $Ce(HPO_4)_2$ is truly a layered one, in order to account for the interlayer distance of 13.1 Å, the distance of the plane of phosphorous atoms from the plane of the tetravalent metal atoms must be higher than that in α-zirconium phosphate while the distance between the planes of fixed charges of two adjacent layers must be higher than that in α-ZrP. These points require additional work.

2. Other Ce(IV) Phosphates

The ion exchange capacity of the CeP materials prepared by Clearfield and Herman are reported in Table 9. Only two of these compounds (A and C) possess significant ion exchange properties in acidic solution. Four others show some ion exchange characteristics in basic media with some of the alkali cations. Compounds B, D, and F exchange Li⁺, but very little Na⁺ while the compound E exchanges Na⁺ and Cs⁺ but no Li⁺ ions. The potentiometric and batch titration curves of these CeP materials are reported in Figure 14a and b, respectively.

The crystalline Ce(IV)-phosphate-sulfates, $CeO_2(HPO_4)_{3-x}(SO_4)_x \cdot 4H_2O$ (with O<x<1) possess ion-sieve properties.[76] Their ion-exchange properties towards several cations, including the trivalent cations of the rare earth elements, were investigated by Konig and Eckstein and some separation of radioelements were carried out with success.[76,77] In acid solution the selectivity sequence Na⁺ > Ag⁺ > Sr²⁺ > Ba²⁺ > Cs²⁺ > Ca²⁺ was found. Furthermore, cations with a hydrated radius larger than 3 Å such as Cs²⁺, Fe³⁺, and Y³⁺, were not exchanged.

C. Cerium(IV) Arsenates

The system cerium(IV)-arsenic acid presents the same complexity as found in the cerium(IV)-phosphoric acid system. Several crystalline products with [As]/[Ce] ratios ranging from 1 to 4 have been obtained[45] but several of these are rather unstable in alkaline, and even in neutral, solution. Thus, several of these materials are poor exchangers and are of interest only in extending our knowledge of crystalline CeP compounds. However, a yellow microcrystalline product with formula $Ce(HAsO_4)_2 \cdot 2H_2O$ and stable at pH values as high as 10 was obtained.[45] This material can be converted into the fully exchanged Li and Na forms (ion exchange capacity 4.3 meq/g) while half conversions (or less) are obtained for K and Cs ions.[78] The apparent distribution coefficients of various trace elements (Na, Sc, Mn, Co, Fe, Zn, and Sr) as a function of time have been determined by Zsinka and Szirtes.[79] Equilibrium was obtained in all cases within a maximum of 2 hr in a single step process.

Infrared and X-ray measurements on $Ce(HAsO_4)_2 \cdot 2H_2O$ and its salt forms have been carried out by Zsinka et al.[80] The two water molecules are lost reversibly in two steps with discontinuous change in the first diffraction reflection.[45]

$$Ce(HAsO_4)_2 \cdot 2H_2O \xrightarrow{60°} Ce(HAsO_4)_2 \cdot H_2O \xrightarrow{110°} Ce(HAsO_4)_2 \qquad (15)$$
$$\text{(10.1 Å} \qquad\qquad\qquad \text{(9.1 Å)} \qquad\qquad\qquad \text{(7.7 Å)}$$

The H^+/K^+ exchange also occurs with discontinuous change in the first d-value. Thus, on the basis of the formula, reversible loss of water, and discontinuous change of the first d-value, it was suggested[45] that $Ce(HAsO_4)_2$ possesses a layered structure of the γ-type.

Recent experiments performed in our laboratory[81] showed that organic polar molecules, such as n-alkylamines, can be intercalated in the structure of $Ce(HAsO_4)_2 \cdot 2H_2O$ with a strong increase in the first diffraction maximum, hence confirming the layer structure. The density of $Ce(HAsO_4)_2 \cdot 2H_2O$ has been determined ($\varrho = 3.73$ g/cm^3) and the n value and a × b product calculated from relationships 1 and 2, respectively; $n = 8.26 \cdot 10^{-10}$ moles/cm^2 and a × b = 39.9 Å^2. These values suggest that the layered structure of $Ce(HAsO_4)_2 \cdot 2H_2O$ is again of γ-type.

D. Titanium Tungstate

A poorly crystalline titanium tungstate with a Ti:W ratio of 1:1.3 has been synthesized[82] by mixing 0.5 M solutions of $TiCl_4$ and sodium tungstate (acidified with HCl) in the volume ratio 1:1. The precipitate obtained was refluxed with its mother liquor for 12 hr. The ion-exchange capacity is low (0.25 meq/g of exchanger). The distribution coefficient of several metal ions have been determined and some separations, such as Hf^{4+} from Zr^{4+} and La^{3+} from Ce^{3+}, Pr^{3+}, Nd^{3+} and Sm^{3+}, were obtained. No other information is available on this material.

REFERENCES

1. **Veselý, V. and Pekárek, V.**, Synthetic inorganic ion-exchangers. I. Hydrous oxides and acidic salts of monovalent metals, *Talanta*, 12, 219, 1972.
2. **Alberti, G. and Costantino, U.**, Recent progress in the field of synthetic inorganic exchangers having a layered or fibrous structure, *J. Chromatogr.*, 102, 5, 1974.
3. **Clearfield, A., Nancollas, G. H., and Blessing, R. H.**, New inorganic ion exchangers, in *Ion Exchange and Solvent Extraction*, Vol. 5, Marinsky, J. A. and Marcus, Y., Eds., Marcel Dekker, New York, 1973, chap. 1.
4. **Alberti, G.**, Syntheses, crystalline structure and ion-exchange properties of insoluble acid salts of tetravalent metals and their salt forms, *Acc. Chem. Res.*, 11, 163, 1978.
5. **Alberti, G. and Torracca, E.**, Crystalline insoluble acid salts of polybasic metals. II. Synthesis of crystalline zirconium or titanium phosphate by direct precipitation, *J. Inorg. Nucl. Chem.*, 30, 317, 1968.
6. **Alberti, G., Allulli, S., Costantino, U., and Massucci, M. A.**, Crystalline insoluble acid salts of tetravalent metals. XX. Forward and reverse Cs^+/H^+ and Rb^+/H^+ ion exchange on crystalline zirconium phosphate, *J. Inorg. Nucl. Chem.*, 37, 1779, 1975.
7. **Alberti, G., Costantino, U., and Giulietti, R.**, Preparation of large crystals of α-$Zr(HPO_4)_2 \cdot H_2O$, *J. Inorg. Nucl. Chem.*, 42, 1062, 1980.
8. **Gill, J. S.**, On the crystallinity of zirconium bis(monohydrogen orthophosphate) monohydrate, *J. Inorg. Nucl. Chem.*, 41, 1066, 1979.
9. **Alberti, G., Bernasconi, M. G., Casciola, M., and Costantino, U.**, Crystalline insoluble acid salts of tetravalent metals. XXXIII. Investigation on the unusual initial shape of the titration curves of layered exchangers of the α-zirconium phosphate type, *J. Inorg. Nucl. Chem.*, 42, 1631, 1980.
10. **Alberti, G., Cardini-Galli, P., Costantino, U., and Torracca, E.**, Crystalline insoluble acid salts of polybasic metals. I. Ion-exchange properties of crystalline titanium phosphate, *J. Inorg. Nucl. Chem.*, 29, 571, 1967.
11. **Clearfield, A.**, Research report, Titanium Alloy Division, National Lead Co., Niagara Falls, New York, 1964.
12. **Weiss, M. A., and Michel, E.**, Kationenaustausch und eindimensionales, innerkristallines Quellungsvermögen bei den isotypen Verbindungen $H_2\{M(X O_4)_2\} \cdot H_2O$ (X = P, As; M = Ti, Zr, Sn), *Z. Naturforsch.*, B22, 1100, 1967.
13. **Kurbatov, D. I. and Pavlova, S. A.**, Composition of titanium phosphate in solutions of phosphoric acid of various concentrations, *Tr. Inst. Khim. Akad. Nauk*, U.S.S.R. Ural Filial, 10, 73, 1966.

14. Landis, A. M., M. S., Thesis, Ohio University, Athens, June 1970, p. 18.

15. Alberti, G., Costantino, U., and Luciani Giovagnotti, M. L., Crystalline insoluble acid salts of tetravalent metals. XXXII. Comparison of ion-exchange properties of crystalline α-zirconium phosphate and α-titanium phosphate, *Gazz. Chim. It.*, 110, 61, 1980.

16. Clearfield, A. and Frianeza, T. N., On the mechanism of ion exchange in zirconium phosphates. XXII. Mixed zirconium titanium phosphates, *J. Inorg. Nucl. Chem.*, 40, 1925, 1978.

17. Alberti, G., Giammari, G., and Grassini-Strazza, G., Chromatographic behaviour of inorganic ions on crystalline titanium phosphate or zirconium phosphate thin layers, *J. Chromatogr.*, 28, 118, 1967.

18. Kobyashi, E., Studies of inorganic ion exchangers. IV. Ion exchange equilibrium between titanium (IV) bis(hydrogenphosphate) and NaCl-KCl aqueous solution, *Bull. Chem. Soc. Jpn.*, 52, 1359, 1979.

19. La Ginestra, A., Massucci, M. A., Ferragina, C., and Tomassini, N., Thermal behaviour of some synthetic ion exchangers: insoluble acid phosphates and arsenates of tetravalent metals, *Thermal Analysis*, Vol. 1, Proc. Fourth Int. Conf. on Thermal Analysis, Budapest, 1974, 631.

20. Cernorukov, N. G., Korschunov, I. A., and Prokofeva, T. V., Ion exchange of Li$^+$ on crystalline titanium phosphate, *V.sb. Ionity i Ionnyi Obmen*, p. 75, 1975.

21. Moraglio, G., Donolato, C., and Provasoli, A., Sul fosfato acido di titanio, *Rend. Ist. Lomb. Sci. Lett. Cl. Sci. Mat. Nat.*, A107, 728, 1973.

22. Torracca, E., Costantino, U., and Massucci, M. A., Crystalline insoluble acid salts of polybasic metals. V. Ion exchange properties of crystalline and amorphous zirconium arsenate, *J. Chromatogr.*, 30, 584, 1967.

23. Clearfield, A., Smith, G. D., and Hammond, B., Zirconium arsenates and their ion exchange behaviour, *J. Inorg. Nucl. Chem.*, 30, 277, 1968.

24. Gupta, J. P., Nowell, D. V., and Reilly, M. F., The mechanism of ammonia/ammonium ion uptake by α-zirconium bis(monohydrogen orthoarsenate) monohydrate, *J. Inorg. Nucl. Chem.*, 41, 749, 1979.

25. Allulli, S., Massucci, M. A., and Tomassini, N., Na$^+$/K$^+$ ion exchange isotherms on crystalline zirconium arsenate in aqueous solution and in molten NaNO$_3$-KNO$_3$ mixtures at 400°C, *J. Inorg. Nucl. Chem.*, 41, 1483, 1979.

26. Clearfield, A. and Duax, W. L., The crystal structure of the ion exchanger zirconium bis(monohydrogen orthoarsenate) monohydrate, *Acta Crystallagr.*, B25, 2658, 1969.

27. Alberti, G. and Torracca, E., Crystalline insoluble acid salts of polyvalent metals and polybasic acids. VI. Preparation and ion-exchange properties of crystalline titanium arsenate, *J. Inorg. Nucl. Chem.*, 30, 3075, 1968.

28. Clearfield, A., Personal communication.

29. Winkler, V. A. and Thilo, E., Uber eine reihe sourer verbindungen HX^{V}P$_2$O$_8$ und H$_2$X^{IV}P$_2$O$_8$ mit schischtstruktur, X^V = As und Sb; X^{IV} = Si, Ge, Sn, Pb, Ti und Zr, *Z. Anorg. Allg. Chem.*, 346, 92, 1966.

30. Costantino, U. and Gasperoni, A., Crystalline insoluble acid salts of tetravalent metals. XI. Synthesis and ion-exchange properties of tin(IV) phosphate and tin(IV) arsenate, *J. Chromatogr.*, 51, 289, 1970.

31. Fuller, M. J., Ion exchange properties of tin(IV) materials. IV. Crystalline tin(IV) phosphate, *J. Inorg. Nucl. Chem.*, 33, 559, 1971.

32. Alberti, G., Costantino, U., Allulli, S., and Tomassini, N., Crystalline Zr(R-PO$_3$)$_2$ and Zr(R-OPO$_3$)$_2$ compounds (R = organic radical). A new class of materials having a layered structure of the zirconium phosphate type, *J. Inorg. Nucl. Chem.*, 40, 1113, 1978.

33. Maya, L., Structure and chromatographic applications of crystalline Zr(OPO$_3$R)$_2$; R = Butyl, Lauryl and Octylphenyl, *J. Nucl. Chem. Lett.*, 15, 207, 1979.

34. Alberti, G., Costantino, U., and Luciani Giovagnotti, M. L., Synthesis and ion-exchange properties of zirconium bis(carboxymethanphosphonate), a new organic-inorganic ion-exchanger, *J. Chromatogr.*, 180, 45, 1978.

35. Clearfield, A., Blessing, R. H., and Stynes, J. A., New crystalline phases of zirconium phosphate possessing ion-exchange properties, *J. Inorg. Nucl. Chem.*, 30, 2249, 1968.

36. Allulli, S., Ferragina, C., La Ginestra, A., Massucci, M. A., and Tomassini, N., Preparation and ion-exchange properties of a new phase of the crystalline titanium phosphate, Ti(HPO$_4$)$_2$·2H$_2$O, *J. Inorg. Nucl. Chem.*, 39, 1043, 1977.

37. Yamanaka, S. and Tanaka, M., Formation region and structural model of γ-zirconium phosphate, J. Inorg. Nucl. Chem., 41, 45, 1979.

38. Alberti, G., Costantino, U., and Luciani Giovagnotti, M. L., Crystallineinluble acid salts of tetravalent metals. XXVIII. Synthesis of crystalline Ti(HPO$_4$)$_2$·2H$_2$O by HF-procedure and some consideration on its formation and structure, *J. Inorg. Nucl. Chem.*, 41, 643, 1979.

39. Kobayashi, E., The synthesis and ion-exchange properties of TiH$_2$(PO$_4$)$_2$·½H$_2$O, *Bull. Chem. Soc. Jpn.*, 48(11), 3114, 1975.

40. **Kobayashi, E.**, Studies of inorganic ion exchangers. II. Effects of sulfuric acid on the synthesis of Ti(HPO$_4$)$_2$·O-½H$_2$O, *Bull. Chem. Soc. Jpn.*, 51(8), 2306, 1978.

41. **Alberti, G., Bernasconi, M. G., Casciola, M., and Costantino, U.**, Crystalline insoluble acid salts of tetravalent metals. XXXIV. Hydrogen ammonium ion exchange on γ-titanium phosphate, *J. Inorg. Nucl. Chem.*, 42, 1637, 1980.

42. **Alberti, G., Costantino, U., and Luciani Giovagnotti, M. L.**, Unpublished data, 1979.

43. **Kobayashi E.**, Studies of inorganic ion exchangers. III. Ion exchange properties of Ti(HPO$_4$)$_2$·½H$_2$O to alkali metal and ammonium ions, *Bull. Chem. Soc. Jpn.*, 52(5), 1351, 1979.

44. **La Ginestra, A. and Massucci, M. A.**, Titanium and zirconium acid phosphate dihydrates: thermal behaviour and phase changes of their hydrogen, sodium and strontium forms, *Thermochimica Acta*, 32, 241, 1979.

45. **Alberti, G., Costantino, U., Di Gregorio, F., and Torracca, E.**, Crystalline insoluble acid salts of polyvalent and polybasic acids. VIII. Synthesis and ion-exchange properties of cerium(IV) arsenate, *J. Inorg. Nucl. Chem.*, 31, 3195, 1969.

46. **Alberti, G., Costantino, U., Di Gregorio, F., Galli, P., and Torracca, E.**, Crystalline insoluble salts of polybasic metals. III. Preparation and ion exchange properties of cerium(IV) phosphate of various crystallinities, *J. Inorg. Nucl. Chem.*, 30, 295, 1968.

47. **Alberti, G. and Costantino, U.**, Italian Applic., 36708 A/67; U.S. Patent 5, 728, 744, 1968.

48. **Alberti, G. and Costantino, U.**, Crystalline insoluble acid salts of tetravalent metals. X. Fibrous thorium phosphate, a new ion exchange material suitable for making (support-free) inorganic sheets, *J. Chromatog.*, 50, 482, 1970.

49. **Alberti, G. and Costantino, U.**, Italian Applic., 52565 A/70; German Patent, 2, 135, 699, 1972.

50. **Alberti, G., Costantino, U., and Luciani Giovagnotti, M. L.**, Unpublished data, 1979.

51. **Alberti, G., Massucci, M. A., and Torracca, E.**, Crystalline insoluble salts of polybasic metals. IV. Chromatography of inorganic ions on (support-free) cerium(IV) phosphate sheets, *J. Chromatog.*, 30, 579, 1967.

52. **Alberti, G. and Costantino, U.**, Italian Applic., 36739 A/67; U.S. Patent, 5, 728, 775, 1968.

53. **Alberti, G., and Costantino, U.**, Italian Applic., 52585 A/70; U.S. Patent, 3, 985, 611, 1976.

54. **Alberti, G.**, Inorganic ion exchange membranes, *"Study Week on Membranes"*, Passino, R., Ed., Pontificiae Academiae Scientiarum Scripta Varia, Vatican City, 1976, 629.

55. **Alberti, G.**, Unpublished data, 1976.

56. **Herman, R. G. and Clearfield, A.**, Crystalline cerium(IV) phosphates. I. Preparation and characterization of crystalline compounds, *J. Inorg. Nucl. Chem.*, 37, 1697, 1975.

57. **Cataliotti, R., Costantino, U., Luciani, M. L., and Paliani, G.**, Comportamento chimico e spettroscopico di scambiatori ionici inorganici della classe dei sali acidi insolubili dei metalli tetravalenti, VII Convegno Nazionale di Chimica Inorganica, B, Associazione Italiana Chimica Inorganica, Pesaro, 1974.

58. **Alberti, G., Casciola, M., Costantino, U., and Luciani Giovagnotti, M. L.**, Crystalline insoluble acid salts of tetravalent metals. XXIV. Ion exchange behaviour of fibrous cerium(IV) phosphate, *J. Chromatog.*, 128, 289, 1976.

59. **Trivedi, J. J., Mandalia, B. T., and Baxi, D. R.**, Preparation and characterization of fibrous ceric phosphate ion exchanger, *Proc. Ion-Exchange Symposium*, Bhavnagar, India, Gadre, G. T., Ed., Sahitya Mudranalaya, Ahmedabad, 22, 5, 1979.

60. **Hagman, L. O. and Kierkegaard, P.**, The crystal structure of NaMe$_2^{IV}$(PO$_4$)$_3$; Me^{IV} = Ge, Ti, Zr, *Acta Chem. Scand.*, 22, 1822, 1968.

61. **Taylor, B. E., English, A. D., and Berzins, T.**, New solid ionic conductors, *Mat. Res. Bull.*, 12(2), 171, 1977.

62. **Allulli, S., Massucci, M. A., and Tomassini, N.**, Italian patent, 26 April, 1979.

63. **Clearfield, A., Duax, W. L., Medina, A. S., Smith, G. D., and Thomas, J. R.**, On the mechanism of ion exchange in crystalline zirconium phosphates. I. Sodium ion exchange of α-zirconium phosphate, *J. Phys. Chem.*, 73, 3424, 1969.

64. **Clearfield, A., Pack, S. P., and Troup, J. M.**, On the mechanism of ion exchange in zirconium phosphates. XVII. Dehydration behaviour of lithium ion exchanged phases, *J. Inorg. Nucl. Chem.*, 39, 1437, 1977.

65. **Goodenough, J. B., Hong, H.Y-P., and Kafalas, J. A.**, Fast Na$^+$-ion transport in skeleton structures, *Mat. Res. Bull.*, 11, 203, 1976.

66. **Clearfield, A. and Blessing, R. H.**, The preparation and crystal structure of a basic zirconium molybdate and its relationship to ion exchange gels, *J. Inorg. Nucl. Chem.*, 34, 2643, 1972.

67. **Kraus, K. A., Phillips, H. O., Carlson, T. A., and Johnson, J. S.**, Ion exchange properties of hydrous oxides, *Proc. Second Int. Conf. Peaceful Uses of Atomic Energy*, Vol. 28, United Nations, Geneva, 1958, 3.

68. **Alberti, G. and Massucci, M. A.**, Crystalline insoluble acid salts of tetravalent metals. IX. Thorium arsenate, a new inorganic ion exchanger specific for lithium, *J. Inorg. Nucl. Chem.*, 32, 1719, 1970.
69. **Alberti, G. and Massucci, M. A.**, German Patent, 1,947,146,1970; U.S. Patent, 3,851,040, 1974.
70. **Sarpal, S. K.**, Personal communication.
71. **Alberti, G., Costantino, U., and Zsinka, L.**, Crystalline insoluble acid salts of tetravalent metals. XII. Synthesis and ion exchange properties of microcrystalline cerium(IV) phosphate, *J. Inorg. Nucl. Chem.*, 34, 3549, 1972.
72. **Herman, R. G. and Clearfield, A.**, Crystalline cerium(IV) phosphates. II. The ion-exchange characteristics with alkali metal ions, *J. Inorg. Nucl. Chem.*, 38, 853, 1976.
73. **Herman, R. G. and Clearfield, A.**, Crystalline cerium(IV) phosphates. III. Preparation and characterization of the isomorphous phases of compounds A, *J. Inorg. Nucl. Chem.*, 39, 143, 1977.
74. **König, K. H. and Meyn, E.**, Amorphe und kristalline Cer(IV)-phosphate als ionenaustauscher. I. Herstellung und chemische eigenschaften, *J. Inorg. Nucl. Chem.*, 29, 1153, 1967.
75. **König, K. H. and Meyn, E.**, Amorphe und kristalline Cer(IV)-phosphate als ionenaustauscher. II. Ionenaustauschereigenschaften gegenuber einwertigen kationen, *J. Inorg. Nucl. Chem.*, 29, 1519, 1967.
76. **König, K. H. and Eckstein, G.**, Amorphous and crystalline cerium(IV) phosphates as ion exchangers. III. Preparation, cation exchange, and chemical properties of crystalline cerium(IV) phosphate sulfate, *J. Inorg. Nucl. Chem.*, 31, 1179, 1969.
77. **König, K. H. and Eckstein, G.**, Amorphe und kristalline cer(IV)-phosphate als ionenaustauscher. IV. Makrosorption, tracersorption und nuklidtrennungen an kristalliner Cer(IV)-phosphatsulfaten, *J. Inorg. Nucl. Chem.*, 34, 3771, 1972.
78. **Kornyei, J., Szirtes, L., and Zsinka, L.**, Investigations on crystalline cerium arsenate and its alkali metal forms. I, *Radiochem. Radioanal. Lett.*, 31(3), 181, 1977.
79. **Zsinka, L. and Szirtes, L.**, Ion exchange studies on crystalline cerium phosphate and arsenate, Radiochem. Radioanal. Lett., 17(4), 257, 1974.
80. **Zsinka, L., Szirtes, L., Mink, J., and Kálmàn, A.**, Infrared and X-ray measurements on various inorganic ion exchangers, *J. Chromatogr.*, 102, 109, 1974.
81. **Alberti, G. and Costantino, U.**, Unpublished data, 1978.
82. **Qureshi, M. and Gupta, J. P.**, Synthesis of a poorly crystalline titanium tungstate. Separation of Hf^{4+} from Zr^{4+} and of La^{3+} from Ce^{3+}, Pr^{3+}, Nd^{3+} and Sm^{3+}, *J. Chromatogr.*, 62, 439, 1971.

Chapter 3

INTERCALATION BEHAVIOR OF GROUP IV LAYERED PHOSPHATES

Umberto Costantino

TABLE OF CONTENTS

I. INTRODUCTION

The reader will probably be surprised to find a chapter on intercalation chemistry in a book that deals with inorganic ion exchange materials, but he will easily recognize that intercalation is strictly connected with the layered crystalline structures of some thoroughly investigated synthetic inorganic ion exchangers such as the insoluble acid salts of tetravalent metals.

As extensively reported in Chapters 1 and 2, some insoluble acid salts of general formula $M(IV) (HXO_4)_2 \cdot nH_2O$ (where $M(IV)$ = Ti, Zr, Ce, Sn, and X = P or As) have a layered structure, each layer consisting of a plane of tetravalent atoms sandwiched between tetrahedral phosphate or arsenate groups.[1-5] The bonds within the layers are strong and primarily covalent, those between adjacent layers are weak, essentially van der Waals'. Consequently, the layers can move in relationship to each other when the protons are replaced by other cations or when the number of water molecules changes. Due to this ability, layered acid salts of tetravalent metals possess the typical characteristic of an intercalating agent. It is significant that the intercalating properties of these compounds were first discovered in 1965 by Michel and Weiss[7,8] (shortly after the layered structure of α-$Zr(HPO_4)_2 \cdot H_2O$ was announced by Clearfield and Stynes[6] but not yet solved[5]) whose contributions in the field of intercalation chemistry are widely known. It is also remarkable to note that from this time up to 1975, no other papers were published on this subject. Only recently has there been a renewed interest in the intercalation behavior of layered insoluble acid salts of tetravalent metals since it was realized that, as written by Lagaly et al.,[9] "zirconium phosphate has a number of superior properties compared with other intercalating compounds". Indeed, apart from graphite[10] and related materials (graphite oxide, boron nitride), few other inorganic materials that crystallize in a layered configuration, such as clays,[11] chalcogenides of group IV and VB metals,[12] crystalline silicic acids,[13] zinc and copper hydroxides,[14] potassium niobate[15], $Zn_2Cr(OH)_6Cl \cdot 2H_2O$,[16] etc., are able to intercalate neutral molecules between the layers of their structure. With respect to the above-mentioned materials, layered insoluble acid salts generally have a higher thermal and chemical stability. Furthermore, the presence of acid groups between the layers makes these exchangers very suitable intercalating agents of polar molecules that are Brönsted bases.

To some extent, layered phosphates and arsenates of tetravalent metals resemble natural clays. First, Leigh and Dyer,[17] and later Yamanaka and Koizumi,[18] pointed out the noticeable analogy between clays of montmorillonite-type and α-zirconium phosphate. Taking into account these analogies, the structural parameters of clays and layered phosphates or arsenates of tetravalent metals will be briefly compared in the following section. Only the features necessary to explain the intercalation behaviour will be recalled, while for a complete description of the structures of layered phosphates or arsenates (of α- and ;-g-type) and for the structure of clay minerals the reader is referred to the previous chapters, and Reference 11.

II. INTERCALATION BEHAVIOR AND STRUCTURE OF THE HOST MATRICES

In the process of intercalation, schematically represented in Figure 1, neutral polar molecules are inserted between the sheets of a layered insoluble compound. The process will occur if some concomitant factors are satisfied; in particular:

1.   The interactions of the guest molecules with the host matrix must be stronger than the mutual interactions of the molecules with themselves (if they constitute the liquid phase) or with the solvent molecules (if they are dissolved). Thus, the

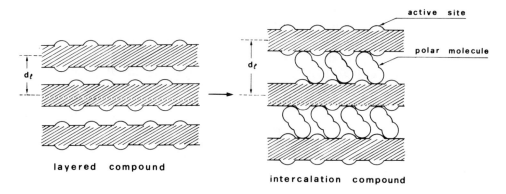

FIGURE 1.   Schematic illustration of the intercalation of polar molecules between the sheets of a layered compound. The increase in the interlayer distance, d_l, is shown.

surface of the layers of the intercalating agent should possess active sites (or groups that can act as Brönsted acid, Lewis acid, etc., or that, generally, have a polar character) with which the guest molecules can interact.

2.   The layers must spread apart to accommodate the guest molecules. Thus, the interlayer bonding must be weak and the stacking of the layers should be such as to not create steric hindrance to the free diffusion of the molecule. Owing to the steric hindrances the intercalation process requires an activation energy.

When the number of molecules taken up per formula unit of intercalating agent is equivalent to the number of the active sites present, intercalation compounds with stoichiometric composition are obtained. Stoichiometric compounds are not formed if the cross diameter of the guest molecule exceeds the free area around the active sites; a "covering effect" of adjacent sites by the guest molecule may in fact take place and sites, partially or completely covered, are unavailable to other molecules.

Let us now examine the structural parameters relative to intercalation in clays and in layered phosphates. It is well known that natural clays have an exceptional ability to accommodate polar molecules between the layers and an extensive literature on reactions of clays with organic compounds may be found in the excellent book by Theng.[11] In clay minerals the active sites are the hydroxyl groups (as in kaolinite and perhaps in montmorillonite), the negative fixed charges arising because of the isomorphous replacement of Si(IV) by Al(III) and Al(III) by Mg(II), Fe(II) etc., and in general the oxygen atoms belonging to the silicate tetrahedra.

With respect to their intercalation ability, the clays are often classified as expanding or nonexpanding lamellar minerals. It has been observed that the expanding clays possess a medium cation density (number of equivalents of cations per formula unit) between the silicate layers.[11] For example, pyrophillite, which does not possess cations between the silicate sheets, and muscovite, having a high cation density (0.8 to 1.0 equivalents of cations per formula weight), do not undergo intracrystalline swelling, while montmorillonite with a medium cation density (0.25 to 0.5 eq/mol) has an extraordinary ability to intercalate polar molecules.[19] In montmorillonite, the surface area associated with each active site range from 50 to 100 Å^2.[20] and the sites are irregularly distributed on the surface of the layers. Steric hindrance is small allowing the diffusion of organic molecules within the layers and intercalation occurs quite easily. ily.

We shall now examine the structural parameters relative to intercalation in layered phosphates. Since only the structures of α-zirconium phosphate-type materials are known, we shall deal essentially with these materials, while we can only speculate about

Table 1
FORMULA, INTERLAYER DISTANCE AND
CALCULATED SURFACE AREA, ASSOCIATED
WITH THE ACTIVE SITES, OF SOME
LAYERED PHOSPHATES AND ARSENATES OF
TETRAVALENT METALS WITH α- OR γ-
STRUCTURES

Compound	Interlayer distance, d_l (Å)	Free area around the active site (Å²)	Ref.
α-Zr(HPO₄)₂·H₂O	7.55	23.99	5
α-Zr(HAsO₄)₂·H₂O	7.78	24.68	21
α-Ti(HPO₄)₂·H₂O	7.56	21.58	2
α-Ti(HAsO₄)₂·H₂O	7.77	22.2ᵃ	22
α-Sn(HPO₄)₂·H₂O	7.76	21.4ᵃ	23
α-Sn(HAsO₄)₂·H₂O	7.87	22.6ᵃ	23
γ-Zr(HPO₄)₂·2H₂O	12.2	17.8	24
γ-Ti(HPO₄)₂·2H₂O	11.6	16.6ᵃ	25

ᵃ   Values estimated by the method described in Reference 25.

layered phosphates with a γ-type structure. In Table 1 the formulas and the interlayer distances, d_1, of some layered phosphates or arsenates are reported. For the sodium forms (but the same holds for the other fully exchanged forms) the cation density between the sheets is very high (2 eq per formula unit) and a strong coulombic force holds the layers together; intercalation should occur with great difficulty and until now no intercalation compounds of these salt forms have been reported. However, taking into account that some dried salt forms of α-zirconium phosphate (e.g., Li⁺, Na⁺, and K⁺ forms), take back all or part of their hydration water,[26] it is probable that, under suitable conditions, intercalation of other polar molecules could occur. For the α-Zr(HPO₄)₂·H₂O, Dyer and Leigh[17] estimated the cation density to be equal to one equivalent per formula weight of exchanger as if one -OH out of two were dissociated. However, more recent results based on neutron diffraction studies[27] and X-ray refinement of the crystal structure[28] have shown that both the protons are covalently bonded to the oxygen atoms. Thus a much smaller cation density is to be expected and this was born out by measurements of the specific conductance of the crystals.[29] Hydrogen forms of layered acid salts are indeed able to intercalate polar molecules. The active sites are the ≡P−OH or ≡As−OH groups, which are Bronsted acids. These are regularly arranged in hexagonal arrays at 5.3 Å away from each other in α-Zr(HPO₄)₂·H₂O[5], 5.4 Å in α-Zr(HAsO₄)₂·H₂O,[21] 5.0 Å in α-Ti(HPO₄)₂·H₂O.[2] The arrangement of the layers is such as to create zeolitic cavities that are interconnected by narrow openings (the maximum diameter is 2.61 Å in α-Zr(HPO₄)₂·H₂O[28]). Thus steric hindrance and hence an activation energy for the process must be overcome. Indeed intercalation occurs in α-zirconium phosphate in a more difficult way than in montmorillonite. Since two phosphate or arsenate groups are present in the (a × b) area, a and b being the lattice constants of the unit cells, the free area surrounding each active site can easily be evaluated and it is reported in Table 1. It can be seen that this area ranges from 24 Å² for α-Zr(HPO₄)₂·H₂O to 21 Å² for α-Ti(HPO₄)₂·H₂O and thus molecules having a cross section higher than this value will give way to the "covering effect". In the layered phosphates of γ-type, because of their interlayer distance much higher than that of the α-ones, steric hindrances are present to a lesser extent and intercalation occurs more easily. However, due to the observation of a more dense structure of the γ-layers, in comparison with the α-ones, the area of the exchange sites is smaller than in α-compounds and the covering effects may also take place with the intercalation of n-alkylamines. The area of the exchange sites has been calculated taking into account the lattice parameters of γ-Zr(HPO$_4$)$_2$·2H$_2$O, recently published by Yamanaka and Tanaka,[24] and the considerations reported by Alberti and co-workers.[25,30]

Finally, but not the last feature of the connection between intercalation behavior and structure, the intercalation process in layered phosphates occurs discontinuously with phase transitions almost exactly as described for the ion exchange processes (see Chapters 1 and 2). In graphite and in some other intercalating agents, the intercalation process also occurs in distinct steps,[10] in which every nth interlayer region is filled until the process is completed. In the case of layered phosphates it is usually thought that the intercalation process proceeds from the external part of the crystals to the internal one with an advancing phase boundary, and that all the interlayer regions are involved in the process.[4] The most appropriate analytical method in the study of the intercalation process is that of the X-ray powder diffraction. Upon intercalation, the d(001) reflection, relative to the basal spacing of the host matrix, is shifted to lower values of 2ϑ and harmonics up to high orders may be detected. The reflections due to other lattice planes are generally weak or absent. The arrangement of the intercalated molecules may be estimated by the analysis of the intensity of X-ray reflections by the one-dimensional Fourier series,[31] but no investigations of this type have been reported for the intercalation compounds of layered phosphates. Phase transitions in the intercalation process are also easily followed by the X-ray powder diffraction technique. The intercalation of polar molecules within the layers of insoluble acid salts very likely proceeds from the external parts of the crystal towards the center with advancing phase boundary, until the fully intercalated compound is completely obtained. Thus, one observes on the X-ray diffractograms of partially intercalated samples, the presence of two diffraction maxima corresponding to the interlayer distances of the original and the new phase. During the intercalation, the intensity of the former X-ray reflection decreases and that of the latter increases, as if two phases, the one transforming into the other, were coexisting. As in ion exchange processes this coexistence should however be thought to occur in a same crystallite of intercalating agent and the layers are only bent to join the region of the crystal with different interlayer distances.[4] Having in mind the above-mentioned observations, let us now examine the data on the intercalation behavior of layered phosphates published to date. The available data are few and mainly refer to α-Zr(HPO$_4$)$_2$·H$_2$O or γ-Zr(HPO$_4$)$_2$·2H$_2$O; however, they are sufficient for a first rationalization of the topic.

III. INTERCALATION OF ALKANOLS AND GLYCOLS INTO α-Zr(HPO$_4$)$_2$·H$_2$O

A. Preparation and Stability of Intercalation Compounds

Unlike montmorillonite, in which the intercalation sometimes occurs when the clay is in contact with an aqueous solution of alkanols,[11] α-zirconium phosphate is not able to take up molecules such as CH$_3$OH, C$_2$H$_5$OH, etc., even when the exchanger is equilibrated with the pure alkanol at the boiling point. To overcome the steric hindrances that prevent the inclusion process, Costantino[32] suggested a simple method based on the regeneration of salt forms of α-zirconium phosphate, e.g., ZrHNa(PO$_4$)$_2$·5H$_2$O, with protonated alkanols, which act as strong Brönsted acids. The reaction between the monosodium form and alkanols, protonated with HClO$_4$,

$$\text{ZrHNa(PO}_4)_2 \cdot 5\text{H}_2\text{O} + \text{R—OH}_2^+ + x\,\text{R–OH} \longrightarrow \text{Zr(HPO}_4)_2 \cdot (1+x)\text{ROH} + \text{Na}^+ + 5\text{H}_2\text{O} \qquad (1)$$

Table 2

METHODS OF PREPARATION, INTERLAYER DISTANCE
AND VALUE OF THE INCREMENT, Δ, FOR SOME
ALKANOL AND GLYCOL INTERCALATION COMPOUNDS
OF α-ZIRCONIUM PHOSPHATE

Intercalated molecule	Method of preparation	Interlayer distance, d_1 (Å)	Increment, Δ, Å	
			d_1-6.3	d_1-9.1
Methanol	a	9.3	3.0	0.2
Ethanol	a	14.2	7.9	5.1
1-Propanol	a	16.6	10.3	7.5
1-Butanol	a	18.7	12.4	9.6
1-Pentanol	a	21.3	15.0	12.2
1-Octanol	b	26.7	20.4	17.6
2-Propanol	a	15.6		
2-Methylpropan-1-ol	b	17.5		
2-Methylbutan-1-ol	b	19.2		
Benzylalcohol	b	21.0		
Ethanediol	a,c	10.3[a]		
1,3 Propanediol	a	11.6		
1,4 Butanediol	a,b	12.7		
2,2'-Dihydroxydiethylether	c	10.5[a]		

Note: a = Equilibration of $ZrHNa(PO_2)_2 \cdot 5H_2O$ with the protonated alkanol or glycol; b = Equilibration of zirconium phosphate-ethanol complex with the alkanol or glycol; c = Equilibration of $Zr(HPO_4)_2 \cdot H_2O$ with the pure liquid.

[a]   Data taken from Reference 18. All other data are from Reference 32.

where R = n-alkylchain, leads to intercalation compounds of α-zirconium phosphate. Reaction 1 fails when R is a long or branched alkyl-chain or contains the benzene ring, e.g., $-C_8H_{17}$, $(CH_3)_2CH\ CH_2\ CH_2-$, $C_6H_5-CH_2-$ but, once one alkanol-intercalate compound has been obtained by Reaction 1, it is easy to replace the intercalated molecule, e.g., C_2H_5OH, with other alkanols by simply contacting the zirconium phosphate-ethanol complex with the pure liquid to be intercalated. A number of zirconium phosphate-alkanol intercalation compounds has been obtained with these two methods and they are listed in Table 2. These complexes are generally unstable since they lose the guest molecules by drying in air or by washing them with polar solvents. However the stability seems to increase with increasing boiling point of the alkanol.

X-ray diffraction patterns show that the intercalated compounds maintain their crystallinity of the host matrix and the integral series of the 002 reflexions are very evident. Figure 2 shows a typical X-ray diffractogram of a zirconium phosphate-alkanol complex compared to the X-ray diffractogram of α-$Zr(HPO_4)_2 \cdot H_2O$. Owing to their instability, the composition of these compounds has not been determined, but there is evidence (see later) to indicate that n-alkanol-zirconium phosphate complexes contain 2 mol of intercalated molecule per mol of exchanger. In the case of isoalkanols or branched alkanols, the "covering effect" should prevent the obtaining of stoichiometric compounds. Glycols can also be intercalated with the procedures described for alkanols. Furthermore, Yamanaka and Koizumi[18] reported the interlayer spacings of α-zirconium phosphate complexes with ethylene glycol and diethylene glycol. These complexes have been obtained by equilibrating the exchanger with the pure glycol at room temperature for one day. Discrepancies between different authors may arise because of the α-zirconium phosphate employed. Preparations having different degrees of crystallinity or different crystal size could lead to different kinetic effects and, in this spe-

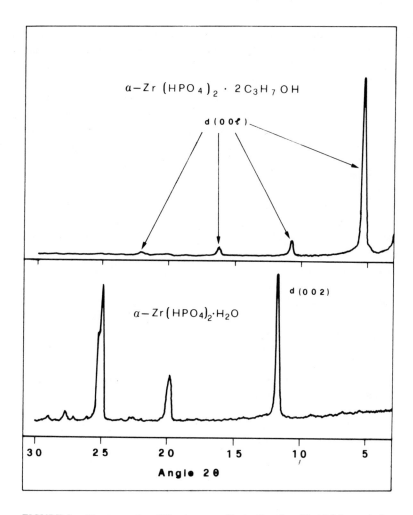

FIGURE 2. X-ray powder diffractograms illustrating the effect of intercalation of 1-propanol between the sheets of α-Zr(HPO$_4$)$_2 \cdot$ H$_2$O. (The intensity of the X-ray reflections of the intercalation compound is five times that of α-Zr(HPO$_4$)$_2 \cdot$ H$_2$O).

cific case, to obtain more easily an intercalation compound. (The effect of the degree of crystallinity is thoroughly discussed in the previous chapters.) The stability of glycol intercalate compounds, which are listed in Table 2, is much higher than that of alkanol ones. These compounds, containing one mol of intercalated molecule per mol of exchanger, can be dried at room temperature and the de-intercalation process may be studied by drying the compounds at different temperatures. The process occurs discontinuously, with phase transitions, as does the dehydration process and leads to α-Zr(HPO$_4$)$_2$ phase.[32]

B. Structural Considerations

In Table 2 the basal spacings of alkanols and glycols intercalation compounds of α-Zr(HPO$_4$)$_2$ are reported. Let us examine more closely intercalates having n-alkanols and glycols as guest molecules. The inter layer distances, d_1, increase linearly with the number of carbon atoms, n_c, in the alkyl-chain and the slopes, $\Delta d_1 / \Delta n_c$, are 2.07 and 1.1 Å/n_c, for alkanols and glycols, respectively. Since the increment of the alkyl-chain length, in conformation trans-trans, is generally estimated as 1.27 Å for each additional carbon atom,[11] it is probable to assume that alkanols are intercalated as a double film while glycols form unimolecular films between the sheets of α-zirconium phosphate. Furthermore, by assuming that the alkyl-chains are in conformation trans-trans, it is possible to calculate that the alkanol molecules are inclined at an angle, $\alpha = $ arcsin $2.07/2.54 = 54.5$ with respect to the sheets.

In the field of intercalation in clays, it is common to speak in terms of Δ, that is the increment in the basal spacing calculated by subtracting from the experimental value d_1, the thickness of the clay sheet.[11] The thickness of the α-zirconium phosphate layer, calculated as the distance between the planes passing through the baricenters of oxygen atoms, carrying the exchangeable protons and placed above and below the zirconium atom plane, is estimated as 6.3 Å. The thickness calculated at the top of the $-OH$ groups will thus be $6.3 + 2x\ 1.4 = 9.1$ Å. (1.4 Å is the generally accepted value of the Van der Waals' radius of oxygen atom.) Table 2 reports the values calculated by subtracting both 6.3 and 9.1 Å from the experimental interlayer distance, d_1. By comparing the values with the dimension of the guest molecules, multiplied by sin 55°, it must be concluded that the oxygens of the alkanol molecules penetrate in the half cavities present on the surface of the layer of α-zirconium phosphate, and that their baricenters are a little higher than the baricenters of the oxygens of the $\gtreqless P-OH$ groups. In other words, the position of the oxygen of the $R-OH$ group is very similar to that of the oxygen of the water molecule in $Zr(HPO_4)_2 \cdot H_2O$.[27,28] Hydrogen bonds must operate between the $R-OH$ and $\gtreqless P-OH$ groups and the arrangement of alkanols and glycols between the layers of α-zirconium phosphate, may be similar to that schematically illustrated in Figure 3 (a) and (b), respectively.

Finally it must be observed that owing to the almost spherical size of CH_3OH, the methanol intercalated compound very probably contains only one mol of CH_3OH per mol of exchanger.[32]

Also in the case of isoalkanols, the interlayer distances increase with the increasing alkyl-chain length, but the numerous configurations that these molecules can assume between the layers prevent us from hypothesizing the arrangement of the guest molecules; it is very likely that bimolecular films, with the polar groups interacting with the $\gtreqless POH$ groups of the exchanger, are formed.

C. Exchange of Intercalated Alkanol Molecules with Other Polar Molecules

Zirconium phosphate-alkanol compounds may be considered as very good starting materials for the intercalation of other polar molecules. In fact, the interlayer distances of these compounds are very large, and no steric hindrance obstructs the diffusion of polar molecules within the layers of the exchanger. Furthermore, alkanols are held with weak forces to the layers and can easily be replaced by other polar molecules. Molecules such as acetonitrile, acetylacetone, dimethylacetone, etc., have been easily intercalated[32] in α-$Zr(HPO_4)_2$ simply by contacting the methanol or ethanol intercalated compounds with the corresponding pure liquids to be intercalated. It must be observed that alkanol-intercalate compounds are stable only in the presence of the pure alkanol, so that dispersion of the exchanger in the solvent, previously standardized (e.g., as mmol of $Zr(HPO_4)_2/m\ell$), must be used. Methanol or ethanol zirconium phosphate complexes dispersed in water give rise to the polyhydrated hydrogen phase[32] with an interlayer spacing of 10.4 Å (designed by Clearfield et al.[2] as ϑ-ZrP). The ethanol-zirconium phosphate is a more effective complex for obtaining intercalation compounds than the methanol one because of its larger interlayer distance (14.2 against 9.3 Å). The interlayer spacing of intercalation compounds obtained with the aforementioned procedure are listed in Table 3. Behrendt et al.,[9] were able to obtain similar intercalation compounds (also reported in Table 3) by contacting α-$Zr(HPO_4)_2 \cdot H_2O$ with the corresponding liquids (or with a concentrated aqueous solution in the case of solid guest molecule), for "several days at 60—80°C".

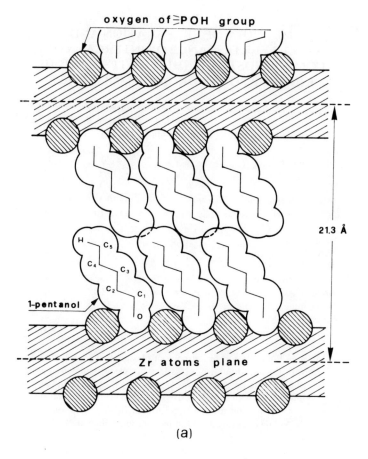

(a)

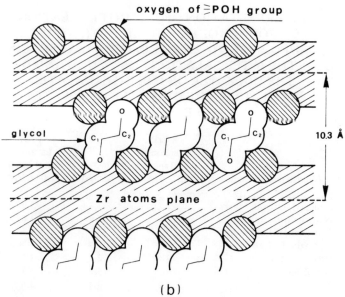

(b)

FIGURE 3. Possible arrangement of 1-pentanol (a) and ethyleneglycol (b) between the sheet of α-zirconium phosphate. (Figure 3a from Costantino, U., *J. Chem. Soc. Dalton Trans.*, 402, 1979. With permission.)

Table 3
METHODS OF PREPARATION AND INTERLAYER DISTANCE OF INTERCALATION COMPOUNDS OF α-Zr(HPO$_4$)$_2$ WITH VARIOUS KINDS OF POLAR ORGANIC MOLECULES

Intercalated molecules	Method of preparation	Interlayer distance, d_l (Å)	Ref.
2-Propanone	a	9.9	32
2-4-Pentanedione	a	13.5	32
Acetonitrile	b	11.3	32
N-Methylformamide	c	10.5	9
N,N-Dimethylformamide	b,c	11.2, 10 7	9, 32, 18
Urea	e,d	9.4	9,32
N,N Dimethylurea	d	10.6	9
N,N'Dimethylurea	d	9.4	9
Hydrazine hydrate	c	9.4	9
Aniline	e	18	32
Decylamine	e	32	32
Piperidine	c	13.4	9
Dimethyl sulfoxide	c	10.8, 11.3	9,18

Note: a = Equilibration of "zirconium phosphate-ethanol" complex with the pure liquid; b = As in a but using "zirconium phosphate-methanol" complex; c = Allowing the corresponding liquid to react with α-Zr(HPO$_4$)$_2 \cdot$H$_2$O for several days at 60-80°C; d = As in c but using a concentrated aqueous solution; and e = As in b but using 0.1 M amine solution in methanol.

Table 4
INTERPRETATION OF THE INTERCALATION COMPOUNDS OF α-Zr(HPO$_4$)$_2 \cdot$H$_2$O (α-ZrP) AND γ-Zr(HPO$_4$)$_2 \cdot$2H$_2$O (γ-ZrP) $\cdot$ d_l IS THE BASAL SPACING OF THE INTERCALATION COMPOUND AND D IS THE DIAMETER OF THE INTERCALATED MOLECULE; THE DIAMETER OF A WATER MOLECULE IS 2.8 A

Intercalated molecule	α-ZrP Increase in basal spacing d_l-7.6 (Å)	D- 2.8(Å)	γ-ZrP Increase in basal spacing d_l-12.3(Å)
Dimethyl sulfoxide	3.2	3.3	3.9
N-Methylformamide	2.9	2.9	3.6
N,N-Dimethylformamide	3.6	3.5	3.5
Hydrazine hydrate	1.8	1.9	2.3
Urea	1.8	2.5	1.3
N,N-Dimethylurea	3.0	3.2	1.8
N,N'-Dimethylurea	1.8	3.4	3.6

From Behrendt, D., Beneke, K., and Legaly, G., *Angew. Chem. Int. Ed. Engl.*, 15, 544, 1976. With permission.

It is not easy to discuss the arrangement of the guest molecules between the layers (infrared spectroscopy would help in this regard), but the mentioned authors observed (see Table 4) that, in the case of molecules that may adopt a spherical shape, the increase in basal spacing Δd_1 is equal to the diameter of the intercalated molecules D minus 2.8 Å (diameter of a water molecule). This observation leads to the conclusion that these molecules replace the water molecules in the cavities of the exchanger.[9]

From a practical point of view, intercalation compounds of α-$Zr(HPO_4)_2$ with polar molecules loosely bonded to the matrix are very attractive materials for several reasons:

1. They may exchange the guest molecules with other polar molecules.
2. They may be considered very suitable materials for ion exchange and adsorption in nonaqueous media. In fact, we are in the presence of a layered exchanger whose replaceable protons can be solvated with the molecules of the solvent used in the ion exchange processes. Owing to their large interlayer distance and to the lability with which the solvent molecules are bonded to the protons, high exchange rates with cations highly solvated or having large size may be expected. Furthermore, zirconium phosphate has easily been loaded with long-chain alkylamines or aromatic amines insoluble in water by contacting the zirconium phosphate-methanol complex with a diluted solution of these amines in methanol.[32]
3. They may improve both the catalytic properties and the ionic conductance of zirconium phosphate. In fact, active substrates may be supported on the exchanger, starting from these intercalated compounds, and the transport phenomena occurring in the interlayer region may be tuned by the presence of different guest molecules.

IV. INTERCALATION OF AMINES INTO α-$Zr(HPO_4)_2 \cdot H_2O$

A. Preparation and Stability of Intercalation Compounds

Owing to the tetrahedral $\gtrsim$POH groups present within its layers, zirconium phosphate shows a high preference for strong Brönsted bases such as ammonia and amines. Thus, unlike alkanols and other molecules possessing a weak basic character, amines are easily intercalated from diluted solutions and, in some cases, also from vapor phase.[33] To hasten the intercalation process and to intercalate amines insoluble in water, zirconium phosphate-methanol complex, dispersed in water or in methanol containing the amines to be intercalated, has been used successfully.[34] Intercalation of amines may be regarded as the protonation of amines with the $\gtrsim$P$-$OH groups of the exchanger. It has been demonstrated[35] that the conversion of α-$Zr(HPO_4)_2 \cdot H_2O$ into the diammonium form results from the diffusion of free NH_3 between the layers and its protonation, according to the process:

$$Zr(HPO_4)_2 \cdot H_2O + 2NH_3 \longrightarrow Zr(NH_4PO_4)_2 \cdot H_2O \qquad (2)$$

At least those amines that are bases stronger than ammonia, are expected to be protonated by the phosphate groups and several authors proposed such a mechanism.[7,18,34] Thus, the intercalation process may, in some case, be followed by titrating the exchanger dispersed in water with a standardized solution of the free amine to be intercalated. The potentiometric titration curves are very useful in obtaining the saturation capacity of the exchanger for a given amine at different pH values and to have information on the intercalation mechanism (see later).

Table 5 shows the interlayer distance and, where known, the composition of intercalation compounds of α-$Zr(HPO_4)_2$ with several amines. These compounds show a remarkable stability to heat and to washing with water and other polar solvents. For

Table 5
INTERLAYER DISTANCE, d_i, AND COMPOSITION OF INTERCALATION COMPOUNDS OF α-Zr(HPO$_4$)$_2$·H$_2$O WITH AMINES

Intercalated amines (In)	Interlayer distance, d_i (Å)	Composition mol In/mol Zr(HPO$_4$)$_2$	Ref.
Methylamine	12.8	2	34
Ethylamine	14.7, 16.3[a]	2	34,39
Propylamine	16.9,17.3[a]	2	34,36
Butylamine	19.0, 18.8, 18.7, 18.6[a]	2	7,37,34,36
Pentylamine	20.9	2	7
Hexylamine	22.8, 23.3	2	7,9
Heptylamine	25.9	2	34
Octylamine	28.0	2	7
Decylamine	32.1 32.0	2	7,34
Dodecylamine	36.4	-	9
Octadecylamine	47.7	2	7
sec-Butylamine	15.7	1.4	34
tert-Butylamine	12.8	1.0	34
Aniline	18.0	2	34
Benzylamine	19.1	2	34
Diethylamine	12.8, 12.6[b]	1.0	34,39
Di n-Propylamine	15.7	1.0	34
Di n-Butylamine	17.0, 17.3	0.8	7,34
Di n-Hexylamine	22.1	0.8	7
Di n-Octylamine	26.8	0.8	7
Di n-Decylamine	35.3	0.8	7
Tri-Ethylamine	12.6, 12.6[b]	0.6	34,39
Tri n-Propylamine	15.7	0.5	34
Tri n-Butylamine	17.2, 16.7	0.3	7,34
Tri n-Hexylamine	19.2	0.3	7
Tri n-Octylamine	26.7	0.3	7
Tri n-Decylamine	31.3	0.3	7
Ethylenediamine	10.7, 11.1	1.0	34,36
Tetramethylenediamine	13.2	1.0	34
Heptamethylenediamine	15.5	1.0	34
Decamethylenediamine	19.8	1.0	34
Pyridine	10.9[a]	0.23	37
Piperidine	13.4	-	9

Note: The different authors have not reported the errors in the interlayer spacings. However it may be evaluated ranging from 0.1 to 0.5 Å.

[a]   These intercalates contain 1 mol of water. The interlayer distance of propylamine and butylamine intercalate does not change for the loss of this mol of water.
[b]   These intercalates contain 2 mol of water. The other samples are anhydrous.

example, Clearfield and Tindwa[36] found that the n−C$_3$H$_7$NH$_2$, n−C$_4$H$_9$NH$_2$, and NH$_2$−(CH$_2$)$_2$−NH$_2$ intercalation compounds begin to decompose at 230 to 250°C.

B. Structural Considerations
Michel and Weiss[7] found that n-alkylamines are intercalated as double packed layers and that the interlayer distance of the host matrix increased by 2 to 2.2 Å for each additional -CH$_2$-group in the alkyl chain. Furthermore, they stated that while primary n-alkylamines form stoichiometric compounds containing 2 mol of amine per mol of exchanger, secondary and tertiary alkylamines give rise to compounds containing 0.8

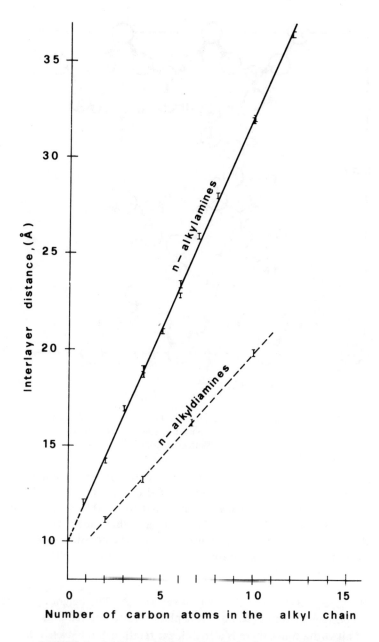

FIGURE 4. Interlayer distances of n-alkylamines and diamines intercalate compounds of α-zirconium phosphate as a function of the number
of carbon atoms in the alkyl-chain.

and 0.3 mol of amine per formula weight of exchanger, respectively. These results
have been essentially confirmed in subsequent studies. In fact, if the interlayer distance
of the n-alkylamine-intercalates is reported against the number of carbon atoms present in the alkylchain (see Figure 4), a straight line is obtained whose slope, $\Delta d_l / \Delta n_c$ is
equal to 2.21 Å per carbon atom and the intercept is equal to 9.9 Å. With considerations similar to those reported for the n-alkanols, it is possible to assume that n-alkylamines are intercalated as a bimolecular film of extended molecules inclined at an
angle of $\sim 60°$ with respect to the sheets. The value of the intercept suggests that the
$-NH_2$ group interacting with the phosphate group is nearer to the oxygen of the phos-

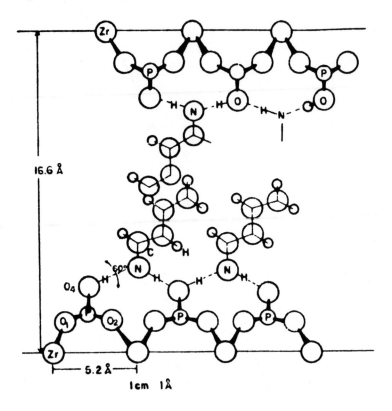

16.6 Å

5.2 Å

1 cm   1 Å

FIGURE 5.   Schematic representation of n-butylamine double layers in α-Zr(HPO₄)₂ at high amine content. (From Clearfield, A. and Tindwa, R. M., *J. Inorg. Nucl. Chem.*, 39, 1057, 1977. With permission.)

phate than the −OH group of alkanols. Clearfield and Tindwa[36] evaluated as 4.5 Å the height of the nitrogen atom above the plane of zirconium atoms, in the case of n-butylamine intercalate compound. They assumed that the −NH₂ is engaged in a symmetrical hydrogen bond with adjacent POH groups and that the O−H ... N bond and angle are 2.8 Å and 180°, respectively. Figure 5 reports the possible arrangement of a double layer of n-butylamine between the sheet of zirconium phosphate as viewed by Clearfield and Tindwa. The trans-trans alkyl-chain forms a 60° angle with the sheets. Adjacent layers are staggered in such a way that the phosphate groups in one layer are shifted with respect to those of the front layer by 3 Å. The height of the terminal −CH₃ group has been evaluated as 9 Å over the plane of zirconium atoms.[36]

In the case of alkyl-diamines there is also a linear relationship between the interlayer distance and the number of carbon atoms in the n-alkyl chain. The data are too few for a reliable analysis but the value of the slope $\Delta d_1/\Delta n_c \simeq 1.1$ Å/carbon atom suggests that the diamines form a unimolecular layer inclined at a ∼60° angle with respect to the sheet. Also in the case of secondary and tertiary n-alkyl amines, the interlayer distance increases with increase in the alkyl chain length, but the numerous configurations that these molecules can assume between the layers prevent us from hypothesizing the disposition of intercalated molecules. However it may be noted that intercalation compounds containing secondary and tertiary amines and having the same n-alkyl radical have about the same interlayer distance and that this value is lower than that of intercalation compounds with the primary n-alkylamines by 1 to 1.2 Å. Thus it can be assumed that secondary and tertiary alkylamines also give rise to bimolecular films between the sheets of the exchanger.

Finally it may be observed that while n-alkylamines and diamines form stoichiometric intercalation compounds containing 2 and 1 mol of intercalate per formula weight of exchanger respectively, substituted amines and some aromatic amines (except aniline and benzylamine) do not saturate all the $\geq$POH groups of the exchanger. As previously discussed, this phenomenon is due to the "covering effect" of the guest molecules; that is, a molecule bonded to a $\geq$POH group concomitantly renders an adjacent site unavailable for bonding since it covers this site. The observations made are quite qualitative and the explanation of the phenomena requires further structural studies.

C. Mechanism of the Intercalation Process

It has already been pointed out that the intercalation of amines may be performed by titrating the exchanger, suspended in water, with dilute solutions of the free amines. The intercalation of some alkyl-monoamines,[33,34,36,37] of ethylenediamine[32,36] and pyridine,[37] has been studied by this method. The titration curves obtained show different steps at various pH' values for each of the amines and in this respect they resemble the titration curves of α-Zr(HPO$_4$)$_2 \cdot$H$_2$O with alkali metal ions (see Chapter 1). In each step of the titration curves two intercalates are generally coexistent, one transforming into the other as the intercalation process proceeds, while in the sloping region of the curves only one intercalate is present. Thus, the intercalation process occurs discontinuously, with phase transitions, it is not easy to foresee the number of steps in which the process occurs since it seems to depend on the basicity of the molecule, the length of the alkylchain, the possible configurations of the guest molecules within the layers, the water content of the intercalated and so on. Yamanaka et al.[37] determined the titration curves of α-Zr(HPO$_4$)$_2 \cdot$H$_2$O with pyridine and butylamine. In the case of pyridine, the curve showed only one end point and the phase Zr(C$_5$H$_5$NHPO$_4$)$_{0.45}$ (HPO$_4$)$_{1.55} \cdot$H$_2$O (interlayer distance 10.9 Å) was identified. Only 25% of active sites of the exchanger are saturated by pyridine and this fact has been explained by considering the weak basic character of the molecule and assuming that α-Zr(HPO$_4$)$_2 \cdot$H$_2$O has different kinds of acidic sites.[37] Under suitable experimental conditions higher uptakes of pyridine are however expected, and this point deserves further attention. The potentiometric titration curve with n-butylamine shows two plateaus, the first ranging from 0 to 5 mmol of n-butylamine added and the second from 5 to 7. The phases Zr(C$_4$H$_9$NH$_3$PO$_4$)$_{1.34}$ (HPO$_4$)$_{0.66} \cdot$0.95H$_2$O (d_1 = 18.2 Å) and Zr(C$_4$H$_9$NH$_3$PO$_4$)$_2$ H$_2$O (d_1 − 18.8 Å) have been identified.

Clearfield and Tindwa[36] have studied in detail the uptake of n-propylamine, n butylamine and ethylenediamine on α-Zr(HPO$_4$)$_2 \cdot$H$_2$O. In the case of n-butylamine the results reported by Yamanaka et al.,[37] were essentially obtained. In addition, it was found that at an amine uptake of about 1.0 mmol/g the original α-Zr(HPO$_4$)$_2 \cdot$H$_2$O was converted in a mixture of two phases, whose interlayer spacings were 10.5 and 18.2 Å. The phase 10.5 Å was found to disappear at slightly higher loading and up to the amine content of 4.0 mmol/g, the 7.6 Å (α-Zr(HPO$_4$)$_2 \cdot$H$_2$O) and 18.2 Å phase were found to coexist.

The titration curve obtained for the intercalation of propylamine was found to be much more complicated.[36] An intercalated phase with interlayer spacing of 10.5 Å is formed at uptakes lower than 0.5 mmol/g. The relative percentage of this phase increased as amine was further intercalated. However the solid becomes entirely amorphous at loadings higher than 2.5 mmol/g. Recrystallization occurred at about 4.5 mmol/g to yield three intercalated phases with interlayer spacings of 14.6, 16.4, and 17.3 Å. The fully intercalated phase having the composition Zr(C$_3$H$_7$NH$_2$)$_2$ (HPO$_4$)$_2 \cdot$H$_2$O has an interlayer distance of 17.3 Å. Also regarding ethylenediamine, an interesting series of phase transitions was found in the intercalation process.[36] Table

Table 6

ETHYLENEDIAMINE PHASES OF
α-ZIRCONIUM PHOSPHATE (α-ZrP),
OBTAINED FROM THE TITRATION
CURVE, AT DIFFERENT LEVELS OF
AMINE ADDITION

Amine added mmol/g	Phases formed with approximate % in parenthesis
0.5	α-ZrP (75), 9.48 (9), 9.83 (5), 10.3 (11)
1.0	α-ZrP (35), 9.83 (41), 10.3 (24)
1.5	α-ZrP (20), 9.83 (48), 10.3 (32)
2.0	α-ZrP (30), 9.48 (35), 10.3 (35)
2.5	α-ZrP (20), 9.48 (38), 10.3 (42)
3.0	9.48 (48), 9.83 (22), 10.3 (30)
3.5	9.48 (50), 10.3 (50)
4.0	9.48 (35), 10.3 (65)
4.5	9.48 (8), 10.3 (92)
5.0	10.3 (100)
5.5	10.3 (82), 11.1 (18)
6.0	10.3 (63), 11.1 (37)
7.0	10.3 (15), 11.1 (85)
8.0	11.1 (100)

From Clearfield, A. and Tindwa, R. M., *J. Inorg. Nucl. Chem.*, 39, 1057, 1977. With permission.

6 reports the phases obtained and their approximate percentage as a function of the amine added. It is clear that a full explanation of the mechanism of intercalation must await the outcome of structural studies; however, the value of the interlayer spacings of the numerous phases obtained could be indicative of the orientation of the amines within the layers.[36] The probable arrangement of alkylamines and diamines in the fully intercalated phases has been already discussed. At partial loading not every available position is occupied by amine molecules and consequently the alkyl chain may incline to the layers at an angle of less than 60°. Thus in the first stages of the intercalation process the alkyl chain may lie parallel to the layers, and the phases with the interlayer distance 10.5 Å have been attributed to the presence of an arrangement similar to the $α_{II}$ type[36] found in clay systems.[11] As the loading increases the amine chains are forced into a more upright position and "kink" and "gauche" arrangement of the alkyl-chains[38] may take place before the final orientation in the fully intercalated compounds is reached.

Finally, considering that a free alkylamine is always in equilibrium with the proton-ated species, exchange between alkylammonium ions and the protons of the exchanger could occur concomitantly to the intercalation process. In a recent paper, Gupta and Nowell[39] reported the titration curves of $α-Zr(HPO_4)_2 \cdot H_2O$ with 0.1 M ethyl-, diethyl- and triethyl-amines in the presence of the respective 0.1 M alkylammonium chlorides. It is noteworthy to observe that the shape of these titration curves is similar to that obtained in absence of the alkylammonium cations but the equilibrium pH values are much lower, this indicating that some exchange has taken place simultaneously with intercalation. However, the phases obtained by titrating $α-Zr(HPO_4)_2 \cdot H_2O$ with these alkylamines in the presence or in absence of the respective alkylammonium chloride are identical. It is a matter for further study to clarify why ethylammonium is ex-changed[39] on $α-Zr(HPO_4)_2 \cdot H_2O$ and ammonium is excluded.[35]

D. Some Properties of Amine Intercalate Compounds

While the alkanols intercalated in $α-Zr(HPO_4)_2$ are loosely bonded to the phosphate

Table 7
INTERLAYER DISTANCE, d_l, OF INTERCALATION COMPOUNDS OF γ-Zr(HPO$_4$)$_2 \cdot$2H$_2$O AND γ-Ti(HPO$_4$)$_2 \cdot$2H$_2$O WITH VARIOUS KINDS OF POLAR ORGANIC MOLECULES

γ-Zr(HPO$_4$)$_2 \cdot$2H$_2$O			γ-Ti(HPO$_4$)$_2 \cdot$2H$_2$O		
Intercalated molecules	Interlayer distance, d_l (Å)	Ref.	Intercalated molecules	Interlayer distance, d_l (Å)	Ref.
Methanol	12.7	18	Propanol	20.0	42
Ethanol	16.6	18	Butanol	21.5	42
Hexanol	24.9	9	Octanol	30.4	42
2-Propanol	19.4	18	Ethylamine	18	25
Ethyleneglycol	13.4	18	Heptylamine	25	25
Dimethylsulfoxide	16.2, 15.8	9, 18			
Acetone	14.4	18	Ethylenediamine	12.5	42
N,N-Dimethylformamide	16.5, 15.8	18, 9	Heptamethylenediamine	18.0	42
N-Methylformamide	15.9	9	Decamethylenediamine	20.5	42
Urea	13.6	9			
N,N'-Dimethylurea	15.9	9			
Butylamine	21.5	18			
Decylamine	33.4	42			
Decylamine	33.4	42			

groups so that they are easily replaced by other molecules, the amine intercalates do not undergo the exchange of the guest molecules with other polar molecules. On the contrary, zirconium phosphate-amines complexes are generally swollen when suspended in different solvents;[7] for example, the interlayer distance of the zirconium phosphate-trimethylcetylamine complex ($d_l = 27.6$ Å) increases up to 38.4 Å when the complex is suspended in n-heptanol.[7]

In a recent preliminary note, Clearfield and Tindwa[40] reported that amine intercalate are capable of exchanging cations, including large complexes. For example, zirconium phosphate-butylamine complex is able to take up Ni^{2+} ions and an exchanged phase, having a composition similar to that of the phase obtained by Ni^{2+} exchange with ZrHNa(PO$_4$)$_2 \cdot$5H$_2$O but with a different interlayer distance, 12.6 instead of 9.5 Å, has been obtained. In addition the butylamine-intercalate exchanges [Cu(NH$_3$)$_4$]$^{2+}$ to give the phase Zr[Cu(NH$_3$)$_4$]$_{0.61}$H$_{0.78}$(PO$_4$)$_2 \cdot$0.8H$_2$O, interlayer distance: 9.3 Å. Also Cu(II) pyridine and ethylamine complexes are taken up to some extent.[40] These results deserve further development with regard to loading zirconium phosphate with active substrates. In this respect it must be noted that La Ginestra was able to load zirconium phosphate with ephedrine.[41]

V. INTERCALATION BEHAVIOR OF OTHER LAYERED ACID SALTS WITH α-TYPE STRUCTURE

Very little work on these materials has been reported to date. Michel and Weiss[8] showed that the phosphates and arsenates of Zr(IV), Ti(IV) and Sn(IV) undergo uni-dimensional swelling when contacted with n-octylamine, di-n-octylamine and tri-n-octylamine. The interlayer distances of the intercalates are very similar for the different exchangers loaded with the same amine. This confirms the fact that the intercalation behavior of these compounds should be similar to that observed for α-Zr(HPO$_4$)$_2 \cdot$H$_2$O. However, the structural differences reported in Table 1 and considerations similar to those reported by Alberti in Chapter 2 lead us to foresee that the intercalation ability may change for the different compounds. Thus, zirconium arsenate, owing to its larger interlayer distance and to the larger (a × b) product, should present less steric hindrance to the intercalation of alkanols and lesser packing density of the alkyl-chains; this fact would facilitate the formation of kink and gauche defects in the bimolecular films. On the other hand, titanium phosphate should present higher steric hindrance and a higher packing density of the alkyl-chains; furthermore, the "covering effect" by large polar molecules should be more marked than in α-$Zr(HPO_4)_2 \cdot H_2O$. Studies on intercalation behavior of these compounds will be useful in confirming these expectations.

VI. INTERCALATION BEHAVIOR OF LAYERED PHOSPHATES WITH γ-STRUCTURE

It is known that layered insoluble acid salts of tetravalent metals exist in at least two modifications, usually indicated as α and γ phases. Until now only γ-$Zr(HPO_4)_2 \cdot 2H_2O$ and γ-$Ti(HPO_4)_2 \cdot 2H_2O$ have been identified to have a γ-structure but much experimental evidence indicates that cerium(IV) arsenate is also a γ-compound (see Chapters 1 and 2).

As previously discussed, the higher value of the interlayer distance, suggests that γ-phases are better able to intercalate polar molecules than α-phases. In Table 7 the interlayer distances of some intercalation compounds of γ-$Zr(HPO_4)_2 \cdot 2H_2O$ and γ-$Ti(HPO_4)_2 \cdot 2H_2O$ are reported. It must be noted that intercalation of alkanols and molecules with weak basic character occurs by simply contacting the exchanger with the pure liquid to be intercalated. No detailed investigations of these compounds have been reported to date, but some considerations may be made:

1.   In each homologous series of intercalated molecules the interlayer spacing increases almost linearly with the increasing number of carbon atoms in the alkyl-chain, and it may be supposed that diamines form a unimolecular film while alkanols or alkylamines give rise to bimolecular films as in α-phases.

2.   According to Behrendt et al.[9] many guest molecules in γ-$Zr(HPO_4)_2 \cdot 2H_2O$ replace only one mol of water. It can be seen from Table 4 that the increase in basal spacing is about equal to the diameter of the guest molecules, D, minus 2.8 Å (diameter of water). In some cases (urea, *N,N*-dimethylurea) both water molecules are replaced by the intercalated molecules.

3.   The composition of some alkyl amine intercalates of γ-$Ti(HPO_4)_2 \cdot 2H_2O$ indicates that bimolecular films are built up with only one mol of guest amine per mol of exchanger.[42] That is, unlike what happens in α-$Zr(HPO_4)_2 \cdot H_2O$, only half of the $\gtrless P-OH$ groups lying in the same plane are engaged in a bond. This probably occurs because the free area surrounding the active site in γ-$Ti(HPO_4)_2 \cdot 2H_2O$ (evaluated as 16.6 Å^2) is much smaller than that of α-$Zr(HPO_4)_2 \cdot H_2O$ (see Table 1). Thus alkylamines, whose cross-sectional diameter is evaluated as 4.4 Å, present a "covering effect" also. This result is a further confirmation of the compact structure of the γ-layers.

VII. ORGANIC DERIVATIVES OF ZIRCONIUM PHOSPHATE

Studies on the intercalation behavior of layered phosphates lead to the conclusion that various kinds of polar organic molecules can be adsorbed in the interlayer spaces of α- and γ-phases. The organic molecules are held between the layers or with weak bonds (hydrogen bonds or Van der Waals' interactions) or with stronger interactions of an ionic type. It seemed of interest to various authors to obtain compounds in which organic groups are covalently bonded to the macro-anions constituting the layers of

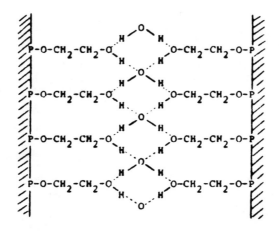

FIGURE 6. Schematic illustration of the arrangement of the glycol chains and water in the interlayer region of 18.4 Å phase with a composition Zr(HOCH$_2$ CH$_2$OPO$_3$)$_2$·H$_2$O. (From Yamanaka, S., *Inorg. Chem.*, 15, 2811, 1976. With permission.)

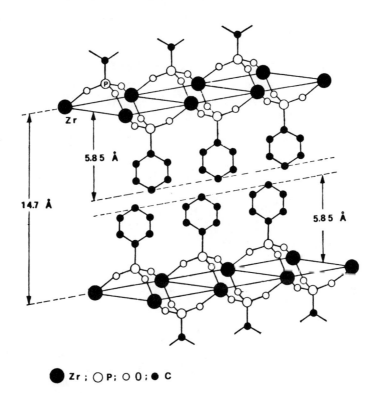

● Zr ; ○ P; ○ O; ● C

FIGURE 7. Idealized crystal structure of zirconium bis(benzene phosphonate). (From Alberti, G., Costantino, U., Allulli, S., and Tomassini, N., *J. Inorg. Nucl. Chem.*, 40, 1113, 1978. With permission.)

the insoluble acid salts. In a series of papers Yamanaka and co-workers[18,43,44,45] reported the reaction between γ-Zr(HPO$_4$)$_2$·2H$_2$O and ethylene or propylene oxide.

In detailed studies, performed with the aid of several experimental techniques,[44] it was demonstrated that ethylene oxide is taken up in the interlayer spaces of γ-

$Zr(HPO_4)_2 \cdot 2H_2O$, where it suffers ring scission and forms P—O—C ester bonds with the monohydrogen phosphate groups of the interlayer surfaces. The amount of reacted ethylene oxide and the basal spacing of the organic derivatives vary depending upon the reaction conditions, and there is a linear relation between the two. Two moles of ethylene oxide react with one mol of exchanger according to the reaction:

$$\gamma - Zr(HPO_4)_2 + 2CH_2 \overset{O}{\overbrace{}} CH_2 \longrightarrow \gamma - Zr(HOCH_2—CH_2OPO_3)_2$$

$$(3)$$

The obtained organic derivative can absorb one mol of water and reach an interlayer spacing of 18.4 Å; its proposed structure is reported in Figure 6. It may be noted that unlike what occurs with alkylamine intercalates of γ-$Zr(HPO_4)_2 \cdot 2H_2O$ where only one $\equiv$P—OH group of two interacts with the guest molecules, in the glycol derivatives of γ-$Zr(HPO_4)_2$ both the $\equiv$POH groups are engaged in the bond. This may be due to some rearrangement of the structure of the layers. A confirmation of this hypothesis may be found in the fact that only one mol of propylene oxide is able to react with γ-zirconium phosphate.[45] In the derivative with more than one mol of propylene oxide, the molecules seem to attack the reacted sites, forming di- and tri-propylene glycol chains.[45] Recently Yamanaka and co-workers[46] showed that other organic derivatives of γ-$Zr(HPO_4)_2$ could be obtained by exchanging, in suitable conditions, the HPO_4^{2-} ions with various kinds of phosphoric ester ions.

A different approach for obtaining organic derivatives of zirconium phosphate has been followed by Alberti and co-workers. As reported in Chapter 2, compounds having the general formula $Zr(R—PO_3)_2$ or $Zr(R—OPO_3)_2$ (where R is an organic radical) have been obtained by using substituted phosphonic acids or phosphoric esters in the synthesis, instead of phosphoric acid.[47] Much experimental evidence indicates that these compounds have a layered structure of α-zirconium phosphate type. As an example, Figure 7 reports the proposed structure of $Zr(C_6H_5PO_3)_2$. These compounds are intercalating agents for polar molecules and the intercalation ability clearly increase with the increasing polarity of the radical, R. Thus while amines have been intercalated in $Zr(HOCH_2PO_3)_2$ and $Zr(HOOCCH_2PO_3)_2$ no intercalation compounds of $Zr(C_6H_5PO_3)_2$ have been so far obtained.[48] It is interesting to note that this new class of layered compounds is a good model for the study of the interactions between intercalated molecules and active sites of the host matrix, since the nature of the sites may be widely varied by changing the organic radical, while the basic structure of the host matrix remains unchanged. Such studies are in progress in this laboratory.

REFERENCES

1. **Vesèly, V. and Pekàrek, V.**, Synthetic inorganic ion exchangers. I, *Talanta*, 19, 219, 1972.
2. **Clearfield, A., Nancollas, G. H., and Blessing, R. H.**, New inorganic ion exchangers, in *Ion Exchange and Solvent Extraction*, Vol. 5, Marinsky, J. A. and Marcus, Y., Eds., Marcel Dekker, New York, 1973, chap. 1.
3. **Alberti, G. and Costantino, U.**, Recent progress in the field of synthetic inorganic exchangers having a layered or fibrous structure, *J. Chromatogr.*, 102, 5, 1974.
4. **Alberti, G.**, Syntheses, crystalline structure, and ion exchange properties of insoluble acid salts of tetravalent metals and their salt forms, *Acc. Chem. Res.*, 11, 163, 1978.
5. **Clearfield, A. and Smith, G. D.**, The crystallography and structure of α-zirconium bis(monohydrogen orthophosphate) monohydrate, *Inorg. Chem.*, 8, 431, 1969.

6. **Clearfield, A. and Stynes, J. A.,** The preparation of crystalline zirconium phosphate and some observations on its ion exchange behaviour, *J. Inorg. Nucl. Chem.,* 26, 117, 1964.

7. **Michel, E. and Weiss, A.,** Kristallines zirkonphosphate, ein kation-enaustauscher mit schichtstruktur und innerkristallinem quellungsvermögen, *Z. Naturforschg.,* 20b, 1307, 1965.

8. **Michel, E. and Weiss, A.,** Kationenaustausch und eindimensionales innerkristallines quellungsvermögen bei den isotypen Verbindungen $H_2\{M^{+4} (X^{+5}O_4)_2\} \cdot H_2O$ (M = Ti, Zr, Sn; X = P, As), *Z. Naturforschg.,* 22b, 1100, 1967.

9. **Behrendt, D., Beneke, K., and Lagaly, G.,** Intercalation compounds of zirconium phosphate, *Angew. Chem. Int. Ed. Engl.,* 15, 544, 1976.

10. **Henning, G. H.,** Interstitial compounds of graphite, in *Progress in Inorganic Chemistry,* Vol. 1, Cotton, F. A., Ed., Interscience, New York, 1959, 125.

11. **Theng, B. K. G.,** *The Chemistry of Clay-Organic Reactions,* Adam Hilger, London, 1974.

12. **Gamble, F. R. and Geballe, T. H.,** Inclusion compounds, in *Treatise of Solid State Chemistry,* Vol. 3, Hannay, N. B., Ed., Plenum Press, New York, 1976, chap. 2.

13. **Lagaly, G., Beneke, K., Diets, P., and Weiss, A.,** Intracrystalline reactivity of phyllodisilicic acid $(H_2Si_2O_5)$, *Angew. Chem. Int. Ed. Engl.,* 13, 819, 1974.

14. **Feitknecht, W. and Bürki, H.,** Zur Kentnis der Metallhydroxyd-Einschlussverbindungen, *Helv. Chim. Acta,* 39, 564, 1956.

15. **Lagaly, G. and Beneke, K.,** Cation exchange reactions of the micalike potassium niobate $K_4Nb_6O_{17}$, *J. Inorg. Nucl. Chem.,* 38, 1513, 1976.

16. **Boehm, H. P., Steinle, J., and Vieweger, C.,** $Zn_2Cr(OH)_6$ X·$2H_2O$, new layer compounds capable of anion exchange and intracrystalline swelling, *Angew. Chem. Int. Ed. Engl.,* 16, 265, 1977.

17. **Dyer, A. and Leigh, D.,** Comments on the structure of zirconium phosphate, *J. Inorg. Nucl. Chem.,* 34, 369, 1972.

18. **Yamanaka, S. and Koizumi, M.,** Structural consideration of zirconium phosphate and its organic complexes, *Clays and Clay Minerals,* 23, 477, 1975.

19. **Hoffman, U.,** On the chemistry of clay, *Angew. Chem. Int. Ed. Engl.,* 7, 681, 1968.

20. **Bradley, W. F.,** Molecular associations between montmorillonite and some polyfunctional organic liquids, *J. Am. Chem. Soc.,* 67, 975, 1945.

21. **Clearfield, A. and Duax, W. L.,** Crystal structure of the ion exchanger zirconium bis(monohydrogen orthoarsenate) monohydrate, *Acta Crystallogr.,* 25, 2658, 1969.

22. **Alberti, G. and Torracca, E.,** Preparation and ion exchange properties of crystalline titanium arsenate, *J. Inorg. Nucl. Chem.,* 30, 3075, 1968.

23. **Costantino, U. and Gasperoni, A.,** Synthesis and ion exchange properties of tin(IV) phosphate and tin(IV) arsenate, *J. Chromatogr.,* 51, 289, 1970.

24. **Yamanaka, S. and Tanaka, M.,** Formation region and structural model of γ-zirconium phosphate, *J. Inorg. Nucl. Chem.,* 41, 45, 1979.

25. **Alberti, G., Costantino, U., and Luciani Giovagnotti, M. L.,** Synthesis of crystalline $Ti(HPO_4)_2 \cdot 2H_2O$ by the HF procedure and some comments on its formation and structure, *J. Inorg. Nucl. Chem.,* 41, 643, 1979.

26. **Zsinka, L. and Szirtes, L.,** Personal communication, 1978.

27. **Albertsson, J., Oskarsson, A., Teligren, R., and Thomas, J. O.,** A neutron powder diffraction study of the hydrogen bond geometry in α-$Zr(HPO_4)_2 \cdot H_2O$. A model for the ion exchange, *J. Phys. Chem.,* 81, 1574, 1977.

28. **Troup, J. M. and Clearfield, A.,** Refinement of the crystal structure of α-zirconium phosphate, *Inorg. Chem.,* 16, 3311, 1977.

29. **Alberti, G., Casciola, M., Costantino, U., Levi, G., and Ricciardi, G.,** Electrical conductance of zirconium bis(monohydrogen orthophosphate) monohydrate with a layered structure, *J. Inorg. Nucl. Chem.,* 40, 533, 1978.

30. **Alberti, G., Bernasconi, M. G., Casciola, M., and Costantino, U.,** Hydrogen-ammonium ion exchange on γ-titanium phosphate, accepted, *J. Inorg. Nucl. Chem.,* 42, 1637, 1980.

31. **Brown, G.,** Fourier investigation of montmorillonite, *Clay Minerals Bull.,* 4, 109, 1950.

32. **Costantino, U.,** Intercalation of alkanols and glycols into zirconium (IV) hydrogen phosphate monohydrate, *J. Chem. Soc. Dalton Trans.,* 402, 1979.

33. **Bettaccini, R.,** Interazioni tra Fosfato Acido di Zirconio e Molecole Organiche Polari: Processi di Intercalazione di Scambio Ionico, Doctoral Thesis, University of Perugia, Italy, 1977.

34. **Alberti, G., Bernasconi, M. G., Casciola, M., Costantino, U., and Luciani Giovagnotti, M. L.,** Intercalation of Amines in the Layered Structure of α-$Zr(HPO_4)_2 \cdot H_2O$ and $Zr(HOOCCH_2PO_3)_2$, presented at XI Congresso Nazionale di Chimica Inorganica, Arcavacata di Rende, 25 to 29 September, 1978, paper no. 1-I.

35. **Alberti, G., Bertrami, R., Costantino, U., and Gupta, J. P.,** Ammonium and ammonia uptake on different ionic forms of crystalline zirconium phosphate, *J. Inorg. Nucl. Chem.,* 39, 1057, 1977.

36. **Clearfield, A. and Tindwa, R. M.,** Intercalation of amines on α-zirconium phosphate, *J. Inorg. Nucl. Chem.,* 41, 871, 1979.
37. **Yamanaka, S., Horibe, Y., and Tanaka, M.,** Uptake of pyridine and n-butylamine by crystalline zirconium phosphate, *J. Inorg. Nucl. Chem.,* 38, 323, 1976.
38. **Lagaly, G.,** Kink-block and gauche-block structures of bimolecular films, *Angew. Chem. Int. Ed. Engl.,* 15, 575, 1976.
39. **Gupta, J. P. and Nowell, D. V.,** Mechanism of some alkylammonium-ion exchanges by α-zirconium bis(monohydrogen orthophosphate) monohydrate, *J. Chem. Soc. Dalton Trans.,* 1178, 1979.
40. **Clearfield, A. and Tindwa, R. M.,** Exchange of large cations and charged complexes with amine intercalates of zirconium phosphate, *Inorg. Nucl. Chem. Lett.,* 15, 251, 1979.
41. **La Ginestra, A.,** Personal communication, 1979.
42. **Isernia, A.,** Sintesi e Proprieta di Scambio Ionico e di Intercalazione di Ti(HPO$_4$)$_2$·2H$_2$O, un nuovo sale Acido con Struttura a Strati di tipo γ, Doctoral Thesis, University of Perugia, Italy, 1978.
43. **Yamanaka, S., Kanamuri, F., and Koizumi, M.,** Organic derivative of γ-zirconium phosphate, *Nature,* 246, 63, 1973.
44. **Yamanaka, S., Synthesis and characterization of the organic derivatives of zirconium phosphate, *Inorg. Chem.,* 15, 2811, 1976.
45. **Yamanaka, S., Tsujimoto, M., and Tanaka, M.,** Synthesis of the organic derivatives of γ-zirconium phosphate by the reaction with propylene oxide, *J. Inorg. Nucl. Chem.,* 41, 605, 1979.
46. **Yamanaka, S. and Hattori, M.,** Exchange reaction between HPO$_4^{2-}$ and C$_6$H$_5$OPO$^{2-}_3$ in a heterogeneous system with γ-zirconium phosphate, Zr(HPO$_4$)$_2$·2H$_2$O, *Chem. Lett.,* 1073, 1979.
47. **Alberti, G., Costantino, U., Allulli, S., and Tomassini, N.,** Crystalline Zr(R-PO$_3$)$_2$ and Zr(R-OPO$_3$)$_2$ compounds (R = organic radical). A new class of materials having layered structure of the zirconium phosphate type, *J. Inorg. Nucl. Chem.,* 40, 1113, 1978.
48. **Costantino, U.,** Unpublished data, 1979.

Chapter 4

URANYL PHOSPHATES

A. T. Howe

TABLE OF CONTENTS

I. INTRODUCTION

Three types of uranyl phosphates are known, namely $UO_2(H_2PO_4)_2 \cdot nH_2O$, $UO_2(HPO_4) \cdot nH_2O$, and $(UO_2)_3 (PO_4)_2 \cdot nH_2O$. Only the monohydrogen type show substantial ion exchange properties. This is because the H^+ ions do not play a unique role in the structure, and their place can be taken by virtually any other cation. The maximum hydrate, the tetrahydrate, does not possess discrete HPO_4^{2-} groups, and is more truly represented by the commonly used formula $HUO_2PO_4 \cdot 4H_2O$ (HUP). A more accurate representation may be $(H_3O) (UO_2PO_4) \cdot 3H_2O$.[1] The UO_2^{2+} and PO_4^{3-} ions are bound together into puckered negatively charged layers that can be stacked in two ways, as shown in Figure 1.[2] In the presence of solution, HUP and the monovalent metal salts adopt the meta-autunite structure, while the divalent metal salts adopt the autunite structure. The exchangeable cations and the water molecules reside between these layers. The general formula can be expressed as $(M^{m+})_{1/m} (UO_2PO_4^-) \cdot nH_2O$, and this chapter will be concerned with these compounds.

These materials function well as high capacity, comparatively fast, ion exchangers in weakly acidic conditions.[3-5] In contrast to the amorphous character of many inorganic ion exchangers, they are crystalline, and as a consequence have good column and filtration properties, would be expected to have well-defined thermodynamic and kinetic properties, and exhibit unusual relative cation affinities. A very strong affinity, in particular, is shown towards NH_4^+. The compounds are stable, insoluble, and easily prepared. The isostructural arsenates have similar properties to the phosphates.

II. PREPARATION

Many of the compounds exist as trace minerals.[6] Synthetic HUP, suitable for ion exchange applications, has been prepared by adding uranyl nitrate, dissolved in a small quantity of water, to 0.84 M phosphoric acid such that the ratio P-U is greater than 2.[3] After a short induction period precipitation will begin, and further digestion for 24 hr will yield well-developed platelet crystals at least 10 μm square and 1 μm thick, which can be filtered, washed with acetone, and dried at 105°C. At this temperature the 2.5-hydrate will be formed[3] which will convert to the 4-hydrate upon standing in air at room temperature.[13] The salts of uranyl phosphate can be prepared by stirring approximately 2 g of HUP for 4 hr with several 250 mℓ portions of a 2 M solution of the respective nitrate.[3]

Changes in the conditions used in the above preparation of HUP can result in other polymorphs being formed.[7] Three polymorphs of the tetrahydrate can be distinguished crystallographically.[7] Because Pekarek and Benesova[3] did not report the X-ray parameters of their preparation, the polymorph identity is not certain. However, judging from the preparative conditions, the commonly studied type I tetragonal form would be expected. Reaction mixtures containing equimolar concentrations of uranyl nitrate and phosphoric acid, each of 1.1 M,[8,9] 0.7 M,[10] 0.5 M,[7] and 0.4 M[11] almost certainly produce the type 1 form. The forms obtained by other workers have been reviewed,[12] and may depend on the presence of other ions such as Ca^{2+}.[7]

Uranium is more chemically toxic than radiologically toxic, and should be handled is a similar manner to lead, since the two are of comparable chemical toxicity. The threshold limit value for uranium is 200 μg $\cdot$ m^{-3}. Commercial products usually contain depleted uranium, where the U-235 content is reduced to between 0.2 to 0.3% compared to the value of 0.71% found in natural uranium. The permissible body burden of natural uranium is 15 mg, as judged radiologically. The specific activity of natural uranium is 0.33 μCi $\cdot$ g^{-1}.

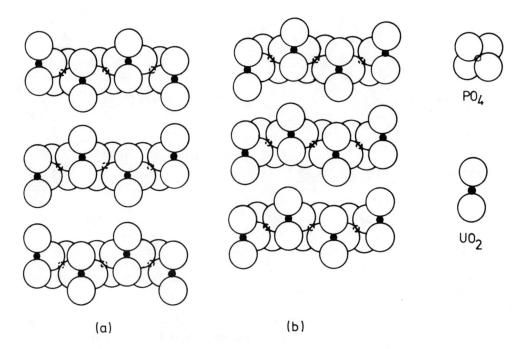

FIGURE 1. Uranyl phosphate layers in the autunite structure (a), and the meta-autunite structure (b). (From Beinteima, J., *Rec. Trav. Chim. Pays-Bas Belg.*, 57, 155, 1938. With permission.)

III. CHEMICAL PROPERTIES

A. Chemical Stability

HUP transforms into $UO_2(H_2PO_4)_2 \cdot 3H_2O$ in solutions more concentrated than 6.1 M phosphoric acid, and into $(UO_2)_3(PO_4)_2 \cdot 6H_2O$ in solutions more dilute than 0.014 M phosphoric acid (pH2.6).[9] The metal salts of HUP are in general stable up to pH 4 to 5,[13] but at lower pH values H^+ exchange needs to be considered, depending on the H^+/metal ratio in solution.

B. Thermal Stability

The equilibrium water vapor pressure of HUP is 0.4 mmHg at 14°C and 16 mmHg at 45°C.[14] Various dehydration products have been found, and are reviewed by Howe and Shilton.[14] Samples dried at 105°C, as in the preparation described above, will quickly rehydrate at room temperature to give the tetrahydrate.[13] In solution, HUP is stable up to 100°C.[12] The metal salts all have 3 to 5 waters of crystallization per metal atom,[6,15] and all begin to dehydrate when heated to between 22 and 40°C, depending on the particular metal.[15]

IV. PHYSICAL PROPERTIES

A. Structure

The disposition of the water molecules in HUP is illustrated in Figure 2. The water molecules are linked to form a puckered two-dimensional H-bonded network,[17,18] in which the water molecules are not liquid-like, but static,[10] with an activation energy for rotation somewhat less than 30 kJ mol⁻¹, as inferred from H^+ conductivity studies.[12] The theoretical density of HUP is 3.43 g·cm⁻³.

The essential arrangement of the water molecules is retained for all analogues having a monovalent cation. Lithium probably enters into the centers of the water squares to

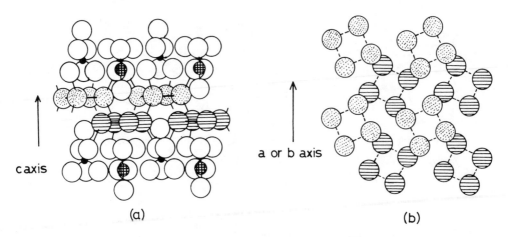

FIGURE 2.   The H-bonded water network in HUP viewed (a) along the a axis, and (b) viewed along the c axis. Water molecules are shaded. One water molecule out of four in each square has an additional H⁺, to form H_3O^+. (From Ross, M. and Evans, H. T., Jr., *J. Am. Mineral.*, 49, 1578, 1964. Copyright by the Mineralogical Society of America. With permission.)

retain a tetrahydrate, while Na^+, K^+, and NH^+_4 probably occupy a water site to give trihydrates.[15,17] Substitution with divalent ions produces the autunite structure (see Figure 1), which permits eightfold coordination around the cations.

B. Solubility and Relative Stability

The solubility of HUP in phosphoric acid pH 2 is approximately 10^{-3} M,[9] and increases considerably at higher acidities. The solubility products K_{sp} = $[M^+]$ $[UO_2^{2+}][PO_4^{3-}]$ are $10^{-24.2}$, $10^{-24.5}$, and $10^{-26.2}$ for M^+ = Na^+, H^+, and NH_4^+.[16] In order to convert HUP into the metal forms, the metal/H⁺ ratio needs to exceed approximately 2 for Na^+, 0.06 for K^+, Rb^+, and Cs^+, and 0.018 for NH_4^+.[16] The strong affinity of the lattice for NH_4^+ is reflected in the ability of dry HUP powder to rapidly incorporate NH_3 from the atmosphere around opened stockbottles containing NH_3 solution.[10]

C. Ionic Conductivities

HUP has recently been shown[12] to exhibit the exceptionally high proton conductivity of 0.4 $ohm^{-1}m^{-1}$ at 17°C. Clear discs can be pressed at room temperature suitable for use in solid-state hydride batteries[19] and electrochromic cells.[11] However, because the conduction mechanism is of the "handing on", or Grotthus type, involving H⁺ transfer between $H_3O^+-H_2O$ pairs, ions other than H⁺ exhibit much lower conductivities.[15] Those of the Li^+, $Na,^+$ K^+ and NH_4^+ forms are, respectively, 4×10^{-7}, 2×10^{-5}, 1×10^{-6}, and 1×10^{-7} $ohm^{-1} \cdot cm^{-1}$ at 20°C.

D. Dielectric Transition

At 1°C the H-bond dipoles in HUP become ordered within the water network[10] to give an antiferroelectric phase with an orthorhombic unit cell.[10] Striations of domains and subdomains are visible under the polarizing microscope. The substituted analogues also show similar behavior.

V. ION EXCHANGE PROPERTIES

A. Rate of Exchange

The rate and extent of exchange of a wide variety of cations for H⁺ in HUP has

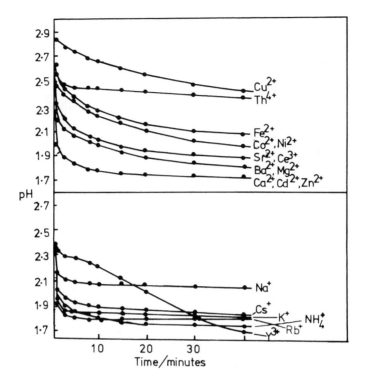

FIGURE 3. H^+ release from HUP in solutions of various salts, using 0.3 g (0.72 meq) of HUP (125-130 mesh) together with 20 mℓ of an 0.1 N solution of the salt (2.0 meq). (From Pekarek, V. and Benesova, M., *J. Inorg. Nucl. Chem.*, 26, 1743, 1964. With permission.)

Table 1

DISTRIBUTION COEFFICIENTS OF MONOVALENT ALKALI
IONS ON HUP (100 MG HUP, 0.24 MEQ, TOGETHER WITH 5 mℓ
SOLUTION CONTAINING 0.08 MEQ OF CATION)

		$K_D \times 10^{-2}$				
Sorbent	Form of the sorbent	Na	K	Rb	Cs	NH$_4$
Uranyl phosphate	H	2.46	63.3	111.0	90.1	154.0
	NH$_4$	No sorption	1.2	106.0	90.1	—

After Pekarek V. and Benesova, M., *J. Inorg. Nucl. Chem.*, 27, 1151, 1965. With permission.

been determined by following the pH changes upon addition of a salt solution to a stirred solution containing powdered HUP. The results are shown in Figure 3. Within a few minutes virtually complete exchange of H^+ by Na^+, K^+, and Rb^+ had occurred, with Cs^+ and NH_4^+ taking about 20 min. Exchange of the higher valent ions took up to 40 min. As might be expected, the extent of the exchange, under conditions of a slight excess of the metal cation, reflect the relative stabilities of the metal uranyl phosphates, as indicated by their relative solubilities, as discussed above.

B. Distribution Coefficients

Titration of HUP with NaOH shows that full utilization of the calculated capacity

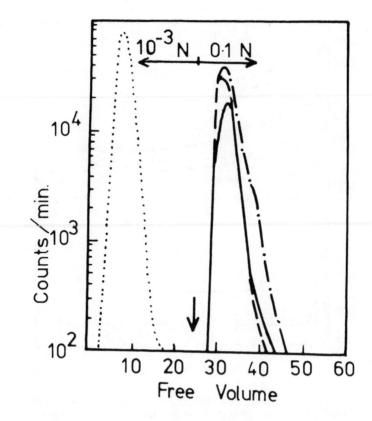

FIGURE 4.   Separation of Na⁺ from K⁺, Rb⁺, and Cs⁺ on HUP. Column: 7.2 × 0.3 cm; particle size 15 to 20 μm; flow rate 0.033 mℓ/min eluting solutions: 0.1 and 10^{-3} M NH₄Cl. Key .... Na, —— K, ---- Rb, and -.-.-.-. Cs. (From Pekarek, V. and Benesova, M., *J. Inorg. Nucl. Chem.*, 26, 1743, 1964. With permission.)

can be achieved. The dried material $HUO_2 \cdot PO_4 \cdot 2.5H_2O$ has a theoretical cation exchange capacity of 240 meq/100 g, while the tetrahydrate has a theoretical capacity of 229 meq/100 g.[4]

The distribution of a small quantity of metal ions between the solid and liquid phases when an excess of the solvent phase is present yields the distribution coefficients K_D, and these are given in Table 1, for sorption on both HUP and ammonium uranyl phosphate. In the case of exchange with HUP, approximately 16% of the total Na⁺ remains in solution, while only 0.3% of NH₄⁺ remains in solution at these concentrations.[3] The distribution coefficients of a number of higher-valent cations have also been determined by Pekarek and co-workers.[4] The distribution coefficients of Cs⁺ on Na⁺, Rb⁺, and NH₄⁺ uranyl phosphates have been determined[3] over a wide range of Cs⁺ concentrations, enabling the respective selectivity coefficients to be evaluated.

The uniquely low distribution coefficient of Na⁺ enables a clean separation to be achieved from K⁺, Rb⁺, and Cs⁺, as illustrated in Figure 4. By this means, using a HUP column, 0.05% Na⁺ was scavenged from an irradiated potassium bicarbonate solution.[3] Attempts have been made to try to separate the ions constituting the second peak in Figure 4 by means of varying the eluting concentration of NH₄Cl.[3] However, a separation of Rb⁺ and Cs⁺ could not be achieved.

C. Mechanism of Exchange

The mechanism of exchange has been considered by Pekarek and co-workers,[4,16] who concluded that exchange proceeds via a solution-reprecipitation mechanism. Evidence for this mechanism is provided by the similar sorption properties of the thermal decomposition products of HUP. In this case it was argued that the uranyl phosphates and pyrophosphates produced by heating HUP to above 200°C in an ion exchange experiment, would provide the ions in solution to enable the metal uranyl phosphates of the HUP structure to precipitate, thereby affecting a take up of the metal ions from solution. In the process, the solute dissolved. The parallel between the distribution coefficients and the solubility products of the various metal forms was cited as further evidence for a dissolution-reprecipitation mechanism.[4,16]

Although the above mechanism, despite being unusual, is a plausible one, it should be noted that the normal mechanism involving interdiffusion of ions within the bulk of the particles cannot, in the case of the uranyl phosphates, be ruled out on kinetic grounds. An estimate of the time required for exchange can be obtained from a knowledge of the ionic conductivities of the various ions. Using the Nernst-Einstein relationship, the self-diffusion coefficient D can be calculated. The root mean square displacement in a given time t is then equal to $(4Dt)^{1/2}$, in the case of diffusion within a plane.[20] In an exchange experiment, diffusion will occur under a concentration gradient, and will also occur in the presence of two cations, in which case chemical interdiffusion coefficients should be used. However, the use of self-diffusion coefficients to calculate exchange times will most likely lead to longer times than would actually be found.

Using this approach, and taking the ionic conductivity of H^+ in HUP as 0.4 $ohm^{-1} \cdot m^{-1}$,[12] the time for an H^+ ion to travel 5 μm (typically half of the length of the crystals) is calculated to be of the order of 1 sec. The ionic conductivities of the alkali metals and alkaline earths are much lower than H^+ in HUP, and are between 10^{-3} to 10^{-5} $ohm^{-1} \cdot m^{-1}$ at room temperature.[15] The time for these ions to travel 5 μm is calculated to be between 5 and 50 min, respectively. These times are similar to those actually observed in exchange experiments,[3] and imply that the exchange data would be kinetically consistent with a mechanism involving genuine bulk interdiffusion.

IV. CONCLUSION

HUP possesses many attractive features for ion exchange applications, namely a very high exchange capacity, a rapid exchange rate for monovalent ions, a high selectivity for NH_4^+, which is strongly exchanged, and for Na^+, which is weakly exchanged, leaving K^+, Rb^+, and Cs^+ towards which HUP exhibits similar behavior. These affinities contrast with those shown by metal ions on amorphous zirconium phosphate upon which NH_4^+ is only weakly sorbed.[5] On the other hand the exchange properties of HUP are closer to those of crystalline zirconium phosphate, which shows an affinity for NH_3 and NH_4^+ ions.[21]

REFERENCES

1. Nikanovich, M. V., Novitskii, G. G., Kobets, L. V., Kolevich, T. A., Sikorskii, V. V., and Umreiko, D. S., IR spectra of the crystal hydrate forms of uranyl hydrogen phosphate, *Koord. Khim.*, 2, 253, 1976; *Coord. Chem. (Russian)*, 2, 192, 1976.
2. Beintema, J., On the composition and the crystallography of autunite and the meta-autunities, *Rec. Trav. Chim. Pays-Bas Belg.*, 57, 155, 1938.

3. Pekarek, V. and Benesova, M., A study on uranyl phosphates. I. Sorption properties of uranyl hydrogen phosphate, *J. Inorg. Nucl. Chem.*, 26, 1743, 1964.
4. Pekarek, V. and Vesely, V., A study on uranyl phosphates. II. Sorption properties of some 1- to 4-valent cations on uranyl phosphate heated to various temperatures, *J. Inorg. Nucl. Chem.*, 27, 1151, 1965.
5. Amphlett, C. B., *Inorganic Ion Exchangers*, Elsevier, Amsterdam, 1964, 8.
6. Weigel, F. and Hoffmann, G., The phosphates and arsenates of hexavalent actinides. I. Uranium, *J. Less - Common Met.*, 44, 99, 1976.
7. Moroz, I. Kh., Valueva, A. A., Sidorenko, G. A., Zhiltsova, L. G., and Karpova, L. N., Crystal chemistry of uranyl compounds-I. Polymorphic modifications of H - meta - autunite, *Geokhimiya U.S.S.R.*, 2, 210, 1973.
8. Schreyer, J. M., *Inorganic Synthesis*, Vol. 5, McGraw-Hill, New York, 1957, 150.
9. Schreyer, J. M. and Baes, C. F., Jr., The solubility of uranium (VI) orthophosphates in phosphoric acid solutions, *J. Am. Chem. Soc.*, 76, 354, 1954.
10. Shilton, M. G. and Howe, A. T., Studies of layered uranium (VI) compounds-III. Structural investigations of hydrogen uranyl phosphate and arsenate tetra-hydrates below the respective transition temperatures of 274 and 301°K, *J. Solid State Chem.*, 34, 137, 1980.
11. Howe, A. T., Sheffield, S. H., Childs, P. E., and Shilton, M. G., Fabrication of films of hydrogen uranyl phosphate tetrahydrate (HUP) and their use as solid electrolytes in electrochromic displays, *Thin Solid Films*, 67, 365, 1980.
12. Howe, A. T. and Shilton, M. G., Studies of layered uranium (VI) compounds. I. High proton conductivity in polycrystalline hydrogen uranyl phosphate tetrahydrate, *J. Solid State Chem.*, 28, 345, 1979.
13. Howe, A. T. and Shilton, M. G., unpublished results.
14. Howe, A. T. and Shilton, M. G., Studies of layered uranium compounds. II. Thermal stability of hydrogen uranyl phosphate and arsenate tetrahydrates (HUP and HUAs), *J. Solid State Chem.*, 31, 393, 1980.
15. Johnson, C. M., Shilton, M. G., and Howe, A. T., Studies of Layered Uranium (VI) compounds - VI. Ionic conductivities and thermal stabilities of $MUO_2PO_4 \cdot nH_2O$, where M = H, Li, Na, K, NH$_4$ or 1/2 Ca, and where n is between 0 and 4, *J. Solid State Chem.*, 36, 3, 1981.
16. Vesely, V., Pekarek, V., and Abbrent, M., A study on uranyl phosphates. III. Solubility products of uranyl hydrogen phosphate, uranyl orthophosphate and some alkali uranyl phosphates, *J. Inorg. Nucl. Chem.*, 27, 1159, 1965.
17. Ross, M. and Evans, H. T., Jr., Studies of the torbernite minerals. I. The crystal structure of abernathyite and the structurally related compounds $(NH_4)(UO_2AsO_4) \cdot 3H_2O$ and $K(H_3O)(UO_2AsO_4)_2 \cdot 6H_2O$, *Am. Mineral.*, 49, 1578, 1964.
18. Morosin, B., Structural Mechanism for H$^+$ ion conductivity in HUP, *Phys. Letts.*, 65A, 53, 1978; idem *Acta Crystallogr.*, B34, 3732, 1978.
19. Childs, P. E., Howe, A. T., and Shilton, M. G., Battery and other applications of a new proton conductor: hydrogen uranyl phosphate tetrahydrate, $HUO_2PO_4 \cdot 4H_2O$, *J. Power Sources*, 3, 105, 1978.
20. Manning, J. R., *Diffusion Kinetics for Atoms in Crystals*, van Nostrand, Princeton, N. J., 1968, chap. 2.
21. Clearfield, A. and Hunter, R. A., On the mechanism of ion exchange in zirconium phosphates. XIV. The effect of crystallinity on $NH_4^+ - H^+$ exchange of α-zirconium phosphate, *J. Inorg. Nucl. Chem.*, 38, 1085, 1976.

Chapter 5

GROUP IV HYDROUS OXIDES — SYNTHETIC INORGANIC ION EXCHANGERS

A. Ruvarac

I. INTRODUCTION

Adsorption properties of alumina, silica, and iron oxides have been known for a long time, and the processes taking place have been often described in terms of ion exchange. Most of these hydroxides show the properties of both cationic and anionic ion exchangers that make them especially interesting. These substances are mainly amphoteric ones and their dissociation could be schematically represented as follows:

$$M - OH \rightleftharpoons M^+ + OH^- \tag{1}$$

$$M - OH \rightleftharpoons M - O^- + H^+ \tag{2}$$

M is the central ion.

Scheme 1 takes place in acid solutions where the substance acts as an anionic ion exchanger. Scheme 2 shows the substance acting as a cationic ion exchanger in basic solutions. Dissociation, near the isoelectric point of the oxide, occurs in both ways which enables simultaneous development of both ion exchange processes.

In recent years a great number of these compounds have been studied. Special emphasis was placed on elucidating the mechanism of the process as well as on the application of these substances for isolation, removal, and treatment of radioactive materials and purification of water. Among the main characteristics of these compounds commending their use are stability in strong radiation fields and retention of ion exchange properties at temperatures higher than 105°C.

II. CHEMICAL CHARACTERISTICS OF THE FOURTH GROUP OF ELEMENTS

The elements of group IV of the periodic table are classified in two subgroups. The first subgroup (IVA) consists of titanium (Ti), zirconium (Zr), and hafnium (Hf). They are rather widespread in nature and their compounds have industrial uses. The second subgroup (IVB) contains the elements, carbon (C), silicon (Si), germanium (Ge), tin (Sn), and lead (Pb).

Each element of the IVA subgroup has in its outer shell two s-electrons (see Table 1). These elements can be divalent and quadrivalent in their compounds; (titanium can also form compounds in which it is tervalent due to different behavior of its 4s and 3d electrons). Quadrivalence of these elements depends on the separation of two electrons from the inner d-shell and two s-electrons from the outer shell. The elements exhibit an increase in electropositive character with increase in atomic weight. Only titanium is soluble in dilute acids, the others are insoluble. These elements are stable at room temperature, while at high temperature they are strongly reactive and easily react with oxygen, halogens, and other elements.

The elements of the IVB subgroup can be considered to be situated in the middle of the periodic table of elements. This is the result of the electronic structure of their atoms, i.e., the outer shell electron configuration of each element is s^2p^2 (see Table 2). For this reason the elements could be expected to form compounds in which they are divalent and quadrivalent.

The tendency of the elements in the IVB subgroups to form positive ions increases with increasing atomic weight. This can be explained by the corresponding increase in the diameter of their atoms which in turn lowers the force of attraction between the nucleus and electrons in an atom. Thus, divalent compounds of carbon and silicon are unstable while those of the other elements are very stable. This results from a decrease in bond energies in going from carbon to lead, which makes the tetravalent state in-

Table 1
ELECTRON CONFIGURATION OF THE ELEMENTS OF THE IVA
SUBGROUP

	K	L		M			N				O			P	
	n = 1	n = 2		n = 3			n = 4				n = 5			n = 6	
Element	s	s	p	s	p	d	s	p	d	f	s	p	d	s	d
Ti	2	2	6	2	6	2	2								
Zr	2	2	6	2	6	10	2	6	2		2				
Hf	2	2	6	2	6	10	2	6	10	14	2	6	2	2	

Table 2
ELECTRON CONFIGURATION OF THE ELEMENTS FROM THE IVB
SUBGROUP

	K	L		M			N				O			P		
	n = 1	n = 2		n = 3			n = 4				n = 5			n = 6		
Element	s	s	p	s	p	d	s	p	d	f	s	p	d	s	p	d
C	2	2	2													
Si	2	2	6	2	2											
Ge	2	2	6	2	6	10	2	2								
Sn	2	2	6	2	6	10	2	6	10		2	2				
Pb	2	2	6	2	6	10	2	6	10	14	2	6	10	2	2	

creasingly unstable relative to the divalent state. The basicity of the dioxides is weaker than that of the corresponding monoxides.

III. SYNTHESIS AND STRUCTURE OF THE GROUP IV OXIDES

Generally speaking the oxides of the group IV elements are obtained by adding an excess of base to solutions of their salts. The gelatinous precipitates so obtained, although often represented as SiO_2, SnO_2, TiO_2, ThO_2, and ZrO_2, are not really well-defined solids. Their chemical composition and properties depend on the method of preparation as well as on the further treatment of the fresh gelatinous precipitate. Amorphous products are most often obtained from these precipitations, but it is also possible, in some cases, to obtain crystalline forms.[1] Transformation of an amorphous gel into a crystalline form of solid is often possible by means of boiling under reflux as in the case of hydrous zirconia. During the boiling, polymerization occurs among tetramer units.[2,3] This kind of polymerization results in the formation of a large number of polymers of varying composition. Most of these group IV hydrous oxides can be obtained in a similar way, and the products of the polymerization process can be expressed by the general formula:

$$[MO_b(OH)_{4-2b} \cdot xH_2O]_n$$

where M = Ti, Zr, Hf, Th, and Si.

A. Hydrous Silica

A large variety of products can be obtained by different methods of preparation. These vary in their sorption behavior, specific surface area, and porosity. Silica gel with a porous structure is obtained by hydration of xerogels:[4]

$$\begin{bmatrix} \begin{array}{ccc} & H & H \\ & | & | \\ O-Si-O-Si \\ & | & | \\ & & O \end{array} \end{bmatrix}_n \longrightarrow \begin{bmatrix} \begin{array}{ccc} & OH & OH \\ & | & | \\ O-Si-O-Si- \\ & | & | \\ & & O \end{array} \end{bmatrix}_n$$

$\equiv$Si $-$ H $+$ H$_2$O $\rightarrow$ $\equiv$Si $-$ OH $+$ H$_2$. Silica gel has on its surface OH-silanol groups, in a density of 4.6 to 8.0 groups per 10.0 nm^2 ($\sim$7.8 μmol OH$-$/m^2).[5] These groups are strong hydrogen-bond donors and can be determined by titration.[6] The conventional silica gel is an agglomeration of spheroids with diameters of the order of 10 nm, bounded by interparticle siloxane ($\equiv$Si $-$ O$-$Si$\equiv$) links.[5] Sorption of the complexes Zn(NH$_3$)$_4$$^{2+}$ and also, Zn(en)$_3$$^{2+}$ is recommended for determination of the specific surface.[27]

B. Stannic Oxide

Hydrous stannic oxide is prepared by the acidification of sodium stannate solution or by the reaction of nitric acid with tin metal.[7] α-Stannic acid is obtained by the first process and β-stannic acid by the latter one. The products are stable in solutions of concentrated nitric and sulfuric acids. X-ray, DTA, and Mössbauer spectra measurements suggest that the exchanger is "wet" SnO$_2$, and that such SnO$_2$ is simply a host for adsorbed water, which itself must act as the exchanger. Thus it may be formulated as SnO$_2 \cdot$xH$_2$O.

C. Titanium Oxide

Hydrous titanium oxide is prepared by mixing titanyl oxalate or titanium (IV) chloride solutions with sodium hydroxide.[8,9] The precipitates obtained are usually dried at room temperature or at 400°C, and white amorphous products are obtained. These lose free or interstitial water up to 200°C and chemically bound water at higher temperatures. The amount of bound water is about 1 to 2%.[8] Infrared measurements[10] show that the molecules of water are more or less bound to the solid, while the OH groups are bound to the metal atoms. Hydrous titanium oxide is expressed by the general formula: TiO$_{(2 - x)}$(OH)$_{2x} \cdot$yH$_2$O, where x is probably 1. Titanium (IV) oxide is insoluble in mildly acidic and basic solutions.[8]

D. Thorium Oxide

Hydrous thorium oxide is obtained by mixing different proportions of thorium nitrate with bases. The product is a white, glassy, amorphous material. This product loses both its free and interstitial water by heating to 200°C. By further rise of temperature to 500°C, the material loses bound water.[9] The results of TGA, DTA, X-ray, and infrared analyses suggest that the samples dried at room temperature contain Th $-$ O and OH groups as well as H$_2$O molecules and that the general formula may be written as ThO(OH)$_n \cdot$nH$_2$O.[9] The exchanger loses water upon heating which results in a decrease of its surface area. At temperatures higher than 300°C the cubic form of ThO$_2$ is obtained.[11]

E. Zirconium Oxide

The gelatinous white precipitate called hydrous zirconia is formed by adding an excess of alkali to a solution of a Zr(IV) salt. The form of this precipitate is very difficult to predict, because its composition and properties are strongly influenced by the mode of synthesis and further treatment of the fresh precipitates. Amorphous forms can be obtained by neutralization of soluble Zr(IV) salts. However, under appropriate conditions some crystalline forms can be obtained.[1] All precipitated forms of hydrous zirconium oxide show ion exchange properties to some extent. The hydroxyl groups can be exchanged with anion at pH values below the isoelectric point, while for the higher pH values protons can be replaced by cations. It is evident that the ion exchange capacity, as with other hydrous oxides, depends on the number of hydroxyl groups on the surface of the hydrous zirconia.

Most precipitation procedures produce amorphous hydrous zirconia. The beginning of precipitation depends on the initial concentration and types of anions in the system involved where the process of precipitation takes place.[12-14] The theoretical end point of neutralization cannot be reached due to incorporation of significant amounts of anions. These anions cannot be completely removed by washing the precipitate with water. Better results are obtainable with dilute solutions of ammonia. The ammonia residue does not interfere significantly with the ion exchange properties of the precipitate.[15]

Boiling of freshly prepared zirconium oxide precipitates in basic solutions leads to the exchange of anions from the solid phase with hydroxyl groups of the aqueous phase.[16] During this procedure amorphous zirconium oxide is transformed into a crystalline form. At the beginning a cubic (or tetragonal) modification of zirconia is formed. Extended boiling of this form of the material leads to the formation of the monoclinic phase of zirconia.[1] These crystalline modifications retain the same ion exchange properties as a gel. The interplanar distances of the crystalline forms of the hydrous zirconia are similar to those of crystalline ZrO_2. Hydrous crystalline zirconium oxide contains approximately 11% of water and this is probably on the surface of the particles.

A study of the behavior of Zr(IV) ions in solutions as well as investigations of the influence of the mode of preparation on the properties of sorbent obtained, enable a proper determination of the mechanism of the formation of hydrous zirconia. It is found that a tetrameric complex ion of zirconium chloride exists in its concentrated solutions.[3,17,18] A model of the complex that exists in solutions is shown in Figure 1. Upon addition of base or upon boiling, such ions tend to polymerize.[19] When the precipitation is carried out slowly, more organized formation of polymers takes place as is shown in Figure 2. In the resultant polymer each zirconium atom is surrounded by eight hydroxyl groups in the form of a distorted cubic arrangement.[20] Oxolation between layers leads to a three-dimensional structure with the following general formula $[ZrO_b (OH)_{4-2b} \cdot xH_2O]_n$. Hydroxyl groups attached to the zirconia are of two types: bridging and nonbridging. The latter type lies on the surface of the crystallites.

The exchange capacity of hydrous zirconia is 1 to 2 meq/g of ZrO_2. This value corresponds to 1 to 2 hydroxyl groups on eight zirconium atoms.

IV. ION EXCHANGE PROPERTIES OF HYDROUS OXIDES

A. Theory

Hydrous oxides of the group IV elements have been used for removing ion impurities from solutions for many years. Hydrous silica has been the most used for this purpose although hydrous zirconia has generated greater interest in recent years. Generally speaking, the tetravalent metal oxides can behave both as cationic and anionic ion exchangers depending on the basicity of the central metal atom as well as on the strength of metal-oxygen and oxygen-hydrogen bonds of the hydroxyl group.

Different behaviors of hydrous oxides can be expected in connection with the physicochemical properties of the solution they contact. Except for silicon, which is a weakly basic metal, the anion exchange process can be performed in acid solutions, while in basic solutions the cationic exchange process takes place. There is not a clearly defined limit for both processes. It depends on the basicity of the metal ion. This shows that exchange sites may be heterogeneous. The ion exchange equilibrium of a hydrous

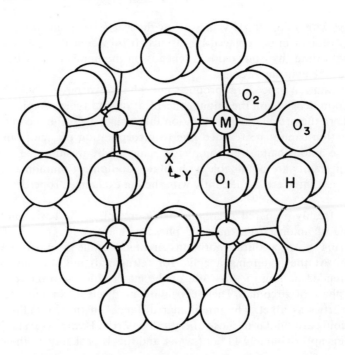

FIGURE 1.   Proposed structure for the zirconyl ion in concentrated zirconyl halide solutions. (From Muha, G. M. and Vaughan, P. A., *J. Chem. Phys.,* 33, 194, 1960. With permission.)

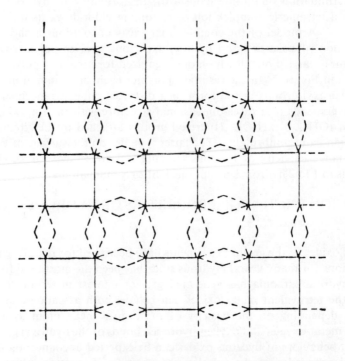

FIGURE 2.   Two-dimensional representation of an ordered sheet polymer produced by refluxing aqueous zirconyl ion solutions. Each dashed line represents an −OH group formed by hydrolysis. A bent dashed line connected to 2 square represents an −ol bridge. (From Clearfield, A., *Rev. Pure Appl. Chem.,* 14, 91, 1964. With permission.)

oxide in a strong basic solution can be expressed by the equation which describes the exchange of cations for one mole of H^+ in the oxide:

$$\frac{1}{(4-2b)} [MO_b (OH)_{4-2b} + \frac{4-2b}{z} A^{z+} \longrightarrow MO_b (OA_{1/z})_{4-2b} + (4-2b)H^+] \qquad (3)$$

Thermodynamic equilibrium constants of the ion exchange reaction are defined by the equation:

$$K = \frac{(\beta_2 g_2) \quad a_{H^+}}{(\beta_1 g_1) \quad a_{A^{z+}}^{\frac{1}{z}}} \qquad (4)$$

In the foregoing H^+, A^{z+} refers to the exchanging ions; Z is the charge of the counter ion A; β_1, β_2-equivalent fraction of the A^{z+} and H^+ forms of the exchangers, respectively; g_1, g_2-corresponding activity coefficient of these components in the exchanger; a_{H^+}, $a_{A^{z+}}$ the ionic activities of the ions solution.

The thermodynamic equilibrium constant, K, can be obtained by procedures given by Hogfeldt,[21] Gaines and Thomas,[22] or by Ruvarac and Vesely.[23] Values of $\Delta G°$ may be derived from the thermodynamic equilibrium constants using Equation 5. Enthalpies of exchange can be obtained from the ion exchange isotherms determined at different temperatures by application of Equation 6 and the corresponding entropies by application of Equation 7.

$$\Delta G° = -RT \ln K \qquad (5)$$

$$\frac{d \ln K}{d(1/T)} = -\frac{\Delta H°}{R} \qquad (6)$$

$$\Delta S° = \frac{\Delta H° - \Delta G°}{T} \qquad (7)$$

In a similar manner it is possible to calculate the thermodynamic equilibrium constant for anion exchange processes on hydrous oxides. In an earlier work[24] were studied the thermodynamics of the exchange between Cl^- and SO_4^{2-} ions with the nitrate form of hydrous zirconia, in the temperature range of 25 to 80°C.

For Cl^-/NO_3^- exchange on hydrous zirconia the following equation can be written:

$$\overline{RNO_3} + Cl^- (Aq) \rightleftharpoons \overline{RCl} + NO_3^- (Aq) \qquad (8)$$

A similar equilibrium holds for the SO_4^{2-}/NO_3^- ion exchange process. The thermodynamic equilibrium constant of Reaction 8,

$$K = \frac{(\beta_{Cl^-} \, g_{Cl^-}) \, (X_{NO_3^-} \cdot \gamma_{NO_3^-})}{(\beta_{NO_3^-} \, g_{NO_3^-}) \, (X_{Cl^-} \cdot \gamma_{Cl^-})} \qquad (9)$$

was calculated by the graphical method developed by Ruvarac and Vesely.[23] In Equation 9, X is the equivalent fraction of the anion in the solution and γ is the mean activity coefficient of the corresponding acid in solution. The graphical method is based on finding a point in the plot of $\log (X_{Cl^-} \cdot \gamma_{Cl^-} / X_{NO_3^-} \cdot \gamma_{NO_3^-})$ vs. $F(\beta_{Cl^-})$ where the activities of the components in the exchanger are equal. In fact, this point was approximated graphically by the inflection point obtained in the graph.

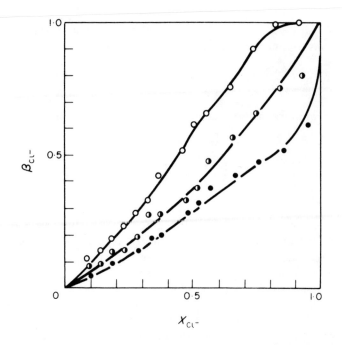

FIGURE 3.   Isotherms of the Cl⁻/NO₃⁻ exchange process on hydrous zirconia at 25°C-O, 50°C- ◓ , 80°C- ● . (From Ruvarac, A. and Trtanj, M., *J. Inorg. Nucl. Chem.*, 34, 3893, 1972. With permission.)

Table 3
THERMODYNAMIC EQUILIBRIUM CONSTANTS AND OTHER THERMODYNAMIC QUANTITIES FOR Cl⁻/NO₃⁻ ION EXCHANGE PROCESS ON HYDROUS ZIRCONIA[24]

Temp. t (°C)	K	$\Delta H°$ KJ/mol	$\Delta G°$ KJ/mol	$\Delta S°$ J/mol/K
25	0.985	−11.0	−0.04	−13.6
50	0.541	−11.0	1.60	−13.8
80	0.386	−11.0	3.04	−13.6

From Ruvarac, A. and Trtanj, M., *J. Inorg. Nucl. Chem.*, 34, 3893, 1972. With permission.

Isotherms for Cl⁻/NO₃⁻ exchange on hydrous zirconia are shown in Figure 3. while the thermodynamic equilibrium constants, calculated by the graphical method are given in Table 3, together with the $\Delta G°$, $\Delta H°$, and $\Delta S°$ values.

The equilibrium constant for the Cl⁻/NO₃⁻ ion exchange process decreases with increasing temperature. Accordingly, the exchange reaction is exothermic. Ion exchange processes can be studied by calorimetric measurements, too. In order to determine the heat of the Cl⁻/NO₃⁻ ion exchange reaction on hydrous zirconia calorimetric studies have been made.

Typical partial heats of the ion exchange process studies as a function of Cl⁻ ion mole fraction in hydrous oxide[25] are shown in Figure 4. The differential heat of exchange defined as

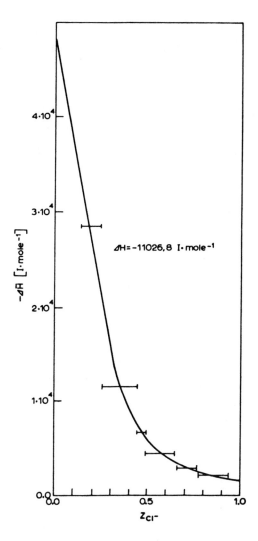

FIGURE 4. Partial molar heat of exchange as a function of the chloride ion mol fraction for the Cl^-/NO_3^- exchange process. (From Trtanj, M., Ruvarac, A., and Susia, M., *Thermochim. Acta*, 23, 303, 1978. With permission.)

$$\Delta H = \delta(\Delta H)/\delta \overline{X}m \tag{10}$$

can be obtained from such a plot (see Figure 4) by applying the Chord-area method.[26] Integral heats of ion exchange per mole of exchanging ion are defined by the relation

$$\Delta H = \int_0^1 \Delta \overline{H} \cdot d\overline{X}m \tag{11}$$

The data obtained by calorimetric measurement ($\Delta H° = -11.03$ kJ/mol^{-1})[25] and $\Delta H°$ from distribution measurements ($\Delta H° = -16.97$ kJ/mol) show a small difference. The source of the difference between these values of $\Delta H°$, would be the graphical nature of the determination of $\Delta H°$ from distribution measurements, where the function of ln K is plotted as a function of reciprocal temp. to give an average $\Delta H°$ over the temperature interval.

In past years, very often the distribution coefficient, K_d, has been used for a qualitative description of the distribution of an ion between an aqueous and solid phase. The distribution coefficient is defined as the ratio of activities of the ion in the solid and in the aqueous phase. In the case of the equilibrium given by Equation 8 the distribution coefficient is

$$Kd = \frac{\beta_{Cl^-} \cdot g_{Cl^-}}{x_{Cl^-} \cdot \gamma_{Cl^-}} \tag{12}$$

For the case of the distributions of ions on the tracer level the activity coefficients are close to one, so that

$$Kd \cong \frac{\beta_{Cl^-}}{x_{Cl^-}} \tag{13}$$

This is due to the asymptotic approach to the standard states for the system. (In this system the solid phase standard state is the pure ion exchanger and for the aqueous phase the standard state is at infinite dilution.) Some of the data which describe ion exchange properties of hydrous oxides will be presented in the following section.

B. Results with Individual Oxides

1. Hydrous Silica

The different types of hydrogels and xerogels are the materials that have received the most attention. Generally, it can be said that silica gel acts as a weakly acidic cation exchanger.[27-29] The surface of this material is covered with OH-silanol groups, with a density of 5 to 8 groups per 10.0 nm.[5,30] The specific surface and porosity of silica gel are the decisive factors influencing its sorption behavior.[31,32]

The changes occurring in silica gel during thermal treatment have been widely examined. The adsorption capacity of silica decreases with an increase of temperature interval 100 to 300°C; at still higher temperatures, in the range of 300 to 1000 °C, the adsorption capacity increases. This increase is explained by the conversion of the original compound to a compound with higher capacity.[33]

The adsorption mechanism on silica gel is mostly interpreted in terms of ion exchange[31,34,35,36]

$$M^{n^+} + m \ Si(OH) \rightleftharpoons M(OSi)_m^{(n-m)+} + mH^+ \tag{14}$$

There are some results which show that in addition to this mechanism other processes (such as physical adsorption and ion exclusion) play a role in determining the total adsorption.[36,37] Adsorbed cations are weakly bound to the surface sites of silica gel and are readily exchangeable.[5] Generally, the affinity increases, in going from univalent to tervalent elements.[29,38] For elements of the same charge, the adsorption is enhanced by a decrease in the ionic radius.[38-40] However, these results depend on the type of sorbent used and on the experimental conditions applied, and because of this large differences in results are observed.

A number of studies have also been reported in which silica gel is one of the main structural components.[41]

2. Stannic Oxide

Stannic oxide behaves both as a cation and an anion exchanger.[42,43] It has been used for separation of bivalent transition elements.[44] The selectivity series Cu > Zn > Co > Fe(II) > Ni > Mn follows the order of the equilibrium constants of the hydrolytic reaction

Table 4
THERMODYNAMIC QUANTITIES OBTAINED FOR SOME ANION EXCHANGE PROCESSES STUDIED AT 25°C ON HYDROUS ZIRCONIUM OXIDE

System	K	$\Delta G°$ KJ/mol	$\Delta H°$ KJ/mol	$\Delta S°$ J/mol/K	Ref.
Cl^-/NO_3^-	1.04	−0.6	4.1	16	52
Cl^-/NO_3^-	0.99	−0.04	−11.03	−37	25
SCN^-/NO_3^-	1.94	−8.6	−7.8	3	53
SCN^-/Cl^-	1.54	−1.2	−4.8	−13	53
SO_4^{2-}/NO_3^-	1.79	−0.3	−12.7	−68	25

$$M^{2+} + H_2O \rightleftharpoons M(OH)^+ + H^+ \tag{15}$$

It leads to the conclusion that the mechanism of cation retention should be described in terms of the hydrolysis process. Alkaline earth metal cations are weakly adsorbed,[45] whereas tervalent metal ions such as Al^{3+} and Cr^{3+} are strongly adsorbed. It appears that a co-precipitation process is taking place in such systems.[42] The selectivity series $PO_4^{3-} > Cr_2O_7^{2-} > Fe(CN)_6^{4-} - > Fe(CN)_6^{3-} > Cl^- > MnO_4^- > Br^- > I^-$ has been reported for the exchange of anions.[43]

3. Titanium Oxide

Titanium oxide is very useful for column operation and can be easily regenerated for reuse.[8]

In the titration process, a curve with three characteristic end points, indicating the polyfunctional character of the exchanger, was obtained.[46,47] It was shown that hydrous titanium oxide possess three exchangeable protons for every ten titanium atoms,[46,47] and dissociation constants for each dissociation step were determined.[46]

The exchange capacity of hydrous titanium oxide, like other hydrous oxides, depends upon the pH value, and goes from ∼2.0 meq/g (at pH ∼12.5 for Ca^{2+} and Sr^{2+}) to ∼1.5 meq/g at pH ∼4 (for Co^{2+}, Ni^{2+}, and Cu^{2+}).[9] The affinity series obtained for alkali metal ions $Na^+ > Rb^+ > Cs^+$, and one for transition metal ions, coincides with the stability order of the complexes, i.e., $Cu > Ni > Co$. A number of thermodynamic equilibrium constants were evaluated for different systems from the adsorption isotherms for the three exchange stages.[48]

4. Thorium Oxide

Thorium oxide exhibits both cation and anion exchange behavior.

The capacity for Ca^{2+} and Sr^{2+} ions have been found (at pH ∼12) to be ∼2.0 meq/g. This capacity depends on the pH value, and decreases with decreasing pH. Hydrous thorium oxide acting as an anion exchanger has a capacity ∼1 meq/g in acid solutions.[8] The distribution coefficients show a regular selectivity series for alkali metal cations ($Cs > Rb > Na$). The series of transition metal ions investigated coincides with the stability order of the respective hydroxo-complexes,[9] similar to the behavior of hydrous tin and titanium oxides.[42,9]

5. Zirconium Oxide

Zirconium oxide in common with the other group IV oxides behaves both as a cation and an anion exchanger.[49,50] The crossover coincides with the zero point of charge at pH 6.05.[51] Kraus and co-workers[52] have demonstrated the reversibility of bromide-nitrate exchange on hydrous zirconia when one ion is maintained at trace concentrations. In later studies[52,55] reversibility of exchange was shown with other anion exchange systems for which the composition of the exchanger varied over wide limits. Thermodynamic equilibrium constants of ion exchange reactions of some alkali metal cations[15] and some anions[24,25,52-54] have been determined. The thermodynamic equilibrium constants for alkali metal cations show the affinity series Li > Na > K.[15] It has also been found[15] that the exchanger in the different alkali metal cation forms contains the same amount of water and leads to the conclusion that the ingoing ions should be substantially dehydrated within the exchanger. Thermodynamic equilibrium constants and values of $\Delta G°$, $\Delta H°$, and $\Delta S°$ obtained at 25° C for the anion exchange processes studies are summarized in Table 4.

Amphlett and co-workers[56] proposed the following approximate affinity series in 0.1 *N* solution of different anions (at 25° C) for hydrous zirconium oxide: Cl^-, Br^-, I^-, $Cr_2O_4^{2-} \gg SO_4^{2-}$.

In addition to the anions mentioned above, it is well known[57] that hydrous zirconia is highly selective towards phosphate ions, even at high temperatures and pressure.[58] The adsorption of phosphates was found even on a sample of zirconium oxide heated for a long period.[59]

The amount of data available on the kinetics of ion exchange on the hydrous oxides is relatively small.[57,60-63] It is estimated that diffusion coefficients of simple ions through amorphous exchangers are between 10 and 20 times lower than in free aqueous solutions. They are therefore similar to those of organic resin exchangers.

The technique of Conway and co-workers[64] was used by Misak and Salama[63] in order to determine the effective diffusion coefficients, D_i, for the exchange of anions and cations on hydrated zirconium oxide. Experimental data obtained with cation exchange processes on hydrous zirconia were computed using the equation for diffusion through the particles of exchanger[65]

$$F = 1 - \frac{6}{\pi^2} \sum_{n=1}^{\infty} \frac{1}{n^2} e^{-n^2 Bt} \tag{16}$$

where $B = \pi^2 \cdot D_i/r^2$, n is an integer, D_i is the effective diffusion coefficient, and F is the fraction of exchange.

For the exchange of Ca^{2+}, Sr^{2+}, and Ba^{2+} on the hydrous oxide particles of 124 μm in diameter the same value of D_i was obtained ($D_i = 8.1 \times 10^{-12}$ cm²/sec) for each cation. Comparing the values obtained by Misak and Salama[63] with those obtained on the same sample of hydrous zirconia for alkali cations[66] allows the following series for the mobility of cations inside zirconia to be written: $Cs^+ > K^+ > Ca^{2+}$, Sr^{2+}, Ba^{2+}, $> Na^+$. This order of mobility is in good agreement with the proposed picture of diffusion of dehydrated cations sorbed by weak acid resins or hydrous zirconia.[15,66]

In a similar way the effective diffusion coefficients were obtained for the exchange of anions by hydrous zirconia.[63] Calculated values of D_i are presented in Table 5. From the data shown in Table 5 it is evident that the diffusion coefficients are almost independent in the range of 0.01 to 1 *M*, which proves particle diffusion control in these cases.

V. APPLICATIONS OF HYDROUS OXIDES AS ION EXCHANGERS

A wide variety of uses has been found for synthetic organic ion exchange resins and for zeolitic inorganic ion exchangers, and new uses are constantly being suggested. Considerable quantities of these materials are used industrially. Ion exchangers find application not only in water purification, the original major application, but also in

Table 5
THE EFFECTIVE DIFFUSION COEFFICIENTS FOR
THE EXCHANGE OF ANIONS ON HYDRATED
ZIRCONIA[63]

Ion	Concentration of Na$^+$ salt (M)	Particle diameter (μ)	D_i (cm^2/sec)
ClO$^-_4$	0.1	124	3.6×10^{-9}
	1.0	260	2.8×10^{-9}
NO$^-_3$	0.1	124	1.8×10^{-9}
	1.0	124	1.3×10^{-9}
	1.0	260	1.3×10^{-9}
Cl$^-$	0.01	70	1.6×10^{-9}
	0.1	124	2.1×10^{-9}
	1.0	260	1.5×10^{-9}
Br$^-$	0.1	124	2.8×10^{-9}
	1.0	260	2.2×10^{-9}
SO$^2_4{}^-$	0.1	124	5.6×10^{-10}
	0.5	260	6.4×10^{-10}

From Misak, N. Z. and Salama, H. N., *Inorg. Nucl. Chem. Lett.*, 11, 559, 1975. With permission.

analytical chemistry, in the separation and isolation of elements, in hydrometallurgy, in organic chemistry and biochemistry, in food technology, and of course in many specialized fields related to the utilization of atomic energy.

The bulk of recent ion exchange literature has dealt with synthetic organic resins. Their availability, stability, and reproducibility is probably largely responsible for the popularity of ion exchange as a separation method. The inorganic zeolites, with which all early ion exchange work was carried out, have with years become less popular for separations mainly because of their instability in strong acid and basic solutions.

The use of organic ion exchangers is limited by virtue of their limited stability under various conditions. The organic resins break down their polymer matrix at higher temperatures, with concommitant decrease in their capacity for exchange. They are very sensitive to exposure to high radiation doses, which causes significant changes in capacity and selectivity, presumably by hydrolysis of functional groups, chain scission, and changes in degree of crosslinking.[67] There is, therefore, a need for ion exchange materials possessing a high degree of stability towards temperature (especially temperatures higher than 150°C) ionizing radiation doses, and which are able to keep appreciable capacity for ion exchange over a wide range of acidity.

The very large class of insoluble hydrous oxides (but mainly those of group IV elements) possess ion exchange and other important properties which make them very useful for the following processes

1. The treatment of high temperature water for removal of corrosion products and ionic impurities. This application is analogous to boiler water treatment as practiced at present, but without the need to lower temperatures in the treatment cycle in order to prevent resin destruction
2. Purification and conditioning of moderator and cooling water in pressurized water nuclear reactors
3. Chemical separation and purification in intense radiation fields
4. Ion exchange catalysis of reactions taking place at temperatures at which organic resins are decomposed
5. Separation of ions from mixtures, metal recovery, and industrial waste treatment processes

Table 6
COLUMN DECONTAMINATION EFFICIENCIES[79]

Average decontamination factor	Zirconium oxide		Test temperature (°C)
	Alkaline pH	Acid pH	
20—300	^{60}Co	Mixed fission products	25
	^{60}Co	—	238
	^{89}Sr	—	25
5—20	—	^{59}Fe	25
	—	^{51}Cr	25
2	—	^{131}I	25
	^{137}Cs	^{137}Cs	25
	^{137}Cs	—	238

From Michael, N., Sterling, P. F., and Cohen, P., *Nucleonics*, 62, 1963. With permission.

In recent years, a number of review papers were written in which the ion exchange properties of hydrous oxides such as SiO_2, SnO_2, TiO_2, ThO_2, and ZrO_2 are described.[57,68-77] In this section some of the applications of hydrous oxides as ion exchangers for various purposes will be discussed with the intention to show the wide range of potential applications in practice.

A. The Treatment of High-Temperature Water

In recent years some attempts were made to use inorganic ion exchangers for the purification of coolant water in closed-cycle nuclear reactor systems. In these systems the temperature of the water is approximately 300°C and the pressure is about 100 atm. To prevent degradation of the organic ion exchange resins usually used to purify coolant water, the stream must be cooled below 100°C before being passed through the resin. Often the water pressure must also be reduced along with temperature. Because of thermal losses in dropping coolant temperature and pressure, only a very small part ($\sim 10^{-4}$ system volume per sec) of the total water flow is purified in a by-pass stream. This low purification rate leaves a lot of radioactive materials in the coolant system, which produced difficulties in the maintenance of equipment and increases the need for chemical decontamination. It was thought that with inorganic ion exchangers the pressurized stream could be purified without temperature lowering.

After considering data on numerous inorganic ion exchange materials, zirconium phosphate and zirconium oxide were selected for this purpose.[78-81] In the experiments done with columns at 25° to 285°C with approximately neutral pH influent solutions, relatively good efficiency for pickup of most fission and corrosion products at trace concentration levels was obtained. The data obtained in column operation tests[79] are shown in Table 6. During these experiments the physical stability of hydrous zirconium oxide was examined. After exposure of zirconium oxide of initially 20 to 30 mesh size for a month to 310°C water in a static autoclave, the mesh size distribution was 97.8% in 20 to 30, 2.2% in 30 to 40, and only 0.3% in 40 to 150 mesh size range.

B. Chemical Separations of Radioactive Ions

Ion exchange is a widely used unit process, and its operation combined with the ready application of remote handling methods render it peculiarly suitable for use in the atomic energy field. The production of a suitable radiation-stable ion exchanger would enable ion exchange processing to be extendd to much higher dose rates such as are involved in the processing of fresh, highly irradiated fuels or of aqueous homogeneous reactor fuel.

Zirconium oxide behaves as a cation exchanger in alkaline solutions towards highly electropositive elements such as the alkali metals and alkaline earth cations, but is capable of absorbing appreciable amounts of polyvalent hydrolyzable ions such as Fe^{3+}, Cr^{3+}, Cu^{2+}, and Ni^{2+} even in acid solutions. The separation of Cs^+ from corrosion products or Sr^{2+} from fission products was obtained[82] on hydrous zirconia, in the process of production of pure radioactive elements.

The hydrous oxides were used with good success in the purification and isolation of trans-uranium elements such as neptunium, plutonium,[83,84] americium, and berkelium[85] from highly radioactive fission products. They have also been used as ion exchange materials in radiochemical separations of target materials in activation analysis. Recently their use has been reported for separation of Te, Sn,[86] and Sb[87] in activation analysis processes. Hydrous zirconium oxide was used as a carrier for production generators of radioactive isotopes [188]Re[88] and [113]In.[89] [188]Re was eluted from the generator with distilled water. The purity of [188]Re was 99.99%, and no adverse changes were encountered in the generator after 6 months of operation.[87]

In recent work done in England, inorganic ion exchangers were used to remove sequentially U, Pu, and fission products from spent nuclear reactor fuels.[88] The spent nuclear reactor fuels were dissolved in nitric acid and the solution passed through columns containing titanium oxide. Uranium and plutonium were recovered by elution with appropriate solutions and the fission products remaining in the columns were processed for waste disposal. This process looks very promising because of the easy way in which disposal of fission products in fully loaded hydrated titanium oxide can be effected by a vitrification process.

Hydrous titanium oxides has been mentioned for use in extraction of uranium from seawater.[89] Since then, a number of new sorbents have been examined but none were superior to titanium dioxide.[90-92] Bettinali and Pantanelli[93] described a plant producing 1000 tons of U per year and estimated production costs at $65 to 120/lb of U_3O_8.

C. Analytical Applications of Hydrous Oxides

The suitability of ion exchangers for analytical purposes has been known for a long time. The separation and identification of uranium fission products and rare earths as a part of the Manhattan Project has introduced inorganic ion exchange into analytical chemistry and afterwards a large number of studies were carried out on application of hydrous oxides for analytical purposes. Selectivity and adsorption characteristics of synthetic inorganic ion exchangers were reviewed by Abe recently.[94] In this section some of the attractive applications in analytical practice will be presented.

Hydrous SnO_2 was used for the determination of impurities in highly pure Fe. This process was fully automated and a process run was obtained in 40 min.[95] Hydrous tin dioxide was also used in the analytical determination of transition elements in hydroorganic media.[96,97] Laskorin and co-workers[98] determined the sorption order in sulfate solutions for copper on various inorganic ion exchangers. According to their data the sorption of copper ion decreases with decreasing pH and in the order SnO_2 > titanium hydroxide > $Zr(OH)_4$ > SiO_2.

An inorganic sorbent having SiO_2 in the matrix was successfully used for the isolation and determination of the amount of heavy metals in petrol and other hydrocarbons.[99] Tustakowski[100] has demonstrated the use of hydrous ZrO_2 for quantitative separation of anions: I^-, Br^-, and Cl^-.

D. Industrial Applications

Although the new ion exchange resins with good characteristics are commercially available, they have not become industrially accepted in a broad field of applications. The ion exchangers are mostly applied in water treatment processes.

Hydrous zirconium oxide has recently become important in water desalination process by hyperfiltration. Dynamically formed membranes made from this material show promising self-rejections by virtue of Donnan electrolyte exclusion.[101]

Inorganic ion exchangers were incorporated into selectively permeable membranes which would have considerable advantages over those based on organic resins. Inorganic membranes would permit higher temperature to be used and higher efficiencies to be attained. Exchange membranes have been made from hydrous thorium oxide and hydrous zirconium oxide by Rajan and co-workers.[102] This type of membrane was found to be useful for demineralization of saline water.

Unfortunately, the introduction of inorganic ion exchangers based on hydrous oxides is making slow progress in industrial applications. Ionescu and co-workers[103] prepared ion exchange membranes based on inorganic ion exchangers with good performances. They demonstrated advantages in comparison to membranes made from organic resins. For example, they do not swell in aqueous medium and they are not subject to drastic chemical modification. Thus, these types of membranes were found suitable in processes concerned with the preparation of pure sodium hydroxide.

A few researchers made attempts to apply hydrous oxides as anticorrosive additives. Labody and Ronay[104] prepared a thin sheet of exchanger. After wetting in 4% $Na_2Cr_2O_7$ solution the sheet was placed around a steel tube and the tube inserted in the earth. The corrosion was lower than a control tube without the sheet. Another example is the determination of the relation between the ion exchange capacity and corrosion protection efficiency of anticorrosion paints containing hydrous oxides.[105]

REFERENCES

1. **Clearfield, A.,** Crystalline hydrous ZrO₂, *Inorg. Chem.,* 3, 146, 1964.
2. **Rijnten, H. T.,** Zirconia, in *Physical and Chemical Aspects of Adsorbants and Catalysts,* Linsen, B. G., Ed., Academic Press, New York, 1970, chap. 7.
3. **Clearfield, A.,** Structural aspects of zirconium chemistry, *Rev. Pure Appl. Chem.,* 14, 91, 1964.
4. **Slinyakova, I. B., Budkevich, G. B., and Neimark, I. E.,** Gels of organosilicon compounds. III. Adsorption and Other properties of a hydrogen-silica adsorbents with Si-H bonds (polysiloxane hydride xerogel), *Kolloidn. Zhur.,* 27, 758, 1965.
5. **Burwell, R. L., Pearson, R. G., Haller, G. L., Tjok, P. B., and Chock, S. P.,** The adsorption and reaction of coordination complexes on silica gel, *Inorg. Chem.,* 4, 1123, 1965.
6. **Rosiliyakova, N. G. and Aleskovskii, V. B.,** Determination of the concentration of silica gel, *Zhur. Prikl. Khim.,* 39, 795, 1966.
7. **Donaldson, J. D. and Fuller, M. J.,** Ion exchange properties of tin (IV) materials. I. Hydrous tin (IV) oxide and its cation exchange properties, *J. Inorg. Nucl. Chem.,* 30, 1083, 1968.
8. **Heitner-Wirguin, C. and Albu-Yaron, A.,** Hydrous oxides and their cation-exchange properties, *J. Appl. Chem. (London),* 15, 445, 1965.
9. **Heitner-Wirguin, C. and Albu-Yaron, A.,** Hydrous oxides and their cation-exchange properties, II. Structure and equilibrium experiments, *J. Inorg. Nucl. Chem.,* 28, 2379, 1966.
10. **Vivien, D., Livage, J., and Mazieres, Ch.,** Nature of the precipitates of hydrated oxides of group IVA metals. I. Thermal analysis and infrared spectroscopy, *J. Chem. Phys. Physicochim. Biol.,* 67, 199, 1970.
11. **Michail, R. Sh. and Fahim, R. B.,** Thermal treatment of thorium oxide gel at low temperatures, *J. Appl. Chem. (London),* 17, 147, 1967.
12. **Larsen, E. M. and Gammill, A. M.,** Electrometric titration of zirconium and hafnium solutions, *J. Am. Chem. Soc.,* 72, 3715, 1950.
13. **Tananaev, I. V. and Bokmel'der, M. Ya.,** Formation of nickelous hydroxide in aqueous solutions, *Zhur. Neog. Khim.,* 2, 2700, 1957.

14. **Singh, R. P. and Banerjee, N. R.,** Electrometric studies on the precipitation of hydrous oxides of some quadrivalent cations. I.Precipitation of zirconium hydroxide from solutions of zirconium salts, *J. Indian Chem. Soc.,* 38, 865, 1967.

15. **Britz, D. and Nancollas, G. H.,** Thermodynamics of cation exchange of hydrous zirconia, *J. Inorg. Nucl. Chem.,* 31, 3861, 1969.

16. **Thomas, A. W. and Owens, H. S.,** Basic zirconium chloride hydrosols, *J. Am. Chem. Soc.,* 57, 1825, 1935.

17. **Clearfield, A. and Vaughan, P. A.,** Crystal structure of zirconium chloride octahydrate and zirconyl bromide octahydrate, *Acta Crystal.,* 9, 555, 1956.

18. **Muha, G. M. and Vaughan, P. A.,** Structure of the complex ion in aqueous solutions of zirconyl and hafnyl oxyhalides, *J. Chem. Phys.,* 33, 194, 1960.

19. **Johnson, J. S., and Kraus, K. A.,** Hydrolytic behavior of metal ions. VI. Ultracentrifugation of zirconium (IV) and hafnium (IV). Effect of acidity on the degree of polymerization, *J. Am. Chem. Soc.,* 78, 3937, 1956.

20. **Fryer, J. R., Hutchinson, J. L., and Paterson, R.,** Electron microscope observations of the initial stages in the hydrolytic polymerization of zirconyl chloride, *J. Colloid Interface Sci.,* 34, 238, 1970.

21. **Hogfeldt, E.,** Ion-exchange equilibria. II. Activities of the components in ion exchangers, *Arkiv. Kemi,* 5, 147, 1952.

22. **Gaines, G. L. and Thomas, H. C.,** Adsorption studies on clay minerals. II. A formulation of the thermodynamics of exchnge adsorption, *J. Chem. Phys.,* 21, 714, 1953.

23. **Ruvarac, A. and Vesely, V.,** Simple graphical determination of thermodynamic equilibrium constants of ion-exchange reactions, *J. Phys. Chem. (N.F.),* 73, 1, 1970.

24. **Ruvarac, A. and Trtanj, M.,** Thermodynamics of anion exchange on hydrous zirconia 1. Cl^-/NO^-_3 and SO_4^{2-}/NO^+_3 ion-exchange processes, *J. Inorg. Nucl. Chem.,* 34, 3893, 1972.

25. **Trtanj, M., Ruvarac, A., and Susic, M.,** Thermodynamics of anion exchange on hydrous zirconia. 4. Calorimetric determination of the heat of anion exchange on hydrous zirconia, *Thermochim. Acta,* 23, 303, 1978.

26. **Yang, T. F. and Vogel, D. G.,** The calculation of partial molal quantities, *J. Am. Chem. Soc.,* 54, 3030, 1932.

27. **Unger, K. and Vydra, F.,** Sorption of $Zn(NH_3)_4^{++}$ and $Zn(en)_3^{++}$ on silica gels of various specific surfaces. The determination of specific surface area of silica gel by sorption of $Zn(en)_3^{++}$, *J. Inorg. Nucl. Chem.,* 30, 1075, 1968.

28. **Parks, G. A.,** The isoelectric points of solid oxides, solid hydroxides and aqueous hydroxo complex systems, *Chem. Rev.,* 65, 185, 1965.

29. **Dolezal, J., Horacek, J., Sramek, J., and Sulcek, Z.,** Use of SiO_2 gel in inorganic analysis. Separation and determination of small amounts of Zr, *Microchim. Acta,* 38, 1966.

30. **Agzamkhodzhaev, A. A., Zhuravlev, L. T., Kiselev, A. V., and Shengeliya, K. Ya.,** Concentration of hydroxyl groups on the surface and within silicas, *Izv. Acad. Nauk SSSR, Ser. Khim.,* 10, 2111, 1969.

31. **Kohlschütter, H. W., Risch, A., and Vogel, K.,** Fundamentals of chromatographic separations by SiO_2 gels, *Ber. Bunsenges. Physic. Chem.,* 69, 849, 1965.

32. **Alekseeva, I. P. and Dushina, A. P.,** Reaction of copper ions with uniformly porous silica gels with different surface areas and porosities, *Kolloid. Zhur.,* 31, 483, 1969.

33. **Kirichenko, L. F. and Vysotskii, Z. Z.,** Sorption of alkali metal cations on SiO_2 gels as a function of the acidity of the solutions, *Dokl. Acad. Nauk SSSR,* 175, 635, 1967.

34. **Vydra, F.,** Application of the ion-exchange properties of SiO_2 gel to the separation of metals, *Chim. Anal.,* 38, 201, 1967.

35. **Kohlschutter, H. W. and Schaefer, L.,** Thin-layer chromatography of inorganic salts on silica gel, *Z. Anal. Chem.,* 245, 129, 1969.

36. **Tien, H. Ti,** Interaction of alkali metal cations with SiO_2 gel, *J. Phys. Chem.,* 69, 350, 1965.

37. **Allen, L. H., Matijevic, E., and Meites, L.,** Exchange of Na^+. for Silanolic protons of silica, *J. Inorg. Nucl. Chem.,* 33, 1293, 1977.

38. **Rubanik, S. K., Baran, A. A., Strazhesko, D. N., and Strelko, V. V.,** Selective adsorption of groups I, II and III cations on various ion-exchange forms of silica gel., *Teor. Eksp. Khim.,* 5, 361, 1969.

39. **Kirichenko, L. F., Strazhesko, D. N., and Yankovskaya, G. F.,** Cation exchange on SiO_2 gels produced in the presence of Al ion, *Ukr. Khim. Zhur.,* 31, 160, 1965.

40. **Dalton, R. W., McClanahan, J. L., and Maatman, R. W.,** Partial exclusion of electrolytes from the pores of SiO_2 gel, *J. Colloid. Sci.,* 17, 207, 1962.

41. **Siclet, G., Lenoir, J., and Eyraud, Ch.,** Ionic exchange reactions between a SiO_2-Al_2O_3 precipitate and an aqueous solution, *Bull. Soc. Chim. France,* 2995, 1966.

42. **Donaldson, J. D. and Fuller, M. J.,** Ion exchange properties of tin (IV) materials. I. Hydrous tin (4.) oxide and its cation exchange properties, *J. Inorg. Nucl. Chem.,* 30, 1083, 1968.

43. Donaldson, J. D. and Fuller, M. J., Ion exchange properties of tin (IV) materials. III Anion exchange and further cation exchange studies on hydrous tin (IV) oxide, *J. Inorg. Nucl. Chem.*, 32, 1703, 1970.
44. Renault, N., Fixation of elements of the first transition series on tin dioxide in hydroorganic media, *Anal. Chim. Acta*, 70, 469, 1974.
45. Donaldson, J. D., Fuller, M. J., and Price, J. W., Ion exchange properties of tin (IV) materials. II. Cation exchange column chromatography on hydrous tin (IV) oxide, *J. Inorg. Nucl. Chem.*, 30, 2841, 1968.
46. Schiewer, E. and Levi, H. W., Exchange of metal and hydrogen ions on hydrous titanium dioxide, in *Radiochem. Cont., Abstr. Pap., Bratislava*, 20, 1966.
47. Levi, H. W. and Schiewer, E., Adsorption exchange of cations on TiO_2, *Radiochim. Acta*, 5, 126, 1966.
48. Levi, H. W. and Schiewer, E., Exchange adsorption on hydrated titanium dioxide. III. Thalium-hydrogen exchange, *Radiochim. Acta*, 14, 43, 1970.
49. Pant, K. M., Amphoterism of hydrous zirconium oxide, *J. Indian Chem. Soc.*, 46, 547, 1966.
50. Belloni-Cofler, J. and Pavlov, D., Positive and negative adsorption of ions, in dilute aqueous solutions, by various metal oxides and hydroxides, *J. Chem. Phys.*, 62, 458, 1965.
51. Smith, G. W. and Salman, T., Zero-point-of-charge of hemolite and zirconia, *Can. Met. Q.*, 5, 93, 1966.
52. Kraus, K. A., Phillips, H. O., Carlson, T. A., and Johnson, J. S., Ion exchange properties of hydrous oxides in *Proc. U.N. Intern. Conf. Peaceful Uses At. Energy*, 2nd, United Nations, Geneva, 1958, 28, 3.
53. Nancollas, G. H. and Paterson, R., Thermodynamics of ion exchange on hydrous zirconia, *J. Inorg. Nucl. Chem.*, 29, 565, 1967.
54. Nancollas, G. H. and Reid, D. S., Calorimetric studies of ion exchange on hydrous zirconia, *J. Inorg. Nucl. Chem.*, 31, 213, 1969.
55. Ruvarac, A. and Turubatovic, L., Thermodynamics of anion exchange on hydrous zirconia. II. Borate ($H_2BO_3^-$)/Nitrate (NO_3^-) ion exchange processes, *J. Inorg. Nucl. Chem.*, 37, 1045, 1975.
56. Amphlett, C. B., McDonald, L. A., and Redman, M. J., Synthetic inorganic ion-exchange materials. II. Hydrous zirconium oxide and other oxides, *J. Inorg. Nucl. Chem.*, 6, 236, 1958.
57. Amphlett, C. B., *Inorganic Ion Exchangers*, Elsevier, Amsterdam, 1964.
58. Ruvarac, A., Purification of cooling water from nuclear reactor RA, *"Boris Kidric" Inst. Nucl. Sci. Report*, IBK-560, Institute Boris Kidric, Beograd, 1967.
59. Vissers, D. R., Sorption of orthophosphate on crystalline metal oxides, *J. Phys. Chem.*, 72, 3236, 1968.
60. Nancollas, G. H. and Paterson, R., Kinetics of ion exchange on zirconium phosphate and hydrated thoria, *J. Inorg. Nucl. Chem.*, 22, 259, 1967.
61. Harvie, S. J. and Nancollas, G. H., Ion-exchange properties of crystalline zirconium phosphate, *J. Inorg. Nucl. Chem.*, 32, 3923, 1970.
62. Gardner, C. R., Paterson, R., and Short, D., Self-diffusion coefficients of chloride ion in membranes and particles of hydrous zirconia as a function of variable chloride ion capacity, *J. Inorg. Nucl. Chem.*, 34, 2057, 1972.
63. Misak, N. Z. and Salama, H. N., Kinetics of exchange by hydrated zirconia, *Inorg. Nucl. Chem. Lett.*, 11, 559, 1975.
64. Conway, D. E., Green, J. H. S., and Reichenberg, D., The kinetics of sodium-hydrogen exchange on a monofunctional cation exchange resin containing carboxyl groups, *Trans. Faraday Soc.*, 5, 511, 1945.
65. Boyd, G. E., Adamson, A. W., and Myers, L. S., The exchange adsorption of ions from aqueous solutions by organic zeolites. II. Kinetics, *J. Am. Chem. Soc.*, 69, 2836, 1947.
66. Halaba, E., Misak, N. Z., and Salama, H. M., Exchange characteristics of hydrated zirconia, *Indian J. Chem.*, 11, 580, 1973.
67. Cathers, C. I., Blanco, R. E., Ferguson, D. E., Higgins, I. R., Kibbey, A. H., Mansfield, R. G., and Wischow, R. P., Radiation damage to radiochemical processing reagents, in *Proc. Intern. Conf. Peaceful Uses of Atomic Energy*, United Nations, Geneva, 1955, 7, 490.
68. Materova, E. A., Belinskaya, F. A., Militsina, E. A., and Skabichevskii, P. A., *Ionnyi Obmen, Lenin. Gos. Univ., U.S.S.R.*, 1965.
69. Tachimori, S. and Amano, H., Inorganic Ion Exchangers. Rep. JAERI-13726, Japan Atomic Energy Commission, Tokyo, 1969.
70. Pai, K. R., Krishnaswamy, N., and Datar, D. S., Properties of hydrous oxide inorganic exchangers in Papers Conf. Ion Exch. Process Ind., Society of Chemical Industry Soc. Chem. Ind. London, 1970, 322.
71. Price, J. W., Inorganic tin compounds paper presented at *Conf. Tin Consumption*, 199, London, 1972.

72. Roslyakova, N. G., Dushina, A. P., and Aleskovskii, V. B., Determination of the composition of cations sorbed by silica gel in *Ionnyi Obmen Ionity, "Nauka" Leningrad. Otd. Leningrad, U.S.S.R.,* 137, 1970.
73. Pekarek, V. and Vesely, V., Synthetic Inorganic Ion-Exchangers. I. Hydrous oxides and acidic salts of multivalent elements, *Talanta,* 19, 56, 1972.
74. Materova, E. A., Ion exchangers based on the elements from groups IV-VI *Neorg. Ionoobmen. Mater.,* 1, 56, 1974.
75. Nikolskii, B. P., Ed., Neorganicheskie Ionoobmenye Materialy, Vyp. I. *Izd. Leninr. Univ. Leningrad, U.S.S.R.,* 1974.
76. Qureshi, M., Structural Aspects and some novel features of synthetic inorganic ion exchangers in Proc. Chem. Symp., 2, Indian Dept. of Atomic Energy, Bombay, 1972, 1.
77. Belinskaya, F. A., Structure of inorganic ion exchangers, *Vest. Leningrad Univ. Fiz. Khim.,* 1, 94, 1974.
78. Michael, N. and Fletcher, W. D., Some performance characteristics of zirconium phosphate and zirconium oxide ion-exchange materials, *Trans. Am. Nucl. Soc.,* 3, 46, 1960.
79. Michael, N., Sterling, P. F., and Cohen, P., Inorganic ion-exchange resins could purify hotter reactor water, *Nucleonics,* 62, 1963.
80. Ruvarac, A. and Tolic, A., Purification of nuclear reactor cooling water at higher temperature and pressures, *"Boris Kidric" Just. Nucl. Sci. Report* IBK-452, Institute Boris Kidric, Beograd, 1966.
81. Ahrland, S. and Carleson, G., Inorganic ion exchangers. VIII. Purification of water on elevated temperatures by a combination of zirconium phosphate and zirconium oxide gels, *J. Inorg. Nucl. Chem.,* 33, 2229, 2977.
82. Amphlett, C. B., Synthetic inorganic ion exchangers and their applications in atomic energy in *Proc. U.N. Intern. Conf. Peaceful Uses At. Energy,* 2nd, United Nations, Geneva, 1958, 28, 17.
83. Korshunov, I. A., Chernorukov, N. G., and Prokof'eva, T. V., Sorption of neptunium and plutonium on several difficulty soluble compounds, *Radiokhimya,* 18, 5, 1976.
84. Kennedy, J., Peckett, J. W., and Perkins, R., The Removal of Plutonium and Certain Fission Products from Alkaline Media by Hydrated Titanium Oxide, U.K. At. Energy Authority Res. Group At. Energy Res. Estab. Rep. AERE-R-4516, United Kingdom Atomic Energy Research Establishment, Harwell, Didcot, Berkshire, 1964.
85. Myasoedov, B. F., Use of higher valence states during isolation and determination of Am and Bk, *Usp. Anal. Khim.,* 148, 1974.
86. Brandona, A., Meloni, S., Girardi, F., and Sabbioni, E., Radiochemical separation by adsorption on tin dioxide, *Analysis,* 2, 300, 1973.
87. Eschrich, H., Herrera-Huertas, M., and Tallberg, K., Sorption of antimony by silica gel from nitric acid and hydrochloric acid solutions, *U.S. A. E. C.,* Rep. NP-18738, 1970.
88. Anon., Reprocessing nuclear fuel, *Res. Discl.,* 179, 104, 1979.
89. Keen, N. J., Extraction of uranium from sea water, *J. Br. Nucl. Energy Soc.,* 7, 178, 1968.
90. Kanno, M., Extraction of Uranium from Sea Water, Rep. IAEA-CN-36/161, International Atomic Energy Agency, Vienna, 1977.
91. Takesute, E. and Miyamatsu, T., Uranium collector, *Japan Kokai,* 77, 114, 511, 1977.
92. Yamashita, H., Ozawa, Y., Nakajima, F., and Murata, T., *Nippon Kagaku Kaishi,* 8, 1057, 1978.
93. Bettinali, C. and Pantanetti, F., Uranium from sea water: possibilities of recovery exploiting slow coastal currents, in *Proc. Advis. Group Meet, 1975,* International Atomic Energy Agency, Vienna, 1976.
94. Abe, M., Analytical application of synthetic inorganic ion exchangers. I. Hydrous oxides and hydroxides, *Bunseki Kagaku,* 23, 1254, 1974.
95. Cleyrergue, Ch. and Deschamps, N., Automation of a systematic analysis scheme for high purity iron, *J. Radioanal. Chem.,* 17, 139, 1973.
96. Renault, N., Fixation of elements of the first transition series on tin dioxide in hydroorganic media, *Anal. Chem. Acta,* 70, 469, 1974.
97. Renault, N., and Deschamps, N., Retention of some transition elements on tin dioxide in water-acetone, nitric acid-acetone and hydrochloric acid-acetone media, *Radiochem. Radioanal. Lett.,* 13, 207, 1973.
98. Laskorin, B. N., Goldobina, V. A., and Kopanev, A. M., Sorption of copper by inorganic ion exchange resins containing titanium, tin and zirconium compounds, *Tsvet. Metal.,* 2, 21, 1973.
99. Whitehurst, D. D., Butter, S. A., and Rodewald, P. G., Sorbent for Removal of Heavy Metals, U.S. Patent 3, 793, 185, 1974.
100. Tustakowski, S., Separation of halide anions on hydroux zirconium oxide, *J. Chromatogr.,* 31, 268, 1967.
101. Kraus, K. A., Shoz, A. J., and Johnson, J. S., Hyperfiltration studies. X. Hyperfiltration with dynamically formed membranes, *Desalination,* 2, 243, 1967.

102. **Rajan, K. S., Boies, D. B., Casolo, A. J., and Bregman, J. I.,** Inorganic Ion-exchange membranes and their application to electrodialysis, *Desalination,* 7, 237, 1966.

103. **Ionescu, T. D., Tudozache, Gh., and Ionita, Ch.,** Obtaining pure sodium hydroxide by diaphragm electrolysis based on inorganic ion exchangers, *Bull. Inst. Politeh. "Georghe Georghiu-Dej" Bucruresti, Rom.,* 34, 41, 1972.

104. **Labody, I. and Ronay, D.,** Ion-exchange anticorrosive pacing for underground metal objects, *Hung, Teljes,* 3327, 1972.

105. **Ularson, U. and Khullar, M.,** Relation between the ion exchange capacity and the corrosion protection efficiency of alkyd based anti-corrosive paints., in *Proc. 6th Scand. Corros. Congr.,* 18, 1, 1979.

Chapter 6

OXIDES AND HYDROUS OXIDES OF MULTIVALENT METALS AS INORGANIC ION EXCHANGERS

Mitsuo Abe

TABLE OF CONTENTS

I. INTRODUCTION

The adsorption properties of hydrous oxides, such as alumina and silica gels, have been studied extensively for many years. Until recently, the major interest in these materials has been related to analytical purposes derived from their abilities to act as substances for adsorption or partition chromatography. Thus their ion exchange properties were somewhat neglected in comparison.

More recently, the ion exchange properties of various oxides and hydrous oxides have been extensively studied since the pioneering work in this field was done by the research group at Oak Ridge National Laboratory led by Dr. Kurt A. Kraus.[1-3] In general, many inorganic ion exchangers have been shown to exhibit good thermal and radiation stability. In addition, some hydrous oxides exhibit excellent selectivities with respect to certain elements or group of elements. Most of these materials can be prepared more easily and more cheaply than organic resins.

Inorganic ion exchangers generally have rigid structures which undergo little swelling or shrinking upon immersion in aqueous solution. This brings about ion-sieve effects or steric effects for various elements. Furthermore, the resistance of many oxides and hydrous oxides towards strong oxidizing reagents and organic solvents offers an advantage over organic resins. The major disadvantage of these oxides is their lower resistance towards strong acid and base solutions at relatively high concentrations as compared with organic resins, although improved resistance can be obtained through aging or heating.

Several reviews on the inorganic ion exchange properties of oxides and hydrous oxides have been published.[4-9] A large number of papers have been reported recently on this subject with particular attention to a deeper knowledge of the adsorption mechanism as well as their application in various fields of interest.

Much has been written on the ion exchange properties of the hydrous oxides, particularly during the last two decades, but as with so much published information that relates to their chemical character, it is often difficult to make valid comparisons between data from different laboratories. The characteristics of these materials depends on the preparative conditions, e.g., starting substances, temperature of preparation, concentration, aging, drying temperature, etc. Furthermore, the crystallinity and surface area are also very important factors in determining ion exchange characteristics. In addition, an accompanying anion or cation may be retained on the surface during processing, and only in a limited number of cases has sufficient attention been paid to removal of this impurity. However, there are cases in which trace or micro amounts of an impurity have an important effect upon the characteristics of the hydrous oxide exchanger, e.g., phosphate ion in hydrous zirconium oxide.[1]

In this chapter, oxides and hydrous oxides as ion exchangers will be first considered as a group in order to develop a coherent comparative discussion of their properties.

II. GENERAL ASPECTS OF OXIDES AND HYDROUS OXIDES AS ION EXCHANGE MATERIALS

In principle, the hydrous oxides and hydroxides of polyvalent metals in the system of metal oxide-H_2O, behave as cation or anion exchangers, depending upon the basicity of the central metal atom and the strength of the metal-oxygen bond relative to that of the oxygen-hydrogen bond in the hydroxyl group. The strength of an acid increases with the number of oxygen atoms per replaceable hydrogen and with the electronegativity of the central atom. An increased number of oxygen atoms combined with the central metal brings about an increase in the strength of the acid.

If hydrous oxides and hydroxides are employed as ion exchange materials, these

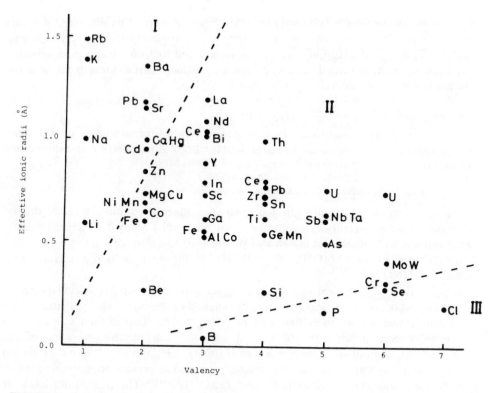

FIGURE 1. Relation between valency and effective ionic radii of elements. Effective ionic radii taken from Reference 81.

materials should be stable in the solution for an extended region above or below pH 7. To illustrate this principle, the effective ionic radii of the central metal in the oxides are plotted against the valency of the metal in Figure 1. The metals with low valency and large radius give soluble hydroxides (group I), while metals with high valency and small radius give soluble oxyacids (group III). Metals in the intermediate range give insoluble hydrous oxides or hydroxides. The oxides listed in region of group II are best suited to use as ion exchange materials.

A. Nomenclature of Hydrous Oxides

The term "hydrous oxide" has been used in its widest sense to refer to insoluble materials with a metal oxide-water system. Different nomenclatures can be found in the literature reported by various authors, i.e., hydroxide, hydrate, oxyhydrate, hydrous, -nic, acid, etc. In many cases the metal oxides combine nonstoichiometrically with water, and in other cases, such as FeOOH and AlOOH the terms oxyhydrate or oxide hydrate are more applicable. However, β-FeOOH contains an appreciable amount of chloride ions in the structure, depending on the method of preparation. In other cases (hydrous oxides of quadrivalent metals) there is no evidence for the existence of a definite hydrate. M-OH groups combine strongly with water molecules, although the isolated M-OH group on dried materials can be detected by infrared (IR) spectroscopy.

As far as possible, the nomenclature in regard to hydrous oxides as ion exchanger will be that of the original authors, because the characteristics of the material depend on their preparation method. The term "oxide" refers to the anhydrous material obtained by, for example, heating the hydrous oxide. However, in some cases, the metal oxides adsorb some water molecules on their surface or recombine with water, and thus exhibit ion exchange behavior. In other cases, the metal oxides contain a very small amount of water which cannot be eliminated completely even at very high temperature. Thus, the distinction between the oxides and hydrous oxides is an arbitrary one, because even in heated oxides, hydration on their surfaces occurs in aqueous solution in which the ion exchange reactions are studied.

B. Preparation and Properties of Hydrous Oxides

Most insoluble hydrous oxides can exist in a number of forms with different chemical and physical properties, depending on their methods of preparation and subsequent treatment.

1. Amorphous Materials

In general, when freshly precipitated from cold aqueous solution, most of the hydrous oxides are apparently amorphous or show very weak X-ray diffraction patterns. The precipitates are usually obtained by hydrolysis of solutions containing metal salts, (e.g., $SbCl_5$ + H_2O or $KSb(OH)_6$ (aq) + HNO_3) or the wet oxidation of metals, (e.g., Sn metal + HNO_3).

Almost all cations of valency 3+ or higher give rise to polynuclear species in aqueous solution over an appropriate pH range. For example, there is little or no convincing evidence for the existence of Zr^{4+} (aq) or ZrO^{2+}(aq) in their salt solutions at moderate concentration.[11] The crystal of zirconium oxychloride octahydrate, $ZrOCl_2 \cdot 8H_2O$, contains the complex ion of $[Zr(OH)_2 \cdot 4H_2O]_4^{8+}$.[10,11] When a zirconium salt is dissolved in water, the cationic species proposed as present are polynuclear cations such as $Zr_2(OH)_2^{6+}$,[12] $Zr_3(OH)_4^{8+}$ and $Zr_4(OH)_8^{8+}$.[12-16] The trimer and tetramer forms are thought to be linear and cyclic respectively. Polymerization occurs between tetramer units in the aqueous species by olation, when alkali is added to these solutions. The rapid precipitation by alkali would be expected to lead to a random arrangement of the tetramer and to form an amorphous or gelatinous modification.[11] In addition, some of the anion associated with the tetramer group is trapped within the polymer.

The polynuclear species of Ti(IV) is uncertain. Infrared spectra have been used to provide evidence for the presence of a Ti–O–Ti unit in weak acid,[17] but dialysis and ion exchange studies were held to prove that Ti(IV) in dilute hydrochloric acid existed as a monomeric cation or as colloidal TiO_2(aq).[18] Such confusion may stem from the very long time (a matter of days or weeks) required to establish equilibrium. It is even more difficult to be definite about the composition and stability of highly polymeric species, because equilibrium is attained so slowly, e.g., 15 years being required for Fe(III) polynuclear species in neutral and alkaline solution.[19] The discussion of various polynuclear cations has been recently reviewed by Burgess.[20]

During preparation of the hydrous oxides as ion exchangers, these complications of polynuclear species may give rise to a lack of reproducibility. Therefore it is very important that care be taken to record the preparative conditions, such as initial concentration, aging time and temperature, history of the solution, initial and final pH, etc. The precipitates of amphoteric oxides, such as $TiO_2 \cdot nH_2O$, $ThO_2 \cdot nH_2O$, etc., usually contain appreciable amounts of co-ion (e.g., K^+ or/and Cl^-) which is difficult to remove completely by washing with water. These oxides exhibit a gradual transition from anion to cation exchange character with increasing pH. There is an equivalent uptake of cation and anion (equiadsorption point −EAP) at a definite pH value, corresponding to the zero point of charge (ZPC) of an individual oxide. This is like the adsorption of nonspecific electrolytes on amphoteric oxides and hydrous oxides. For example, when hydrous thorium oxide is prepared by hydrolyzing a thorium chloride solution with aqueous ammonia, the precipitate obtained contains appreciable amounts of chlo-

Table 1

SURFACE AREAS OF VARIOUS METAL HYDROXIDE GELS

Aluminum hydroxide gel[23]		Ferric oxide gel[24]		Silica gel[29]		Ceric oxide gel[28]	
Hydrolysis of Al(C₄H₉O)₃		FeCl₃ + NH₃(aq)		Hydrolysis of Si(OC₂H₅)₄		Ce(NO₃)₃ + NH₃(aq) + H₂O₂	
$S(m^2g^{-1})$	Aged at R.T. (hr)	$S(m^2g^{-1})$	Heating temp. (°C)	$S(m^2g^{-1})$	Treatment	$S(m^2g^{-1})$	Heating temp. (°C)
391[a]	0	390[b]	50	557	Without	92.9[c]	35
415[d]	2	294	100	388.0	Hydrothermal in open system	88.8	100
251[e]	24	217[f]	150	320.4		70.2	300
37[g]	2352	186	300	203.4		63.1	500
438 (98% EtOH)	20	105[h]	400	139	In an autoclave	52.4	600
		66	500	61.8		38.6	700
		11	800	34.6		7.9	1000
				237—727	Commercial		

[a] Amorphous.
[b] 0.495 g H₂O/g of Fe₂O₃.
[c] 14.4% H₂O (weak ceria patterns).
[d] Pseudoboehmite.
[e] Al₂O₃ · 2.3H₂O (bayerite patterns).
[f] 0.083 g H₂O/g of Fe₂O₃.
[g] Al₂O₃ · 2.99 H₂O (bayerite patterns).
[h] 0.0101 g H₂O/g of Fe₂O₃.

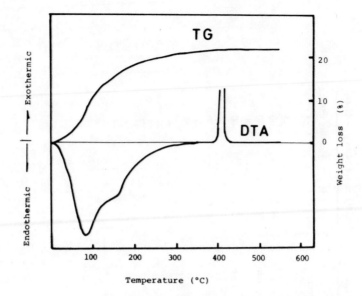

FIGURE 2.   Thermal analysis of hydrous zirconium dioxide dried at room temperature. Heating rate; 10°C/min.

ride ions which cannot be removed completely by washing with water, because the thorium hydrous oxide has an EAP of 8.0, which is higher than the pH value of the water (~pH 6). Successful removal of the adsorbed electrolytes on the hydrous thoria can be achieved by washing with water after removing chloride ions with dilute aqueous ammonia.[21, 22]

A different treatment, washing with water after removing adsorbed cation with dilute hydrochloric acid solution, is needed for the preparation of hydrous titanium oxide free from electrolytes, because the oxide has an EAP of 4.5, which is lower than the pH value of the water. If certain polyvalent anions are adsorbed by a positively charged oxide matrix, the resulting material will exhibit cation exchange behavior, e.g., hydrous zirconium dioxide to phosphate, hydrous cerium dioxide to sulfate, etc. Some confusion related to ion exchange properties of the hydrous oxides may arise because of the presence of these undesirable cation or anion impurities.

Surface areas have been determined on the basis of nitrogen and argon adsorption (BET method) on a number of dried hydrous oxides, e.g., of Al,[23] Fe(III),[24] Si(IV),[25] Sn,[26] Th,[27] and Ce(IV)[28] (see Table 1). The surface areas are generally decreased by increasing the temperature of heating and period of aging. A limited number of attempts have been made to correlate ion exchange properties with their surface areas. The amount of sodium ions and zinc ion complexes absorbed show a linear relationship with BET surface areas in the case of silica gel.[29,30]

If gels or gelatinous hydrous oxides are dried at relatively low temperature they undergo considerable shrinking to become a glassy gel. The dried gels, such as hydrous oxides of Ti(IV), Sn(IV), and Zr(IV), break down by immersion in water to give small granular particles suitable for column operations.

Thermal analysis in conjunction with IR and Mössbauer spectra is an excellent way to study the characteristics of water and M—OH bonding in the hydrous oxides. Most amorphous hydrous oxides begin to lose interstitial water (free water or zeolitic water) at 100 to 150°C and chemically bonded water at higher temperature (200 to 250°C). The typical example is hydrous zirconium dioxide as illustrated in Figure 2.[31] The first dehydration step is mainly reversible and little change in ion exchange properties occurs. The adsorption ability of the heated samples is dependent on their thermal stability and on their mode of preparation. For example the adsorption ability of silica gel gradually decreases as it is heated to 100 to 300°C, but in the temperature range of 300 to 1000°C substantially increases for the adsorption of Rb^+.[32] This phenomenon can be explained by the increase in surface area with conversion from

$$\equiv Si\begin{matrix} OH \\ \\ OH-----H_3O^+ \end{matrix} \quad to \quad =Si\begin{matrix} OH \\ \\ OH \end{matrix} \quad and \quad -Si(OH)_3$$

This increase is called the activation of silica gel (and alumina gel) and produces highly active sorbents, as is well known. Hydrous ZrO_2 and amorphous or glassy antimonic (V) acid show a steady decrease in exchange as a result of thermal treatments, the capacities of the materials heated at 300°C being about 20 to 30% of the values of the air-dried materials. With hydrous TiO_2, different results can be found in the literature: one group of workers has reported that the material heated at 300°C for 5 hr loses its ion exchange properties,[33] whereas other workers found it to retain 40% of its initial capacity after heating at 400°C.[34] However, at present, insufficient systematic studies of the ion exchange properties on heated materials are available.

The ion exchange selectivities of the heated samples depend on the chemical species in the solution as well as the materials used, pH, concentration of the species, co-ion present, and drying temperature. For example, hydrous TiO_2 heated at 400°C shows an increase in the selectivity for Cu^{2+} as compared with other transition metals and alkali metal ions (see Table 2).[35] With hydrous ZrO_2, a marked decrease is observed in the adsorptive ability for Ca^{2+} by heating at 140°C in comparison to those for transition metal ions. This phenomena can be applied for the separation of transition metal ions from a large amount of Ca^{2+}.[36]

2. Crystalline Materials

On aging in various solutions, amorphous materials or lower polynuclear species undergo polymerization (actually condensation) reactions with structure ordering of the precipitate. The crystallization process involves the supersaturation and formation of nuclei, growth of crystals, and recrystallization. The whole process is complicated and depends on the nature of the nuclei, concentration of acid or base, presence of impurities, temperature, etc. The crystalline material may be formed either by internal structure modification of the amorphous polymer or alternatively via a crystal growth process involving dissociation of mononuclear entities from amorphous polymer particles as shown below.

$$MOH^{n+}\begin{matrix} A \rightleftharpoons Amorphous \longrightarrow Crystalline\ (I) \\ (Polymer) \\ \\ B \longrightarrow Crystalline\ (II) \end{matrix}$$

A and B represent the nuclei with low molecular weight precursors of polymer and crystalline precipitates, respectively. All processes from left to right are accompanied by an increase of hydrogen ion concentration. For example, the formation of hydrous iron(III) oxide in high molecular species may be represented by:[37]

$$pFeOH^{2+} \rightleftharpoons [Fe_pO_q(OH)_{p+r}]^{(2p-2q-r)+} + (2q+r)\,H^+ \tag{1}$$

When the rate of formation of crystalline (I) is slower than that of crystalline (II), crystalline (II) may form, because the increased hydrogen ion concentration may cause

Table 2

DISTRIBUTION COEFFICIENTS OF VARIOUS METAL IONS ON HEAT-TREATED HYDROUS OXIDES OF TiO_2, ZrO_2, and ThO_2

Exchanger	Drying temp. (°C)	Na^+	Rb^+	Cs^+	Sr^{2+}	Cu^{2+}	Ni^{2+}	Co^{2+}	Fe^{3+}	Cr^{3+}	Ref.
H–TiO_2 (0.01 M soln.)	30	38	8.5	0	61	112	40	6.15	5	40	34
	400	0	0	0	2.5	8.25	5	1.75	0	0	
H–ThO_2 (0.01 M soln.)	30	130	160	194	151	270	405	795	34	52	34
	400	13	15	16	28	225	115	111	21	51	

Exchanger	Drying temp. (°C)	Ca^{2+}	Mn^{2+}	Ni^{2+}	Co^{2+}	Cd^{2+}	Zn^{2+}	Cu^{2+}	Ref.
H–ZrO_2 (final pH = 7.0)	40	2.4×10	2.7×10^2	8.6×10^2	1.4×10^3	1.6×10^3	1.6×10^4	4.6×10^4	35
	140	5.8	1.6×10^2	6.3×10^2	8.5×10^2	1.2×10^3	3.9×10^4	1.0×10^6	

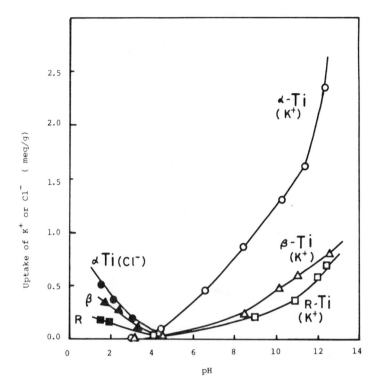

FIGURE 3. The pH dependence of the capacities of hydrous titanium dioxides at different crystallinities. Ionic strength, O.1M(HCl + KCl) or (KOH + KCl); total volume, 12.5 cm³; temperature, 25°C; exchanger, 0.25 g; α-Ti, amorphous; β-Ti, anatase; R-Ti, rutile. (From Abe, M. and Ito, T., *Nippon Kagaku Zasshi*, 86, 1259, 1965. With permission.)

preferential dissolution of nuclei or polymers of low molecular weight during slow establishment of equilibrium.

The crystalline hydrous oxide can be identified by analytical, crystallographic, and thermal analysis. The amorphous hydrous oxide freshly prepared has a large surface area with relatively high ion exchange capacities and poor stability, whereas the aged hydrous oxides with increased degree of ordering have better stabilities for various reagents, but a decrease in the capacity. For example, active α-hydrous SnO_2 is prepared by hydrolysis in cold solution, while the less active β-form is prepared by hydrolysis in hot solution. The α-form is also transformed to the β-form by aging for a long time. The difference between the two forms is believed to be simply one of primary particle size. Figure 3 indicates that the capacity of different hydrous Ti(IV) oxides decreases with increased degree of structure ordering: amorphous < anatase type < rutile type.[22]

One hydrous oxide cation exchanger, which does not conform to the above general discussion on the change in the capacity in going from amorphous to crystalline, is crystalline antimonic(V) acid whose capacity decreases for Li⁺ with increasing aging time, while it increases for K⁺.[38] This is attributed to the transformation from an amorphous structure to a zeolitic structure.

3. Surface Charge Characteristics

There is a characteristic value of the pH for any particular oxide at which the overall charge on the surface is zero; this arises from adsorption equilibrium associated with

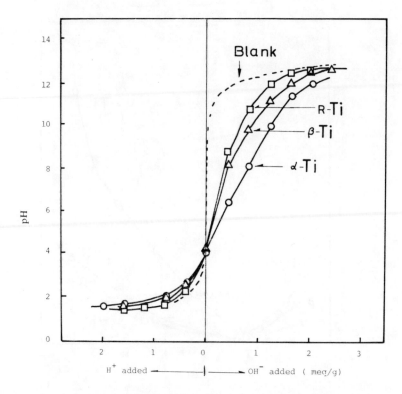

FIGURE 4.   The pH titration curves of hydrous titanium dioxides at different crystallinities. Ionic strength; 0.1 M (HCl + KCl) or (KOH + KCl) total volume, 12.5 cm³; exchanger, 0.250 g; temperature, 25 C°; α-Ti, amorphous; β-Ti, anatase; R-Ti, rutile. (From Abe, M. and Ito, T., *Nippon Kagaku Zasshi*, 86, 1259, 1965. With permission.)

the hydrogen ion being potential determining. This pH value is called the zero point of charge (ZPC) and is readily determined by potentiometric titration. A similar situation exists in electrokinetic experiments; the isoelectric point (IEP) is obtained from electrophoteric mobility and streaming potential data. The IEP equals the ZPC when there is no specific adsorption in the inner regions of the electric double layer associated with the oxide/solution interface. When the adsorption of an element occurs at the oxide/solution interface, the ZPC and IEP move in opposite directions by increasing the concentration of supporting electrolyte.[39,40] The adsorptive properties of cation and anion much depend on the chemical species in the solution because of their different selectivities. Thus the ZPC and IEP also vary with the cation and anion used as well as ionic strength. Parks has reviewed the existing zero point data for solid oxides, hydroxides, and aqueous hydroxo complex systems.[41]

C. pH Titration Curves of Various Hydrous Oxides

Titration curves are frequently used to characterize the functional groups of ion exchangers. Typical pH titration curves for different types of hydrous TiO_2 are illustrated in Figure 4.[22] When the material is insoluble throughout in the range to be measured, the uptake of K^+ (or Cl^-) is practically equivalent to the difference in the amounts of OH^- (or H^+) added at the same pH as indicated on the pH titration curves between blank and sample suspension. In this case, the buffering action is attributed to the adsorption of OH^- (or H^+) on the hydrous oxide. When the oxide is soluble, either above or below a certain pH, the buffer action is due to contributions from both uptake of OH^- (or H^+) and the solubility of the oxide.

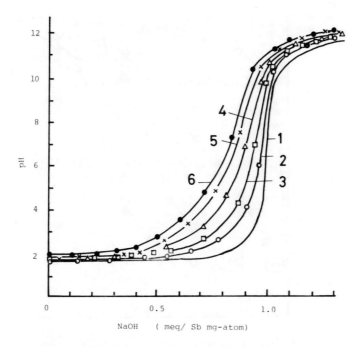

FIGURE 5. The pH titration curve of precipitated antimonic(V) acid. 1, published titration curve for hydrogen hexahydroxo-antimonate, H[Sb(OH)$_6$]; 2, freshly precipitated; 3, after 5 months; 4, after 10 months; 5, after 1.5 years; 6, after 2 years. (From Novikov, B. G. Materova, E. A., and Belinskaya, F. A., *Zh. Neorg. Khim.*, 20, 1566, 1975. With permission.)

Most hydrous oxides exhibit weakly acidic and/or basic ion exchange behavior. Although the lack of inflexion points is indicative of monofunctional behavior, the pH titration curves would be expected to show several inflexions corresponding to the number of the functional groups with overlapping different pK$_a$ values arising from their position in the gel structure.

The shape of the pH titration curve depends on the aging of materials. For example, it has been known that amorphous antimonic (V) acid is gradually transformed into crystalline materials by aging in the acidic solution.[38] Novikov et al.[42] give the pH titration curves for the same specimen at different stages of aging (Figure 5). It can be seen that the monomeric species of H[Sb(OH)$_6$] exhibits strong acid behavior as the fresh precipitate. In the subsequent structure ordering to the crystalline state the solids retain their acidic properties. Crystallization does not alter the total quantity of hydrogen ions capable of being neutralized, but merely leads to partial hindering of the dissociation of the acid.

The shape of the titration curves also depends on various factors, e.g., the chemical species to be measured, co-ion present, ionic strength, ratio of the solution and the sample, temperature, etc. When the exchanger exhibits large steric and ion-sieve effects, the shape much depends on the chemical species in the system. One typical example is illustrated in Figure 6.[43]

A systematic study of pH titration curves has been reported by Abe and Ito,[21,22] including a number of hydroxides and hydrous oxides of multivalent metals. They have selected an ionic strength of 0.1 in (HCl + KCl) or (KOH + KCl), because K$^+$ and Cl$^-$ have almost the same hydration volume and mobility in aqueous solution. The pH titration curves for various hydrous oxides are shown in Figures 7A to 7Q. If the

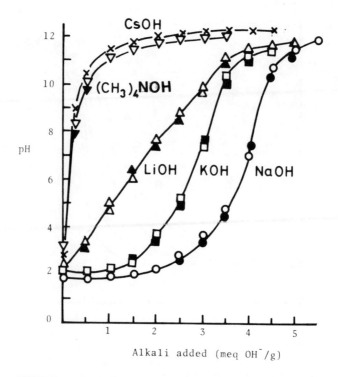

FIGURE 6.   The pH titration curves of crystalline antimonic acid with various hydroxide solutions; ionic strength, 0.1 M with (MOH + HCl). (From Novikov, B. G., Belinskaya, F. A., and Materova, E. A., *Vestn. Leningrad Univ. Fiz. Khim.*, No. 4, 29, 1971. With permission.)

polymerization (such as Equation 1) or depolymerization occurs during the ion exchange reaction, the adsorption of H^+ or OH^- would be observed, although no exchange reaction takes place. Thus, the determination of the adsorbed amounts for cations and anion is necessary in order to know the contribution from this source.

As mentioned above, the pH titration curve of a hydrous oxide much depends on its preparation. In an attempt at better understanding the character of the exchanger, detailed descriptions of the preparation of hydrous oxides are given.

1. Beryllium Hydrous Oxide

Beryllium hydrous oxide exists in three different forms, a gelatinous material produced by adding the stoichiometric quantity of alkali to a cold beryllium salt solution, and two crystalline forms; a stable orthorhombic and a metastable tetragonal modification.[44] These crystalline forms are obtained by aging the amorphous product, by preparing the precipitate from a hot solution or boiling a beryllate solution. Recent work has shown that the latter method can afford either polymorph, depending on the choice of hydrolytic conditions.[45] The amorphous product contains a small amount of sulfate or carbonate ions which are difficult to remove. The composition varies with preparative and dehydration conditions and ranges from $BeO \cdot 16H_2O$ to $Be(OH)_2 \cdot 2\frac{1}{3}H_2O$. The amorphous precipitate obtained by adding aqueous ammonia to a beryllium salt solution was washed with dilute ammonia until free from Cl^- and then with water and finally dried at room temperature.[21] The pH titration curve of the amorphous $BeO \cdot 1.7H_2O$ obtained by this preparation exhibits amphoteric ion exchange behavior, and the uptake of K^+ increases with increasing pH, while the uptake of Cl^- decreases (see Figure 7A).[21] Changes in the pH do not corresponded to uptakes

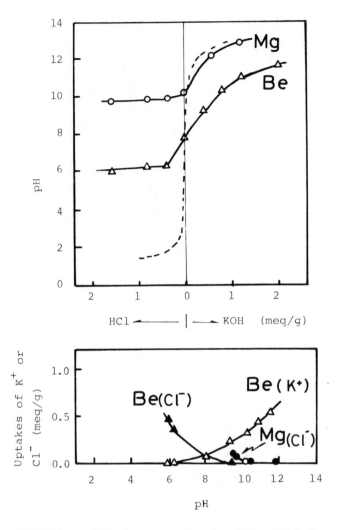

FIGURE 7A. pH titration curves and uptakes of K$^+$ and Cl$^-$ for hydrous beryllium oxide and magnesium hydroxide. Exchanger, 0.25 g; total volume, 12.5 cm³; ionic strength, 0.1 M (HCl + KCl) or (KOH + KCl). (From Abe, M. and Ito, T., *Nippon Kagaku Zasshi*, 86, 817, 1965. With permission.)

of K$^+$ or Cl$^-$ because of the dissolution of the hydrous beryllium oxide in the solution at pH values lower than 6 or higher than 10.

2. Magnesium Hydroxide

Magnesium hydroxide (the mineral brucite) has the cadmium iodide layered structure in which each cation is surrounded by six anions. Each OH forms three bonds with three magnesium cations in its own layer and is in contact with three OH in the adjacent layer.[46] The environments of OH$^-$ in Mg(OH)$_2$ shows that there are no hydrogen bonds in the structure. As in LiOH the OH$^-$ ions in the hydroxide are oriented with their H atoms on the outer surface of the layers, as shown by an nmr study of Mg(OH)$_2$.[47]

Magnesium hydroxide is prepared by addition of aqueous ammonia to a magnesium chloride solution. The precipitate is treated in a similar manner as described above in order to remove adsorbed Cl$^-$.[21] Magnesium hydroxide behaves only as an anion ex-

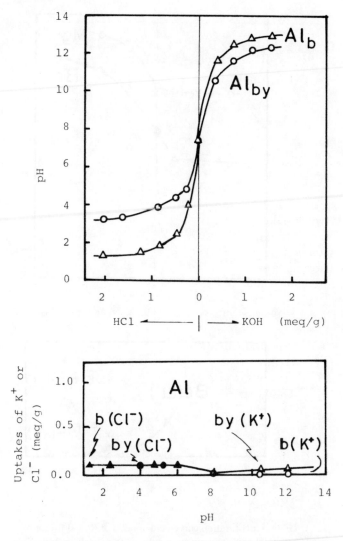

FIGURE 7B.   pH titration curves and uptakes of K^+ and Cl^- for hydrous aluminum oxides. Al_{by}, bayerite; Al_b, boehmite; exchanger, 0.250 g; ionic strength, 0.1 M (HCl + KCl) or (KOH + KCl); total volume, 12.5 cm^3. (From Abe, M. and Ito, T., *Nippon Kagaku Zasshi*, 86, 817, 1965. With permission.)

changer. The pH titration curve shows the presence of a plateau pH 10, because of its solubility (see Figure 7A).

3. Hydrous Aluminum Oxide

Various modifications of aluminum trihydroxide are described in the literature, the most common being gibbsite (in German and French studies called hydrargillite), bayerite, and norstrandite. Aluminum oxide hydroxide (AlOOH) is known to exist in two modifications, diaspore and boemite. Three types of alumina are commercially available; neutral alumina (pH 6.9 to 7.1), basic alumina (pH 10 to 10.5), and acid alumina (pH 3.5 to 4.5). Most chromatographic aluminas are a mixture of γ-alumina with a small amount of aluminum oxide-hydroxide (and perhaps a little sodium carbonate left during manufacturing).[48] The pH titration curve for bayerite shows amphoteric behavior. However, the determination of K^+ and Cl^- in the supernatant solution indi-

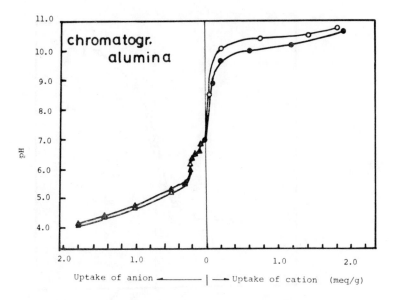

FIGURE 7C.   Titration curves obtained on titration of Brockmann 1 alumina with alkali and acid.[49] Concentration, 0.02 M; -O- LiOH; —●— - KOH; - ▲ - HCl; - △ -, HNO₃. Replotted by author.

cates small uptakes by the material.[21] It is quite difficult to obtain pure bayerite without any contamination of amorphous aluminum hydroxide, gibbsite, and boemite. The amorphous aluminum hydroxide is easily soluble in both weak acidic and basic solutions. Thus the pH titration curve obtained may be due to both a contribution of ion uptake and of the dissolution of amorphous aluminum hydroxide present as an impurity. Boemite shows only anion exchange properties in the pH range studied (see Figure 7B).

Churms has reported[49] that, amphoteric behavior with high ion-exchange capacities is observed for chromatographic alumina, probably gibbsite, of Brockmann number 1 (adsorptive activity decreases as Brockmann number increases) (see Figure 7C).

4. Hydrous Gallium Oxide

The hydrous oxide of gallium(III) is obtained by the action of acids on a solution of gallates or by adding base to aqueous gallium salts. Basic salts are frequently formed in the presence of potentially coordinating anions (e.g., sulfate ions). The freshly precipitated hydrous oxide gel is amorphous and GaOOH is obtained by aging.[50]

The hydrous gallium oxide, $Ga_2O_3 \cdot 2.4H_2O$, prepared in a manner similar to beryllium hydrous oxide behaves as an amphoteric ion exchanger (see Figure 7D).[21] Hydrous gallium oxide is soluble in acidic solution at pH values below 3 and in basic solutions with pH 10. Thus, there is a pH limit for its application as an ion exchanger.[21]

5. Hydrous Indium Oxide

On adding aqueous alkali or ammonia to a solution of an indium(III) salt (e.g., nitrate), the precipitation of the hydrous oxide begins at pH 3.41 to 3.43; indium sulfate and chloride form basic salts in addition to the hydrous oxide.[51] The phase precipitated at room temperature is not quite amorphous to X-rays and may be considered a crystalline hydrate of the hydroxide $In(OH)_3 \cdot xH_2O$.[52] At least three compounds $In(OH)_3$, oxyhydroxide InOOH and sesquioxide In_2O_3 can be prepared by hydrothermal methods in the temperature range 25 to 800°C at pressures of 3.5 to 1406 kg/cm². $In(OH)_3$, cubic, occurs as the stable phase up to 245 ± 10°C at 703 kg/cm² and can

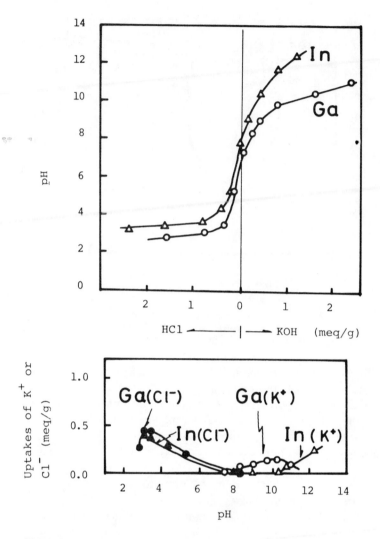

FIGURE 7D.   pH titration curves and uptakes of K⁺ and Cl⁻ for hydrous oxides of gallium and indium. Exchanger, 0.250 g; total volume, 12.5 cm³; ionic strength, 0.1 M (HCl + KCl) or (KOH + KCl). (From Abe, M. and Ito, T., *Nippon Kagaku Zasshi*, 86, 817, 1965. With permission.)

easily be prepared in large quantities by boiling the precipitated hydroxide. When prepared in this manner and dried at 110°C, it is quite stoichiometric: it may adsorb some water from the atmosphere, but the water does not enter the structure in any way. It has the ReO₃ structure with a = 7.97₉ Å, slightly distorted to allow hydrogen bonding between OH groups.[52] Differential thermal analysis indicates that In(OH)₃ is transformed to cubic In₂O₃ at 300°C.[53]

InOOH is prepared in the temperature range of 330 to 415°C at a pressure ranging from 124 to 827 kg/cm² by treating amorphous indium hydrous oxide with water or with a dilute (0.1-0.5 M) sodium hydroxide solution. InOOH is orthorhombic; space groups is Pnnm with a = 5.26, b = 4.56, and c = 3.27 Å.[54]

One cannot convert In₂O₃ to InOOH, nor will InOOH once formed revert to In(OH)₃ even in a period of two months within the formation range of the individual oxide.

Hydrous indium oxide, In₂O₃·3.5H₂O, in amorphous form is prepared in similar

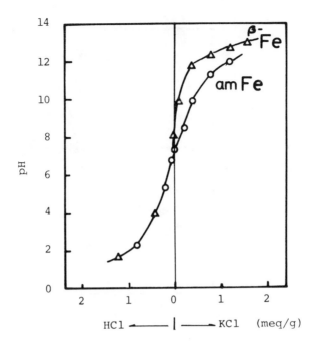

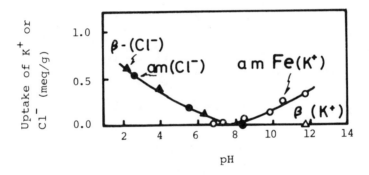

FIGURE 7E.   pH titration curves and uptakes of K^+ and Cl^- for hydrous iron(III) oxides. amFe, amorphous; β-Fe, β-FeOOH; exchanger, 0.250 g; total volume 12.5 cm^3; ionic strength, 0.1 M (HCl + KCl) or (KOH + KCl). (From Abe, M. and Ito, T., *Nippon Kagaku Zasshi*, 86, 817, 1965. With permission.)

manner to hydrous gallium oxide.[21] The pH titration curve shows amphoteric behavior with uptakes of K^+ and Cl^-. The hydrous oxide is stable in the basic solution studied, while it is soluble in acidic solution at a pH below 4 (see Figure 7D).[21]

6. Hydrous Iron(III) Oxide

Various types of hydrous iron(III) oxides are known to exist with different crystalline forms depending on the method of preparation; these are amorphous, α-FeOOH(goethite), β-FeOOH, and γ-FeOOH(lepidocrocite). The red-brown precipitate, referred to as amorphous hydrous iron(III) oxide, is obtained by adding aqueous ammonia or alkali to the solution of iron(III) salts at low temperature. The pH titration curve of amorphous iron(III) oxide, of composition $Fe_2O_3 \cdot 2H_2O$, exhibits typically amphoteric ion exchange behavior, while β-FeOOH shows only anion exchange behavior (see Figure 7E).[21] Both samples are practically insoluble in the solution above

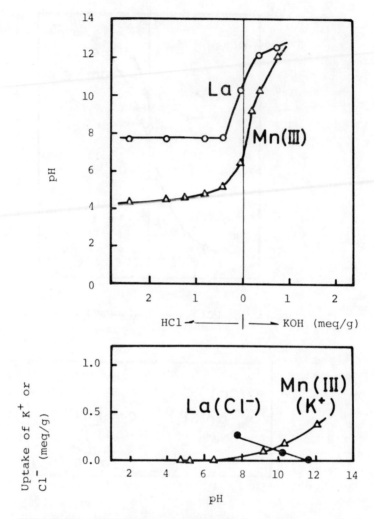

FIGURE 7F.   pH titration curves and uptakes of K$^+$ and Cl$^-$ for hydrous manganese(III) oxide and lanthanum hydroxide. Exchanger, 0.250 g; total volume, 12.5 cm^3; ionic strength, 0.1 M (HCl + KCl) or (KOH + KCl). (From Abe, M. and Ito, T., *Nippon Kagaku Zasshi*, 86, 817, 1965. With permission.)

pH 1.6, whereas they are transformed to α-Fe$_2$O$_3$ by immersing in strong alkaline solution for a long time.

7. Hydrous Manganese (III) Oxide

There are at least three different substances prepared by oxidation of Mn(II) ion in basic solution. However, well defined γ-MnOOH, which corresponds to a natural substance manganite, can be prepared by adding aqueous ammonia to manganese(II) sulfate solution in the presence of hydrogen peroxide under boiling conditions. The precipitate obtained is washed with water until free from sulfate ions and is dried at 50°C.[55] The structure of γ-MnOOH has a monoclinic (pseudo-orthorhombic) cell with a superstructure of marcasite FeS$_2$ type.[56]

The pH titration curve for hydrous manganese(III) oxide shows apparent amphoteric behavior. However, γ-MnOOH exhibits only cation exchange properties for K$^+$ in solution above 6.0, and is soluble in acidic solution at pH values below 5.0 (see Figure 7F).[21] The exchange capacity is about 0.4 meq/g at pH 12.

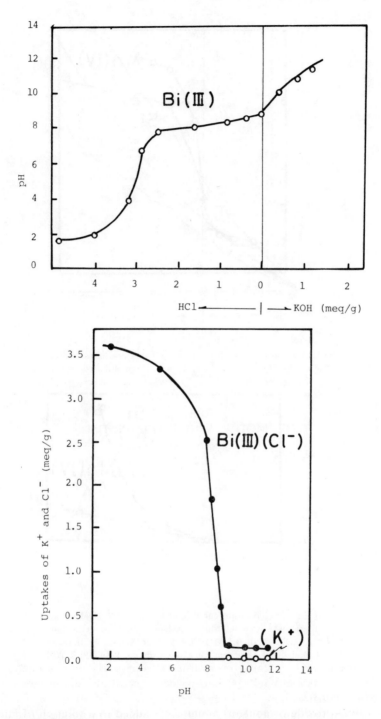

FIGURE 7G. pH titration curve and uptakes of K$^+$ and Cl$^-$ for bismuth hydrous oxide. Exchanger 0.25 g; total volume 12.5 cm^3; ionic strength, 0.1 M (HCl + KCl) or (KOH + KCl). (From Abe, M. and Ito, T., *Nippon Kagaku Zasshi*, 86, 816, 1965. With permission.)

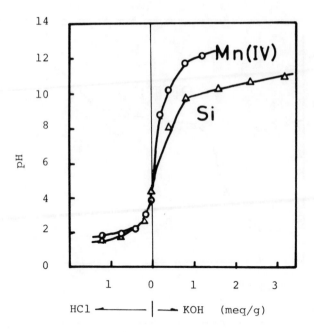

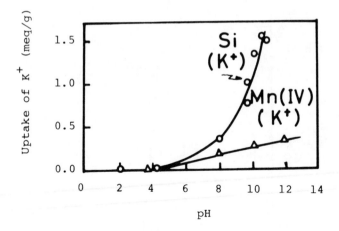

FIGURE 7H.   pH titration curves and uptakes of K^+ and Cl^- for chromatographic silica and β-MnO$_2$. Exchanger, 0.250 g; total volume 12.5 cm³; ionic strength, 0.1 M(HCl + KCl) or (KOH + KCl). (From Abe, M. and Ito, T., *Nippon Kagaku Zasshi,* 86, 1259, 1965. With permission.)

8. Lanthanum Hydroxide

When alkali hydroxide or aqueous ammonia is added to a solution of lanthanum salts, a gelatinous precipitate is obtained. The precipitate was washed with 2 M alkali hydroxide until free of chloride ion, and then washed with water in order to remove alkali hydroxide, and finally dried at 50°. Lanthanum hydroxide prepared this way exhibited anion exchange properties, but was soluble at pHs below 8.0 (see Figure 7F).[21]

9. Hydrous Bismuth(III) Oxide

Hydrous bismuth oxide, Bi$_2$O$_3 \cdot$3H$_2$O or Bi(OH)$_3$, is prepared by addition of an ex-

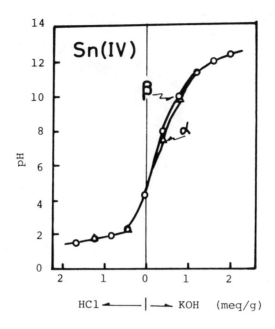

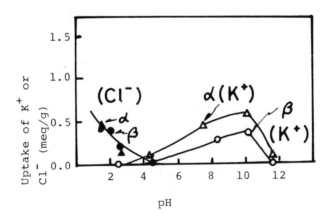

FIGURE 71. pH titration curves and uptakes of K^+ and Cl^- for α- and β-hydrous tin (IV) dioxide. Exchanger, 0.250 g; total volume, 12.5 cm³, ionic strength, 0.1 M (HCl + KCl) or (KOH + KCl). (From Abe, M. and Ito, T., *Nippon Kagaku Zasshi,* 86, 1259, 1965. With permission.)

cess of concentrated aqueous ammonia to a bismuth nitrate solution stabilized with a small quantity of nitric acid. The precipitate was first washed with water then with a dilute solution of sodium carbonate and finally with water. The material usually contains an appreciable amount of nitrate ions. The best way to prepare the hydrous oxide free from basic salt is to add a glycerol or mannitol complex of a bismuth salt to sodium hydroxide and immediately to neutralize the excess alkali with dilute nitric or acetic acid.[57] However, this oxide contains a few percent of organic substance.[60] It is not known definitely whether it is a trihydrate, $Bi_2O_3 \cdot 3H_2O$, or a dihydrate. The dehydration isobar for an electrolyte free solid showed a strong inflection at 300°C, corresponding to the composition $Bi_2O_3 \cdot 2H_2O$.[58] The dehydration of hydrogels of $Bi_2O_3 \cdot nH_2O$ precipitated at 0°C and pH 9.3 and 11.5 was studied by isothermal and

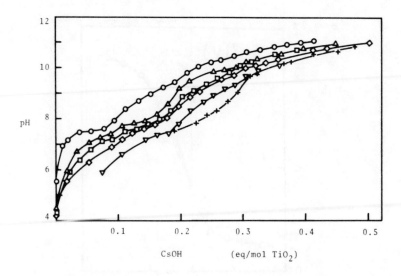

FIGURE 7J.   pH titration of TiO₂ suspension with CsOH. Initial concentration of Cs: (O), 0; (△), 2.5×10^{-3} *M*; (□) 5×10^{-3} *M*; (◇), 1.2×10^{-2} *M*; (▽), 1.2×10^{-1} *M*; (+) 1.0. (From Schiewer, E., Austaushadsorption von Kationen an Titandioxidhydrat, Dissertation, Technischen Universitat, Berlin, 1967.)

thermal analysis methods.[59] The hydrogels lose water to yield orthobismuthic acid, H_3BiO_3, and metabismuthic acid, $HBiO_2$.[59] However, neither the presence of BiOOH nor acidic character has been validated.

The pH titration curve for the hydrous oxide shows a strong basic type of anion exchange behavior similar to that observed with strong basic quaternary ammonium anion exchange resins (see Figure 7G).[21] The strong preference of the hydrous oxide for chloride ions reflects the fact that the amorphous material readily forms BiOCl.[21,60] The adsorption capacity is 3.0 to 3.8 meq/g.[21,60] The oxychloride is transformed to α- and/or γ-Bi_2O_3 by regeneration with 2 *M* NaOH.[61]

10. Hydrous Silica

The use of silica gel as an ion exchange material has been extensively studied for many years. Various activity grades of silica can be prepared by controlled water content of activation. Silica gel generally acts as a weakly acidic cation exchanger, although the ionic adsorption mechanism has thus far not been fully established.[29,41,62] The pH titration curve of chromatography grade silica gel shows a weakly acidic cation exchange behavior and the maximum uptake of K^+ is 1.5 meq/g at pH 10.2.[22] Silica gel is stable in acidic solution, but is soluble in basic solution e.g., pH 10.5 (see Figure 7H). Recent investigations indicate that silica gel also exhibits anion exchange behavior at pHs below 3.[41,63,64]

11. Hydrous Manganese Dioxide

Increased attention has been devoted to a study of the ion exchange properties of hydrous manganese dioxide because of its selectivities for certain elements. There are at least four different manganese dioxides which are formed, with structures close to α, β, γ or $\delta-MnO_2$, depending upon the method of preparation and the drying temperature. Manganese dioxide contains some water in the structure with empirical formula $(MnO_x)_2(OH)^6$. The pH titration curve of $\beta-MnO_2 \cdot 0.6H_2O$ shows that only cation exchange behavior, with a maximum uptake of 0.3 meq K^+/g at pH 12, takes place (see Figure 7H).[22] β-MnO₂·0.6H₂O is stable in the pH range studied. The titration of β-MnO₂ indicates that this exchanger contains two functional groups with different

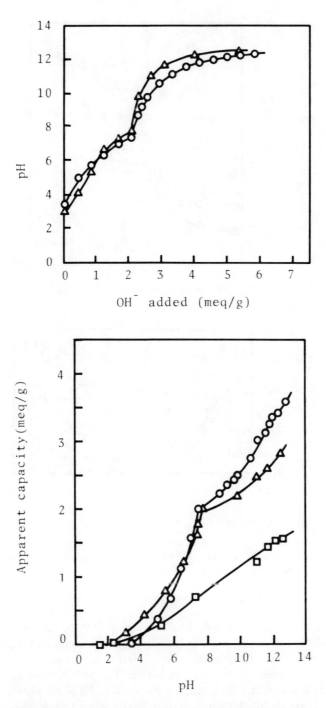

FIGURE 7K.   pH titration curves and uptakes of alkali metal ions for hydrous titanium dioxide. O, Na⁺; △, Cs⁺ (from Reference 74); □, Na⁺ (From Ref. 22) ionic strength, 0.1 (from Reference 75).

pK_a values of 3.8 and 5.2.[65] More recent work suggests a third functional group with a pK_a value of 9.3.[66]

12. Hydrous Tin (IV) Oxide

The freshly prepared material from cold solution is called α-stannic acid and is easily

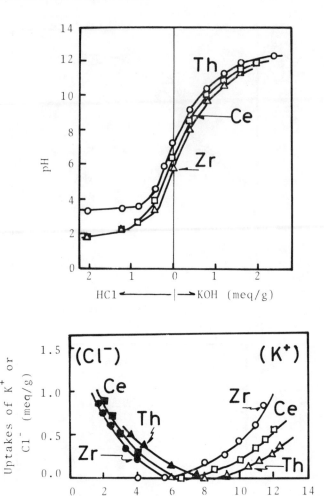

FIGURE 7L.   pH titration curves and uptakes of K⁺ and Cl⁻ for hydrous oxides of Zr, Ce(IV) and Th. Exchanger, 0.250 g; total volume, 12.5 cm³; ionic strength, 0.1 M(HCl + KCl) or (KOH + KCl). (From Abe, M. and Ito, T., *Nippon Kagaku Zasshi*, 86, 1259, 1965. With permission.)

soluble in acidic solution. β-stannic acid is prepared by the reaction of concentrated nitric acid with tin metal and is more inert in highly concentrated nitric acid and sulfuric acid solutions. It is believed that the differences between α- and β-SnO$_2$·nH$_2$O are solely due to differences in the particle size. The pH titration curves for the two hydrous oxides demonstrate their amphoteric nature.[22] The uptakes of K⁺ and Cl⁻ on α-hydrous oxide are slightly higher than those on β-hydrous oxide, because of its higher surface area. Both oxides are practically stable in acidic solution, while they are soluble in basic solutions (pH > 10) (see Figure 7I).[22]

13. Hydrous Titanium(IV) Dioxide

Increased attention has been paid to the development of hydrous titanium(IV) dioxide as an ion-exchanger for the selective adsorption of uranium from sea water on a commercial scale.[67-70] Hydrous titanium(IV) dioxide "so-called titanic acid", is formed by hydrolysis of titanium(IV) chloride or by air oxidation of Ti$_2$O$_3$·nH$_2$O.

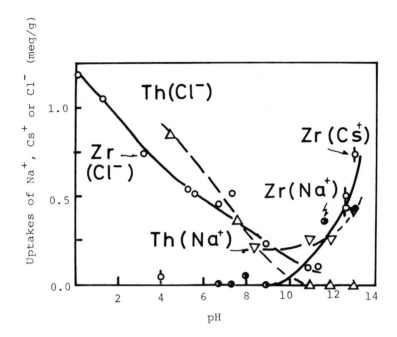

FIGURE 7M. Uptakes of cations and Cl⁻ on hydrous oxides of Zr and Th. (From Amphlett, C. B., McDonald, L. A., and Redman, M. J., *J. Inorg. Nucl. Chem.*, 6, 236, 1958. With permission.)

There are four different types of the hydrous oxide; amorphous, anatase, rutile, and brookite. Amorphous $TiO_2 \cdot nH_2O$ is obtained by hydrolysis of an HCl solution of $TiCl_4$ with aqueous ammonia at room temperature. Oxidation in air of $Ti_2O_3 \cdot nH_2O$ also yields an amorphous Ti(IV) product. Aging under water of the amorphous precipitate at room temperature for 14 weeks produces no change detectable by X-ray diffraction methods. Further aging of this precipitate for 30 weeks at room temperature or 6 hr at 100°C under water gave an X-ray diffraction pattern of anatase.[71]

The pH titration curves for various hydrous titanium(IV) oxides show typical amphoteric character and the increased order of the capacities is rutile < anatase < amorphous. This order parallels the surface areas of the materials (see Figure 3).[22] Hydrous Ti(IV) oxides are practically insoluble in the pH range of 1 to 12.

The pH titration curve of the suspension of TiO_2 prepared by hydrolysis of the tetraethyl ester of orthotitanic acid, shows a polyfunctional cation exchange behavior with $pK_1(Na-H) = 3.81$, $pK_2(Na-H) = 6.28$, $pK_1(Cs-H) = 3.29$, and $pK_3(Cs-H) = 7.60$ (see Figure 7J).[72,73]

Amorphous hydrous titanium dioxide having high exchange capacity is prepared by drying without washing out excess alkali, and is then washed with dilute hydrochloric acid and finally with water. The titration curve shows two functional acid groups with $pK_1 (Na-H) = 5.2$, $pK_2 (Na-H) = 9.0$, $pK_1 (K-H) = 5.42$, and $pK_2 (K-H) = 9.27$ at an ionic strength of 0.1 (see Figure 7K).[74]

14. Hydrous Zirconium Oxide

Three hydrous zirconium oxides are known; amorphous, monoclinic, and cubic. Some interest has been shown to these oxides as adsorbents for the extraction of uranium from sea water.[75] The amorphous hydrous oxide is usually prepared by addition of alkali to a solution of zirconium salts at room temperature. Monoclinic hydrous oxide is prepared by refluxing a 1 *M* zirconium chloride solution adjusted to the pH values between 1 and 2.5 by addition of aqueous ammonia or by refluxing slurries of

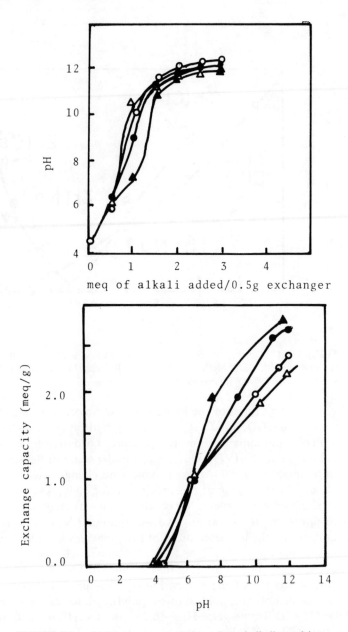

FIGURE 7N.   pH titration curves and uptakes of alkali metal ions on hydrous cerium oxides. Preparation 1, (cerium sulfate is added to NaOH solution); ▲ , NaOH; ● , KOH; preparation 2 (the order of addition is reversed), NaOH; △, KOH; ○, ionic strength, 2. (Top replotted by author from Figure 2 and 3. Bottom plotted by author from Table 2 of Reference 78.)

amorphous zirconium hydrous oxide.[76] Cubic hydrous oxide is obtained by heating the amorphous hydrous oxide in the presence of aqueous NaOH or KOH solution.[76]

   The pH titration curve (see Figure 7L) indicates that the amorphous hydrous zirconium dioxide behaves as an amphoteric ion exchanger with an EAP of 6.0. A large variety of values for ZPC or IEP are found in the literature, ranging from 4 to 11.[64,77] This large variation may result from differences in surface preparation, impurity content, and whether the solid is synthetically or naturally produced. If the value is very

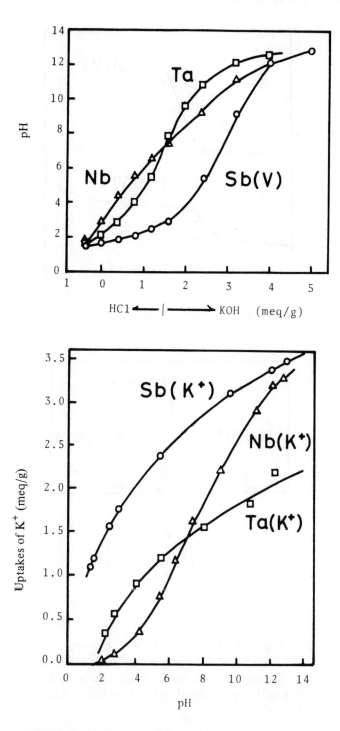

FIGURE 7O. pH titration curves and uptakes of K⁺ for hydrous oxides of niobium, tantalum and antimony (V). Exchanger, 0.250 g; total volume, 12.5 cm³; ionic strength, 0.1 M(HCl + KCl) or (KOH + KCl). (From Abe, M. and Ito, T., *Nippon Kagaku Zasshi*, 86, 1259, 1965. With permission.)

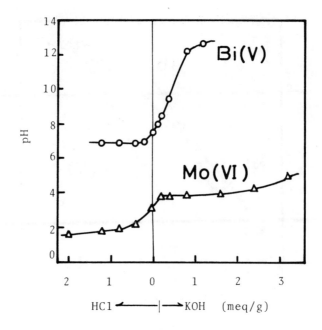

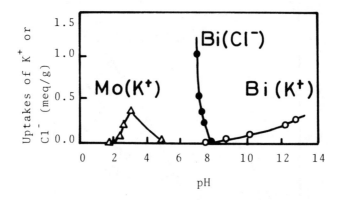

FIGURE 7P.   pH titration curves and uptakes of K^+ or Cl^- for hydrous oxides of Bi(V) and Mo(VI). Exchanger, 0.250 g; total volume, 12.5 cm^3; ionic strength, 0.1 M(HCl + KCl) or (KOH + KCl). (From Abe, M. and Ito, T., *Nippon Kagaku Zasshi*, 86, 1259, 1965. With permission.)

close to the pH of water, it is very difficult to remove adsorbed cations or anions by washing with water. Thus, very small amounts of electrolyte are retained in the solid. The pH dependence for the exchange of alkali metal cations and chloride ions on hydrous zirconium oxide and thorium oxide dried at 50 to 100°C is illustrated in Figure 7M.[77]

15. Hydrous Cerium(IV) Oxide

When aqueous ammonia or alkali is added to a solution of cerium(IV) salt, a yellow gelatinous precipitate of hydrous cerium(IV) oxide is formed. This hydrous oxide is liable to be contaminated with basic salt as well as adsorbed alkali metal ions. Undesirable adsorbed anions are removed by washing with dilute aqueous ammonia and the adsorbed ammonium ions are removed by washing with water for a long time.[22] The pH titration curves show that hydrous cerium oxide behaves as both a cation and

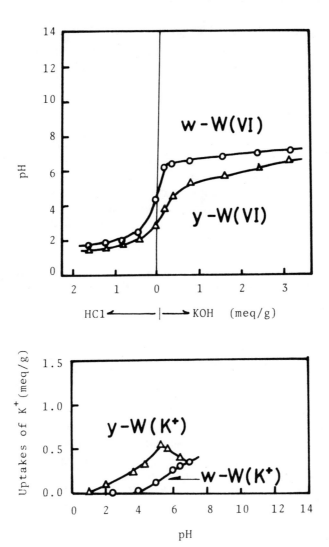

FIGURE 7O. pH titration curves and uptakes of K⁺ or Cl⁻ for hydrous tungsten oxides. Hydrous oxide; y-W, yellow hydrous tungsten oxide; w-W, white hydrous tungsten oxide; exchanger taken, 0.250 g; total volume, 12.5 cm³; ionic strength, 0.1 M(HCl + KCl) or (KOH + KCl). (From Abe, M. and Ito, T., *Nippon Kagaku Zasshi*, 86, 1259, 1965. With permission.)

anion exchanger with an IAP of 6.8 (see Figure 7L).[22] When cerium sulfate solution is added to 1 M sodium hydroxide solution, an amber colored crystalline material is obtained. However, if the order of addition is reversed, a yellow amorphous material is obtained.[78] The results of the pH titration and uptakes of alkali metal ions indicate that the ion exchange properties depend on the order of addition of the reagents, although other variables are held constant, e.g., final pH, aging time, etc. (see Figure 7N).[78] Hydrous cerium(IV) oxide is fairly stable in 0.1 M HNO₃, 0.1 M HClO₄ and 0.05 M H₂SO₄. When the exchanger is converted to the hydrogen ion form by immersion in 0.05 M acid, the exchanger is likely to contain partially dissolved Ce(IV) as a complex anion, $Ce(SO_4)_3^{2-}$, which is very difficult to remove.

16. Hydrous Thorium Oxide

Hydrous thorium oxide is usually prepared by mixing thorium salt solutions with alkali in various ratios. A white glassy product is obtained by drying at relatively low temperature. The pH titration curve indicates that hydrous thorium oxide behaves as both a cation and anion exchanger and is stable in the solution at pH 2 (see Figure 7L).[22,76]

17. Hydrous Niobium(V) Oxide

Hydrous niobium(V) oxide, or niobic acid, is formed as a gelatinous precipitate when niobium oxychloride, $NbOCl_3$, or niobium pentachloride, $NbCl_5$, is hydrolyzed by water. It is very difficult to remove traces of chloride ion from the precipitates. Hydrous niobium oxide is stable towards most reagents, except hydrofluoric acid, concentrated sulfuric acid and hydrochloric acid. The pH titration curve indicates that hydrous niobium oxide behaves only as a cation exchanger containing two functional acidic groups (see Figure 7O). The uptake of K^+ is 3.3 meq/g at pH 12.5.[22]

18. Hydrous Tantalum Oxide

Hydrous tantalum(V) oxide is obtained as a gelatinous precipitate by hydrolysis of tantalum pentachloride with an excess of water or by addition of aqueous ammonia. It is also obtained by treating sodium tantalate with acid. The Ta(V) hydrous oxide is more stable than hydrous niobium oxide towards most chemical reagents.

The pH titration curve indicates that hydrated tantalum oxide behaves only as a cation exchanger of the monofunctional acid type and has a fairly large capacity of about 2 meq/g at pH 12 (see Figure 7O).[22]

19. Hydrous Antimony(V) Oxide (Antimonic Acid)

Hydrous antimony(V) oxide, "so-called antimonic acid," is obtained as an amorphous, glassy, or crystalline material, depending on the method of the preparation.[38] Amorphous antimonic acid is prepared by hydrolysis of antimony pentachloride with a large amount of water or by treating a potassium antimonate solution with an acid and aging for a relatively short time at low temperature. On prolonged aging in the mother solution, the amorphous material is gradually transformed into a crystalline product.[38]

The pH titration curve indicates that amorphous antimonic acid behaves as a cation exchanger of the monofunctional acid type and has a relatively large ion exchange capacity for K^+, e.g., 3.5 meq/g at pH 12 (see Figure 7O).[22] Titration curves for the aged materials were shown earlier (see Figure 5).

Further details are given in Section III.A of this chapter.

20. Hydrous Bismuth(V) Oxide[22]

When hydrous bismuth(III) oxide is suspended in a 20% sodium hydroxide solution and is then oxidized by passing in chlorine gas, a hydrous oxide of higher valency, probably $HBiO_3$, is obtained upon washing with dilute nitric acid solution. It is very difficult to obtain a definite hydrous oxide because some reduction to Bi(III) occurs during removal of sodium ions by washing with a dilute nitric acid solution.

The pH titration curve for this hydrous oxide (see Figure 7P) shows similarities to that obtained for hydrous bismuth(III) oxide (see Figure 7G).[22] The cation exchange capacity is only 0.25 to 0.3 meq/g for K^+ but high for chloride ion adsorption. This is attributable to incomplete formation of Bi(V) oxide or some reduction to bismuth (III) oxide. Thus, this material is of little practical importance as an ion exchanger.

21. Hydrous Molybdenum(VI) Oxide

Two types of hydrous molybdenum(VI) oxide may exist, e.g., $MoO_3 \cdot H_2O$ and $MoO_3 \cdot 2H_2O$. $MoO_3 \cdot 2H_2O$ is obtained by slowly acidifying a molybdate solution at room temperature. From hot solution, the monohydrate $MoO_3 \cdot H_2O$ is obtained rapidly. These compounds are hydrated and do not contain discrete H_2MoO_4 molecules; broad line nmr of these compounds indicates that all of the hydrogen is present in the form of water molecules.[79]

The pH titration curve for $MoO_3 \cdot 2H_2O$ shows two stages of neutralization (see Figure 7P).[22] However, in the long buffering range starting at pH 4, $MoO_3 \cdot 2H_2O$ is soluble. A relatively small exchange capacity of 0.4 meq K^+/g is observed.

22. Hydrous Tungsten(VI) Oxide

Two hydrous tungsten(VI) oxides, "so-called" white tungstic acid $WO_3 \cdot 2H_2O$ and yellow tungstic acid $WO_3 \cdot H_2O$ are known.[80] A white voluminous precipitate of $WO_3 \cdot 2H_2O$ is obtained by adding dilute hydrochloric acid to ammonium tungstate solution at 0 to 10°C. The material usually contains a little more water than corresponds to $WO_3 \cdot 2H_2O$ when dried to constant weight in air.

The pH titration curve shows two stages of neutralization which is similar to the behavior of hydrous molybdenum oxide. Hydrous tungsten oxide exhibits cation exchange properties at pH values between 1 and 7. However, the material is soluble at pH 7 (see Figure 7Q).[22] Similar conclusions were also obtained by De and Chowdhury.[81]

D. Acidities of Hydrous Oxides

Cation or anion exchange by hydrous oxides is known to occur predominantly by displacement of hydrogen ions and hydroxide ions from the sorbents, provided that these have previously been washed free from impurity ions.

These substances are mostly amphoteric and their exchange reactions may be schematically represented as follows;

$$X–OH + K^+ \rightleftharpoons X–OK + H^+ \tag{2}$$

$$X–OH_2^+ + Cl^- \rightleftharpoons X–OH_2 Cl \tag{3}$$

or

$$X–OH + Cl^- \rightleftharpoons M–Cl + OH^- \tag{4}$$

(X represents any central metal atom).

Such acids and bases all contain the fundamental structure $:\ddot{X}: \ddot{O}: H$ from which it is apparent that the oxygen will be pulled more towards those metal atoms, X, with small radii, and the proton can be removed by a suitable base.

For the OH group in the X–O–H bonding, we may imagine typically three types of behavior; (a) as an ion with effective spherical symmetry, (b) OH$^-$ is oriented towards the central atom with cylindrical symmetry, and (c) polarized with a tetrahedral charge distribution as shown below.

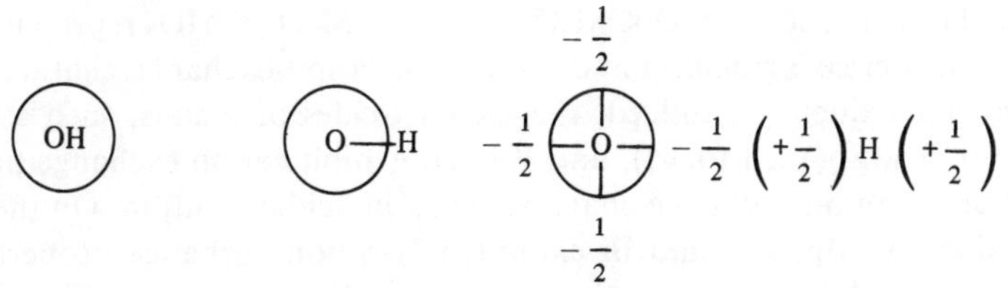

(a)   (b)   (c)

Case (a), implying random orientation or free rotation, is apparently realized in the high temperature form of KOH. The transformation from (b) to (c) is to be expected with increasing charge and decreasing size of the cation. If as far as possible the charge is neutralized locally, the discussion is put in a more precise form by defining the electrostatic bond valency (e.s.v.) in the following way. If a cation with charge $+Ze$ is surrounding by n oxygens, the strength of bonds from the cation to its oxygen neighbors is Z/n (if O^{2-} forms part of several coordination polyhedra, the sum of the e.s.v. would be equal to 2, corresponding to the numerical value of the charge on O^{2-}).

The e.s.v. in the $X-O-H$ system can be classified into the following three types:[8]

1. e.s.v. $\leqslant \frac{1}{2}$:   hydroxides of alkali metal, alkaline earth metals, transition metals etc. (hydroxy bond)
2. $\frac{1}{2} \leqslant$ e.s.v. $\leqslant 1$: $Be(OH)_2$, $Al_2O_3 \cdot nH_2O$, $Fe_2O_3 \cdot nH_2O$
        $TiO_2 \cdot nH_2O$, $ZrO_2 \cdot nH_2O$, $Sb_2O_5 \cdot nH_2O$ (hydrogen bond with OH)
        $WO_3 \cdot nH_2O$, $MoO_3 \cdot nH_2O$ etc.
3. e.s.v. > 1: H_2SO_4, $HClO_4$, $HBrO_4$, H_3PO_4 (isolated hydrogen bond)

For example, in the $Mg-O$ bond with a coordination group MgO_6, the e.s.v. is $1/3$, and for $Al-O$ in AlO_6 and $Be-O$ in BeO_4, they are $\frac{1}{2}$. In type (1), there are no hydrogen bonds in the structures. Oxy-hydroxides, having values between 0.5 and 1, are expected to be ion exchange materials.

It is well established, particularly for SiO_2 gel, that the first layer of adsorbed water is present as $X-OH$ groups and that the second layer is hydrogen bonded to the first. Thus, arrangements such as

$$X-O-H\text{---}O\begin{smallmatrix} \diagup H \\ \diagdown H \end{smallmatrix}$$

should be present on immersed surfaces. Proton transfer may occur in the following ways (1) rupture of the OH bond in XOH, (2) formation of an OH bond in hydronium ion, and (3) removal of the proton from the electrostatic field of the central metal-oxygen anion.

If X has a small radius and is a highly electronegative element, acidic properties will appear. With increase in the size of X or with a decrease in its electronegativity, amphoteric behavior will result first and this will be followed by basic behavior. If we consider the polarizing power of a cation M^{n+} to be proportional to Z/r^2, it can be readily understood why there is hydrogen bonding in, for example, $Al(OH)_3$ but not in $Ca(OH)_2$ or $La(OH)_3$, the numerical values of the polarizing powers being 2.0(Ca), 2.67(La), and 10.67(Al). Various hydroxides and hydrous oxides of polyvalent metals can be classified, in terms of the polarizing power of the metal, as anion exchangers (I), amphoteric exchangers (II), and cation exchangers (III) (see Figure 8). The hydroxides are included in this figure.

The presence of additional oxygen attached to X increases the acid strength of the compound. Thus, the series $MO < M_2O_3 < MO_2 < M_2O_5 < MO_3$ represents an approximate order of increasing acidity and increasing cation-exchange character for the insoluble hydrous oxides.[22,83] Indeed, the higher oxides of metals, such as the hydrous oxides of Nb, Ta, Sb(V), Mo(VI), and W(VI), exhibit cation exchange properties and show little or no anion exchange character even in acidic solution. On the other hand, hydrous oxides of Mg, La, and Bi exhibit only anion exchange properties and little cation exchange behavior even at the high pH of 12. Amphoteric ion exchangers are found mainly among the hydrous oxide of ter- and quadrivalent metals.

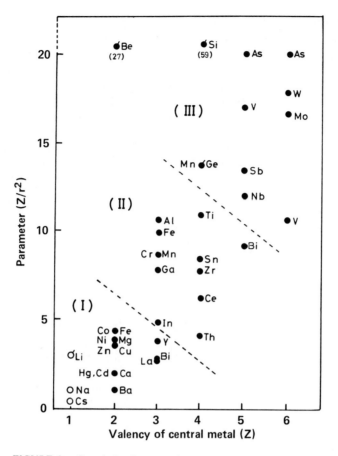

FIGURE 8.   Correlation between the parameter (Z/r^2) and valency of the central metal. Values of r are taken from Ref. 82, assuming that the metals have a coordination number of 6 (●), except Li, Be, Si, and Mn which have CN4 (◖).

Amphoteric exchange reaction can be deduced by following the progressive dissociation reaction of an acid;

Anion exchange reaction: $-XOH_2^+ \rightleftharpoons XOH + H^+$ K_1
   (reverse reaction)

$$(5)*$$

Cation exchange reaction: $-XOH \rightleftharpoons -XO^- + H^+$ K_2

$$(6)$$

Since

$$K = K_1 K_2 = \frac{[-XO^-][H^+]^2}{[-XOH_2^+]}$$

$$(7)$$

$$[-XOH_2^+] = [-XO^-]$$

---

* Or $XOH \rightleftharpoons X^+ + OH^-$

At EAP, $[-XOH^+_2] = [-XO^-]$

$$pH(\text{at EAP}) = 1/2(pK_1 + pK_2) \tag{8}$$

This pH indicates the average value of pK_1 at first dissociation and pK_2 at second dissociation. This relationship (Equation 8) is very close to that of IEP.

Parks[41] has pointed out that there is a good correlation between the IEP of a solid surface and $(Z/R)_{eff}$, corrected for crystal field effects, coordination, hydration, and other factors. He also indicates that the broad probable IEP range characteristic of a cation oxidation state may be selected from about 170 data in his Table 1, as shown below.

M_2O;	IEP > pH 11.5
MO	8.5 < IEP > pH 12.5
M_2O_3;	6.5 < IEP < 10.4
MO_2	0 < IEP < 7.5
M_2O_5, MO_3;	IEP < 0.5

A quantitative explanation of acid strength was carried out for oxyacids in aqueous solution by Kossiakoff and Harker,[84] by assuming a charge distribution and their structure configurations. Unfortunately, no structural data is available for the hydrous oxides because many of them are amorphous.

The extent to which anions are polarized increases with increasing cation charge and decreasing cation radius. It would be desirable to combine the two in some fashion and this has been done empirically by Cartledge,[85] in terms of ionic potential (ϕ), which is defined by the relation:

$$\phi = \frac{\text{Cation charge}}{\text{Cation radius}}$$

Ion hydration, complex formation, and acid-base behavior among oxygen-hydrogen compounds may be correlated with ionic potential data.

A fairly good linear relationship is obtained by plotting EAP versus ionic potential values rather than that between EAP and $(Z/R)^*_{eff}$, except for Be, Al, Fe(III) (see Figure 9). Similar arguments have been used for the interpretation of the change in IEP of a solid in terms of the strength of the oxyacids, $MO_m(OH)_n$.[86,87] In the latter case an increase in the ratio, m/n, is said to result in an effective increase in ϕ, and consequently in the acid strength.

The pH titration curves show quantitatively the uptakes of the exchanging ions provided the ion exchangers are practically insoluble. However, pK values cannot be obtained directly from such curves. The relation between the pK of an ionogenic group in the exchanger and the pH of the aqueous solution must be established. "Apparent" pK values can be obtained in the following way:[88]

The pK value of an acid group RH is defined as the negative logarithm of the dissociation constant K.

$$K = \frac{[\overline{R^-}][\overline{H^+}]}{[\overline{RH}]} \tag{9}$$

The degree of dissociation α and the pH in the exchanger are defined by

$$\alpha \equiv \frac{[\overline{R^-}]}{[\overline{R^-}] + [\overline{RH}]} \qquad \overline{pH} \equiv -\log[\overline{H^+}] \tag{10}$$

---

* The term R is the sum of the average diameter of the oxide ion (2.80 Å) and ionic crystal radius of the metal atom.

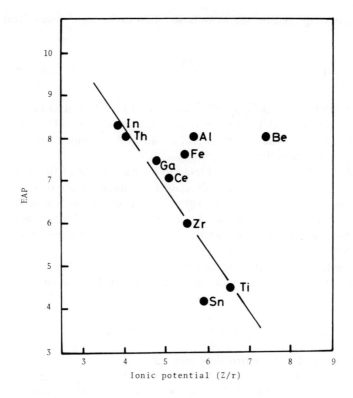

FIGURE 9. Correlation between ionic potential and equiadsorption points(EAP) of amphoteric hydrous oxides of ter- and quadrivalent metals. Values (r) are taken from Reference 82, EAP data from Reference 22.

From Equations 9 and 10 one obtains

$$\overline{pH} = pK - \log \frac{1-\alpha}{\alpha} \qquad (11)$$

The second term in Equation 11 vanishes when $\alpha = 0.5$(50% exchange). As a first approximation, it can be assumed that the concentration ratio $[Na^+] / [H^+]$ is the same in the ion exchanger and in the aqueous solution.

$$[\overline{H^+}] = [H^+] [\overline{Na^+}]/[Na^+] \qquad (12)$$

At 50% exchange, the Na$^+$ concentration in the exchanger is

$$[\overline{Na^+}] = \frac{[\overline{X}]}{2} \quad (\alpha = 0.5) \qquad (13)$$

where $[\overline{X}] = [\overline{RH}] + [R^-]$ is the total concentration of (dissociated and undissociated) ionogenic groups.

One obtains from Equations 10 to 12

$$pK = pH + \log[Na^+] - \log \frac{[\overline{X}]}{2} \qquad (14)$$

The corresponding relation for weak-base anion exchangers, when titrated with HCl, is

$$pK_1 = pH - \log[Cl^-] + \log \frac{[\overline{X}]}{2} \qquad (15)*$$

Equation 14 can be used for computing pK values of weak-acid cation exchangers from pH titrations. The pK values of the different groups in polyfunctional exchangers can also be calculated, provided that the values differ sufficiently (more than 3) so that the titration curves show distinct steps.

Most hydrous oxides may be considered to have a number of functional groups with overlapping different pK values, as described previously. Care must be taken for the determination of the 50% exchange value for an individual functional group, when Equation 14 is employed. Equations 14 and 15 were derived with a number of simplifying assumptions and thus give approximate values.[88] However, they are sufficient for most practical applications.

From the extensive pH-titration and pH-capacity data of Abe and Ito,[22] the following approximate acidity series can be deduced for hydrous oxides of quinquevalent metals

$$Nb_2O_5 < Ta_2O_5 < Sb_2O_5$$

for the hydrous oxides of quadrivalent metals

$$ThO_2 < CeO_2 < ZrO_2 < TiO_2 < SnO_2 < SiO_2 < MnO_2$$

for hydrous oxides of tervalent metals

$$La_2O_3 < Bi_2O_3 < Al_2O_3 < In_2O_3 < Ga_2O_3 < Mn_2O_3$$

and for hydrous oxide of divalent metals

$$MgO < BeO$$

As described earlier, it was believed until recently that silica gel showed no anion exchange character at all,[89] even in acid solution, but anion exchange has occurred at pH 3.[5] The isoelectric point of silica gel is generally accepted to about 2.[41,64]

Acid-base character is relative, varying with the polarizing tendency of the metal in the surface XOH groups. Furthermore, the adsorption properties of hydrous oxides are very specific for certain elements, and the pH titration curve may vary with the chemical species to be titrated.

It has been known that the IEP for amphoteric oxides is affected by the presence of impurities. This is called specific adsorption, using the term in the sense used by Graham.[90] The specific adsorption of an anion would be expected to produce a negative surface charge under conditions otherwise identical with the IEP, and to increase cation exchange ability. When alkali or cations are introduced into an amphoteric hydrous oxide, the material would be expected to behave as an anion exchanger. In con-

---

* K_1 is the same definition as Equation 5. Overall anion-exchange reaction can be represented by $\overline{RH} + H^+ + Cl^- \rightleftharpoons \overline{RH_2 + Cl^-}$. Thus,

$$\frac{1}{[H^+]} = \frac{1}{Ka} \cdot \frac{[Cl^-]}{[Cl^-]} \cdot \frac{[\overline{RH}]}{[\overline{RH_2^+}]}$$

trast, when amphoteric hydrous oxides react with polyvalent anions, the materials behave as cation exchangers.

III. HYDROUS OXIDES OF QUINIQUE- AND SEXIVALENT METALS

Hydrous oxides of Nb, Ta, Sb(V), Mo(VI), and W(VI) exhibit cation exchange properties, as described in Section II.

Among them hydrous antimony(V) oxides (so-called antimonic acid or polyantimonic acid) has been one of the most intensively studied, owing to its high exchange capacity, a reasonable rate of exchange and desorption, and high selectivities for certain elements.

A. Antimonic Acid (Polyantimonic Acid)

In 1923, Jander and Simon[91] reported that "so-called" antimonic(V) acid adsorbed lithium ions form a dilute lithium sulfate solution, giving an amorphous mass of indefinite composition which has been mistaken for definite antimonates similar to phosphates. Jander[92] indicated that this adsorption behavior might be attributed to the chemical action of the oxide gel. Ghosh and Dhar[93] reported that the coagulation values of Sb_2O_5 gel obeys the Shulz-Hardy rule.

In recent years, Abe and Ito,[22,94,95] and Lefebvre[96] have reported that the adsorption and desorption of potassium ions on antimonic acid have been found to be attributable to the exchange between the hydrogen ions in the acid and potassium ions in the external solution. Lefebvre and Gaymard[97] have also reported that the adsorption of alkali and alkaline earth metals on antimonic acid is governed by an ion exchange mechanism with a selectivity sequence in the order: $Na^+ > K^+ > NH_4^+ > Rb^+ > Cs^+$ and $Ba^{2+} > Sr^{2+} > Ca^{2+} > Mg^{2+}$. Baetsle et al.,[98,99] have also reported that polyantimonic acid shows promise for ^{90}Sr and ^{137}Cs recovery from acid reprocessing effluents. The adsorption properties of antimonic acid cation exchangers depend on their preparative conditions, e.g., aging, drying conditions, etc.[38] Crystalline antimonic acid (C—SbA) shows extremely high values of distribution coefficients for Na^+,[100,101] Sr^{2+},[98,102-104] Cd^{2+}[102,105-106], and Hg^{2+}.[107] Hydrated antimony pentoxide(HAP) also exhibits extremely high adsorptive ability for Na^+, Ag^+, Ta^+ even in concentrated mineral acids.[108]
tive ability for Na^+, Ag^+, Ta^+ even in concentrated mineral acids.[108]

These properties can be applied widely for the selective removal of Na^+ from biological materials or high purity substances for the determination of trace elements by neutron activation analysis.

1. Preparation of Antimonic(V) Acid (Polyantimonic Acid)

Much pertinent information relating to the preparation of antimonic acid or hydrous antimony pentoxide is to be found in the literature. The early information was summarized in the standard books of Mellor[109] and Gmelin.[110] Even here, much confusion is apparent, and contradictory statements are not hard to find. For example, Fremy and Senderens* showed that the water content in the antimonic acid varies according to the kind of starting antimony salt. However, Conrad and Daubrawa* showed that a definite hydrate was obtained under the same drying conditions regardless of different starting salts. Senderens and Delacroix[109] showed the presence of a soluble and insoluble form in the antimonic acid obtained from different antimony salts, but the relation between the forms and starting salts is not clear.

Simon and Thaler[111] proved that hydrated antimony pentoxide crystallized when heated at 300°C with water under pressure, and a definite hydrate, $3Sb_2O_5 \cdot 5H_2O$,

* See Table 3.

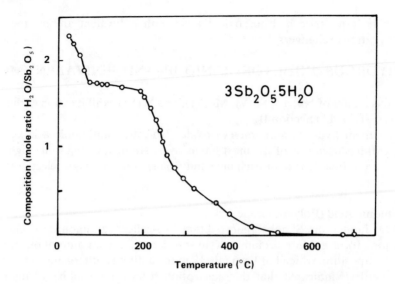

FIGURE 10.   Dehydration isobars for hydrous $3Sb_2O_5 \cdot 5H_2O$. (From Simon,
A. and Thaler, E., *Z. Anorg. Allg. Chem.*, 161, 113, 1927. With permission.)

existed which had a point of inflection for its dehydration curve (see Figure 10). Natta
and Baccaredda[112] concluded from systematic examination of the hydrated Sb_2O_5 prepared by decomposition of $KSb(OH)_6$ by HNO_3 that it was amorphous at first, but
after 5 years became crystalline, with a density of 3.647 gcm^{-3}, so that it is not necessary to heat this compound to make it crystalline. Such confusion is still a part of the
recent literature.

a. Amorphous and Crystalline Antimonic Acid

Recently, an extensive study of the preparation of antimonic acid has been carried
out by Abe and Ito,[38] and Novikov et al.[42] The precipitate of antimonic acid was obtained by one of several methods; hydrolysis of $SbCl_5$ in water,[92] by adding acid into
antimonate, and by passing a $KSb(OH)_6$ solution over a strong cation exchange resin
in the H^+ —form.[42,113] The precipitate is amorphous at first, but is gradually transformed to crystalline material by keeping it in the acidic solution for a long time.[38]
The crystallization is very sensitive to increasing temperature and concentration of
acid. Novikov et al.[42] indicated that the appearance of a weak indication of crystallinity
in the specimen was detected after approximately three months of aging the precipitate
(obtained by hydrolysis of $SbCl_5$) in 0.55 *M* acid. The time of aging can be reduced
by increasing the temperature to 80°C and by increasing the concentration of acid.
When the hydrochloric acid in the precipitate was decreased by washing with water, it
became colloidal passing through fine filter paper. Therefore, it is very difficult to
wash the precipitate free of chloride ions by a filtration procedure. Very pure antimonic acid is obtained by washing the precipitate with cold water with the aid of a
centrifuge.[38] Another preparation is based on passing a dilute aqueous solution
through a column of Dowex® 50[96] or KU-2[42] followed by subsequent evaporation or
treating the effluent with nitric acid. The evaporated material is obtainable as a glassy
and/or crystalline solid, depending on the subsequent treatment, e.g., time and temperature of aging etc.[38, 114-116] The sample treated with nitric acid solution is obtainable
as a crystalline material, if the concentration of the acid and the temperature are high
enough.[38]

Some other methods of preparation include oxidation of $SbCl_3$[104] with nitric acid or aqua regia and subsequent hydrolysis[38] or neutralization of Sb(V) salts with aqueous ammonia, and thermal polymerization of $NaSb(OH)_6$ at 250°C and subsequent treatment with nitric acid.[117] Whenever antimonic acid is prepared from solutions of antimonate salts or by addition of ammonia, appreciable amounts of cations are present in the precipitate due to an ion exchange reaction. These elements cannot be washed out with water, but can be removed by washing with a dilute nitric acid solution. When this procedure is carried out at a selectively high temperature, the amorphous material is easily transformed into crystals.[100]

b. Glassy Antimonic Acid[38]

When freshly prepared antimonic acid (in a wet state) is dissolved in a large amount of water, the clear solution gradually becomes turbid because of the formation of crystalline antimonic acid. However, if the freshly prepared antimonic acid is rapidly dissolved in a limited amount of hot water, a glassy material is obtained by evaporation. The glassy material is also obtained by hydrolysis of $SbCl_5$ at 90 to 89°C. Colin and Lefebvre[113] have reported that a stable form of amorphous antimonic acid can be obtained from antimonic acid prepared by the ion exchange procedure if the acid is immediately plunged into ethanol cooled at −4°C. The precipitate obtained is immediately filtered and dried at 25°C. X-Ray diffraction shows the product to be amorphous. The material may be a mixture of the glassy and amorphous forms.

c. Hydrothermal Treatment of Antimonic Acid

In the hydrothermal treatment of the freshly prepared antimonic acid at 300°C, the material (S_{300}) obtained consists of thin hexagonal crystals having a relatively small water content of $Sb_2O_5 \cdot O.49H_2O$.[38] There is no evidence for a definite hydrate. $3Sb_2O_5 \cdot 5H_2O$, as reported by Simon and Thaler.[111] More recently, Jansen[118] has reported that $Sb_2O_5 \cdot 3/5H_2O$ or $Sb_5O_{12}(OH) \cdot H_2O$ is obtained by hydrothermal treatment under pressure (6×10^7 Pa = 600 bar) at 550°C for 14 days. The crystal structure has been solved. The lattice constants are a = 5.518, b = 16.50, c = 5.519 Å, and β = 107.0° with the space group $P2_1/m$. Sb is centered on distorted oxygen octahedra which are linked by common corners and edges to form layers of the composition $Sb_5O_{13}^-$.

Girardi and Sabbioni[108] have reported that the precipitate obtained by hydrolysis of $SbCl_5$, washed and dried at 270°C for 5 hr, shows a cubic structure with a = 10.326 Å. However, Abe indicated that crystallization from the amorphous antimonic acid does not take place even at 270°C. The same conclusion is obtained by Novikov et al. (see Section III.2.d).

To summarize the preparative methods, amorphous antimonic acid is obtained by hydrolysis of $SbCl_5$ or by adding acid to antimonate salts at low temperature and subsequent aging for short times in the acid solution of low concentration. Crystalline antimonic acid is obtained by aging for a long time in an acid solution of relatively high concentration or by hydrolysis of $SbCl_5$ at 60 to 70°C. The glassy antimonic acid is obtained by hydrolysis of $SbCl_5$ at 90 to 98°C, or by dissolving the freshly prepared precipitate in hot water and subsequent evaporation of the liquid. The important factors are the temperature and period of time on aging, and concentration of acid to obtain these modifications, although different starting materials have been used. X-Ray diffraction patterns for antimonic acid obtained by various procedures are illustrated in Figure 11.[38]

2. Physical and Chemical Properties of Antimonic Acid

a. Water Composition in Antimonic Acid

In early studies, much attention was directed towards whether or not several hy-

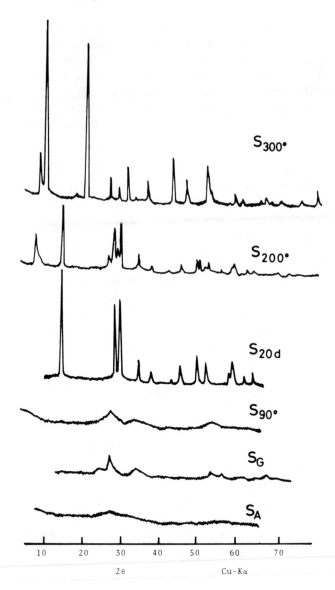

FIGURE 11.   X-ray powder diffraction patterns of antimonic acids obtained by various preparations. S_A; aged in 1 M HCl for 1 day at 25-30°C. S_G: dissolved in hot water and dried. S_{90}: hydrolyzed at 90-98°C. S_C: aged for over 20 days at 30°C S_{200}: hydrothermal treatment at 200°C. S_{300}: at 300°C. (From Abe, M. and Ito, T., *Bull. Chem. Soc. Jpn.*, 41, 333, 1968. With permission.)

drates, such as ortho-($Sb_2O_5 \cdot 3H_2O$), pyro-($Sb_2O_5 \cdot 2H_2O$), and meta-($Sb_2O_5 \cdot H_2O$), well known is the case of hydrated P_2O_5, existed.

Antimonic acid is usually regarded as hydrous antimony pentoxide, $Sb_2O_5 \cdot nH_2O$, with various water contents;[110] e.g., n = 1 to 6. The water contents found in early reports are summarized in Table 3. Conflicting results are not hard to find because conditions for preparation of antimonic acids were inadequately described. Furthermore, when the water content is determined by heating the material, no conclusive evidence has been available until recently on whether the heated material is Sb_3O_6OH, Sb_6O_{13}, or Sb_2O_4.

Table 3
COMPOSITION OF HYDROUS
ANTIMONY PENTOXIDE

H_2O/Sb_2O_5	Drying conditions	Ref.
6[a]	Exposed to air for 3 months at ambient temp.	1
5[a]	Stream of air	1
4	Dried in air for 3 months	1[b], 2[c], 4, 7
4	On gypsum plate	3
3	On conc. H_2SO_4	1, 3, 4, 6
2	At 100°C	3, 4, 5
2	At about 200°C	1
1.66	Hydrothermal	
1	Between 175 and 200°C	3, 4, 7
1	Between 100 and 200°C	5
1	About 300°C	1
0.5	At 300°C	5
0	At 275°C	3, 4
0	About 400°C	1

[a] Oxidized $SbCl_3$ with concd. HNO_3 and then hydrolyzed.
[b] Turbid material from 2.2 aqueous solution of Sb_2O_5.
[c] $SbCl_5$ + H_2O and $KSb(OH)_6$ + HNO_3.

References

1. Senderens, J. B., *Bl. Soc. Chim.,* 21, 48, 1899.
2. Fremy, E., *Ann. Chim. Phys.,* 23, 405, 1848.
3. Daubrawa, H., *Lib. Ann.,* 186, 118, 1871.
4. Geuther, A., *J. Pr. Ch.,* 4, 438, 1871.
5. Conrad, C. P., *Chem. N.,* 40, 198, 1879.
6. Beilstein, F., Blaese, O. V., *Acad. Petersb.,* 1, 97, 1890.
7. Berzelius, J., *Schw. J.,* 6, 158, 1812, data taken from Ref. 109 and 110.

Jander and Simon[91] prepared hydrates of antimony pentoxide by these methods: (1) the hydrolysis of the $SbCl_5$ at 0 to 1°C; (2) hydrolysis at 100°C; and (3) oxidation of the $SbCl_3$ by concentrated nitric acid and then hydrolysis of the product at 60°C. The speeds of dehydration of these acids in vacuo over concentrated sulfuric acid at room temperature, are indicated by the curves shown in Reference 109. Abe and Ito[38] revealed that slow dehydration of amorphous and glassy antimonic acid continued for a long time even if they were dried for a period of about 6 months. The crystalline acid gave an almost constant weight with a composition of $Sb_2O_5 \cdot 4H_2O$ on drying for a relatively short time of about 3 weeks (Figures 12 A and B). Similar slow dehydration is also observed for the dull semitransparent material prepared by Colin and Lefebvre.[113] The rate of dissolution in a solution of 0.05 M KI and 3 M HCl decreases with increasing age of the acid. This can be explained in that further polymerization occurs at room temperature even *in vacuo.*

The water composition of various antimonic acids reported recently by different authors is summarized in Table 4.

The composition of crystalline antimonic acid approaches $Sb_2O_5 \cdot 4H_2O$ at room temperature and the mol ratio of H_2O/Sb_2O_5 decreases with increasing drying temperature. The amorphous materials have relatively high water contents (4 to 6 H_2O) and the glassy materials have the compositions of $Sb_2O_5 \cdot 3.3$ to $4.5H_2O$, depending on the age of the acids because of further polymerization.

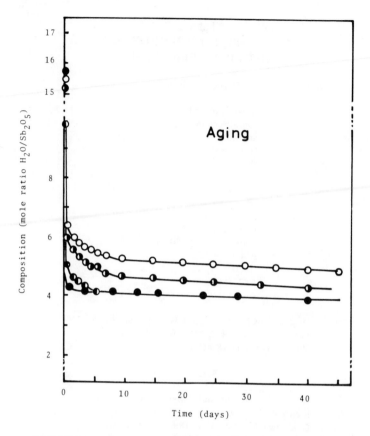

FIGURE 12A.   Effect of aging on the rate of dehydration of the precipitated antimonic acids. Aging: 1 day, ○; 3 days, ◑ ; 5 days, ◓ ; 7-30 days, ● ; Hydrolysis: 25°C. (From Abe, M. and Ito, T., *Bull. Chem. Soc. Jpn.*, 41, 333, 1968. With permission.)

b. X-Ray Diffraction Analysis

The X-ray diffraction patterns of antimonic acid or polyantimonic acid are well defined as the cubic pyrochlore(P) type (space group Fd3m).* However, slightly different values are found for the lattice constant and relative diffraction intensities with their methods of preparation and drying temperature.[38,108,117,119-123] As mentioned in a later section, crystalline antimonic acid may adsorb appreciable amounts of metal ions by ion exchange reaction, affecting the lattice constant and diffraction intensities. The data relative to crystalline antimonic acid reported by Abe and Ito[38] are essentially similar to those of the polyantimonic acid of Baetsle and Huys,[117] antimonic acid by Novikov et al.,[42] and Sb_2O_5 by Hanawalt, et al.[121] Accurate diffraction data reported recently are shown in Table 5 Baetsle and Huys[117] indicate that, based on the empirical formula $Sb_2O_5 \cdot 4H_2O$, a density of 4.27 gcm^{-3} and lattice parameter a = 10.3 Å, the molecular weight is about 2800 with 14 antimony atoms per unit cell. The structure proposed by Baetsle and Huys,[117] based on the powder pattern, is built up essentially of two polymeric structures based on $Sb(OH)_6^-$ octahedra; a trimeric structure unit empirical formula $H_3Sb_3O_4(OH)_{10}$ $(OH)_{10}$ with 4 oxygen atoms common to 3 Sb atoms, and a pentameric structure unit, empirical formula $H_5Sb_5O_4(OH)_{22}$, with 4 oxygen at-

---

*   The X-ray powder data of $Sb_2O_5 \cdot nH_2O$ are found in the ASTM card file of 2-1183($Sb_2O_5$3 H_2O), 2-1358(Sb_2O_5), 2-1386($Sb_2O_5H_2O$), 16-938(Sb_3O_6OH), 1-0154($Sb_2O_5 \cdot H_2O$), 11-690(Sb_2O_5), 20-111($Sb_2O_5 \cdot 4H_2O$) and 21-803($Sb_2O_5 \cdot 4H_2O$).

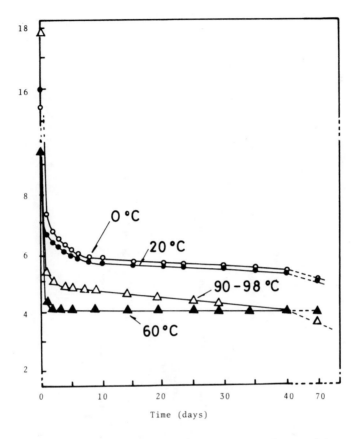

FIGURE 12B.   Effect of hydrolysis temperature on the rate of dehydration of the precipitated antimonic acids. All samples aged for 4 hr and dehydrated at room temperature. (From Abe, M. and Ito, T., *Bull. Chem. Soc. Jpn.*, 41, 333, 1968. With permission.)

oms of the central Sb octahedron linking 4 Sb(OH)$^-_6$ group around it (see Figure 13A). Three trimeric units and one pentameric unit constitute one unit cell of an empirical formula

$$[H_3Sb_3O_5(OH)_8]_3[H_3Sb_5O_6(OH)_{18}]$$

The empirical formula takes into account the interconnections of the units to each other. A proposed sketch of the unit cell of polyantimonic acid is shown in Figure 13B. The fourteen hydrogen ions associated with Sb polymers in maintaining electrical neutrality in the crystal are considered to be exchangeable ions, corresponding to the theoretical capacity of 5.05 meq/g.

A structural study has also been carried out by Olen'kova and Plyasova[124] showing that the Sb^{5+} cations occupy centers of oxygen octahedra and the overall structure is of the pyrochlore type.

C. Chemical Stability

The solubilities of the antimonic acids decrease with the time of aging or with increasing temperature of the hydrolysis up to 70°C. It can be concluded that amorphous and glassy forms are soluble and the crystalline form is insoluble. Dehydration at elevated temperatures result in improved stability because of further polymerization for the former two acids. The soluble forms are more stable in dilute solutions of acid

Table 4
WATER CONTENTS OF VARIOUS ANTIMONIC ACIDS

Antimonic acid type	Mol ratio (H_2O/Sb_2O_5)	Drying method	Density (g/cm³) and/or lattice constant (Å)	Preparation	Remarks	Ref.
Amorphous	3—4	70—90°C		Dowex® 50X2 + KSb(OH)₆		96
Crystalline	4			0.1 M HSb(OH)₆. Standing for 2—3 days	β-form	116
Amorphous	4.70—5.15	25—30°C (after 6 months)		SbCl₅ + H₂O, KSb(OH)₆ + HNO₃ (pH = 1.0), or metatic Sb + aqua regia. (short aging, and low acidic reagents.)	Sb₂O₄ at 900°C	38,95
Crystalline	3.70—4.07	25—30°C (after 6 months)	a = 10.38	(long aging, and highly acidic solution)	Sb₂O₄ at 900°C	38,95
Glassy	3.65—4.50	25—30°C (after 6 months)		SbCl₅ + H₂O at 90—98°C, or dissolution and drying	Sb₂O₄ at 900°C	38,95
Crystalline	4.3	Room?	(4.27) a = 10.25	KSb(OH)₆ + 1.5 M HNO₃, washed with 0.75 M HNO₃		117
	3.55	Room temp.	a = 10.338	SbCl₅ + H₂O (ice)		135
	3.67	Room temp.	a = 10.337	SbCl₅ + H₂O (ice) + H₂O₂		135
	3.51	Room temp.	a = 10.387	KSb(OH)₆ + excess HNO₃		135
	4	Room temp.		SbCl₅ + H₂O		153
Amorphous	4.04—5.75[a]	20°C(over P₂O₅)	(2.35—3.50)	KSb(OH)₆ + KU2, KSb(OH)₆ + HNO₃ or SbCl₅ + H₂O	Sb₂O₄ at 1000°C	42
Crystalline	3.12—3.99[a]	Dried at 60 ∿ 180°C	(3.96—4.37)	KSb(OH) + Ku2, KSb(OH)₆ + HNO₃ or SbCl₅ + H₂O		42

[a] Water contents calculated by author.

Table 5
ACCURATE X-RAY POWDER DIFFRACTION DATA FOR ANTIMONIC ACID AND POLYANTIMONIC ACID

	Crystalline antimonic acid[38]			Polyantimonic acid[117]		Antimonic acid[123]			
						150°C*		18°C*	
hkl	d(Å)	I/I₀	a*(Å)	d(A) (I/I₀)$_{cal}$	(I/I₀)obs	d(Å)	I/I₀	d(Å)	I/I₀
111	5.985	100	10.366	5.831(100)	100	6.17	s	5.93	vs
311	3.128	70	10.374	3.097(74)	62--70	3.15	vs	3.09	vs
222	2.995	75	10.375	2.957(69)	62—70	3.03	vs	2.98	vs
400	2.594	15	10.376	2.569(11)	14—17	2.614	w	2.57	m
331	2.381	11	10.379₅	2.355(27)	10—13	2.391	w	2.359	w
422	2.119	2	10.380₉	—		—		—	
511	1.998₄	17	10.382₉	1.981(14)	14—18	2.004	m	1.984	m
440	1.835₈	31	10.384₈	1.822(32)	31—36	1.840	s	1.819	s
531	1.754₅	22	10.381₅	1.741(12)	22—23	1.756	m	1.739	m
533	1.583	11	10.380₄	—		—		—	
622	1.565₂	24	10.382₄	1.555(24)	22—29	1.568	s	1.552	s
444	1.498₃	6	10.380₅	1.490(10)	3.5—6	1.501	w	1.484	w
711	1.453₈	12	10.382₂	1.445	10.4—14.7	1.455	w	1.441	w
731	1.351₆	12	10.381₈	1.343	8.6—11.8	1.350	w	1.341	
800	1.298	3	10.384	—		1.298	vw	1.287	vw
733	1.268₄	1	10.382₃	—		—		—	
822	1.223₃	1	10.380	—		—		—	
751	1.1987	4	10.381	—					
662	1.190₇	8	10.380₃	1.185	7—10	1.192	w	1.181	w
840	1.160₈	7	10.382₅	1.155	6—13	1.161	w	1.151	w
911	1.139₅	5	10.381₃	—		1.140	vw	1.130	vw
931	1.088₃	4	10.381₇						
844	1.059₇	4	10.382₈						
933	1.0434	3	10.3817						
951	1.0035	4	10.3803						
10·2·2	0.9989	6	10.381						
953	0.9677	2	10.377₄						
11·1·1	0.9362	1	10.383						
880	0.9174	1	10.379₂						
11·3·1	0.9070	1	10.381₁						
11·3·3	0.8807	4	10.383₃						
10·6·2	0.8776	8	10.383₉						
12·0·0	0.8652	5	10.382₄						
11·5·1	0.8566₅	2	10.386₂						
11·5·3	0.8337₈	2	10.380₅						
12·4·0	0.8209	4	10.383₆						

and salts than water. Therefore, they can be used as cation exchangers in these solutions. However, if the samples are immersed in an acid solution at relatively high concentration and temperature, they are gradually transformed into crystalline material without change in apparent shape.

Crystalline antimonic acid is extremely stable to most reagents, and is very difficult to dissolve, even by heating it with a concentrated hydrochloric acid or 1 M potassium hydroxide solution. However, peptization occurs when crystalline antimonic acid is kept for a long time in contact with pure water. Furthermore, the acid is physically unstable as compared with glassy gels, such as silica gel, zirconium oxide gel, and titanium oxide gel. Some attempts have been made to stabilize it by supporting it on silica gel[125-129] or active carbon.[130] Especially, Kourin et al.[129] have reported that a large particle size of 0.5 to 1.0 mm is obtained when the sol-gel method is employed for the preparation of particles in a silica gel matrix.

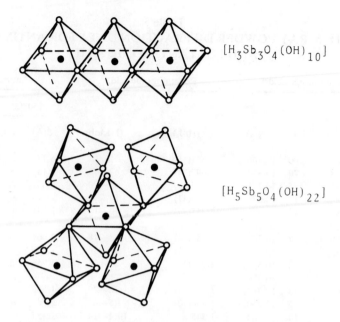

$[H_3Sb_3O_4(OH)_{10}]$

$[H_5Sb_5O_4(OH)_{22}]$

FIGURE 13A.   Antimonic- acid polymers; filled circles are Sb and open circles are O^{2-} or OH^-. (Reprinted with permission from *J. Inorg. Nucl. Chem.*, Vol. 30, Baetsle, L. W. and Huys, D., structure and ion-exchange characteristics of polyantimonic acid, Copyright 1968, Pergamon Press, Ltd.)

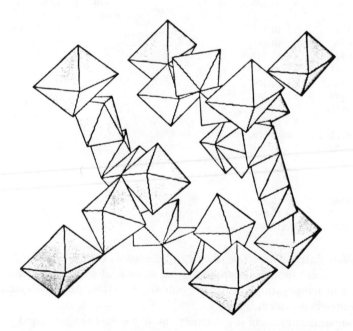

FIGURE 13B.   Unit cell of polyantimonic acid. (Reprinted with permission from *J. Inorg. Nucl. Chem.*, 161. 30, Baetsle, L. H. and Huys, D., structure and ion-exchange characteristics of polyantimonic acid, Copyright 1968, Pergamon Press, Ltd.)

d. Thermal Analysis of Different Antimonic Acids

It is very important to identify and distinguish the different antimonic acids from each other, to determine their water compositions, and to know the nature of water and hydroxyl groups in the matrix.

The existence of two forms of Sb_2O_3, servantite and senarmontite, is unquestioned, and both the Sb_2O_4 dimorphs (α- and β-) have been well characterized by single-crystal X-ray studies. However, much confusion can be found in the literature regarding the higher oxides and their hydrous oxides.

Szilagyi[131] indicated that Sb_2O_5 began to decompose to Sb_2O_4 at temperatures higher than 300°C. Thermal gravimetric analysis by Goto[132] revealed that Sb_3O_4 was formed by heating the antimonic acid at 610°C. From a study of the isobaric (10 torr) "equilibration curve" for antimonic acid, Simon and Thaler[133] proposed the following two steps of thermal reactions:

$$3Sb_2O_5 \longrightarrow Sb_6O_{13} + O_2 \tag{16}$$

$$2Sb_6O_{13} \longrightarrow 6Sb_2O_4 + O_2 \tag{17}$$

The deoxidation of Sb_2O_5 begins at 380°C and Sb_6O_{13} appears to have been assigned to an apparent plateau (620 to 720°C). Sb_2O_4 is formed by further heating at 750°C and Sb_2O_3 at 920°C. However, the material corresponding to this plateau range (750 to 920°C) gave an X-ray powder pattern of the cubic (P) type rather than that of Sb_2O_4, which prompted Dihlstrom and Westgren[120] to reassign the 750 to 900°C plateau to the composition Sb_3O_6OH. Nevertheless, both these compounds are accepted by many present day texts, as is anhydrous Sb_2O_5 whose formation by dehydrating antimonic acid was questioned as long ago as 1927. The X-ray powder data for "Sb_2O_5" by Swanson et al.[122] is listed in the 1966 edition of the ASTM X-ray powder data card file (No. 11-690) with an erroneous composition.[134,135] This "Sb_2O_5" was prepared by dissolving antimony metal in hydrochloric acid. Nitric acid was then used to precipitate an oxide, which then was heated at 780°C for 30 min. The commercial products listed as "Sb_2O_5" have been found to be either α-Sb_2O_4 or Sb_6O_{13} by Stewart et al.[135] Therefore, the water content of antimonic acid or hydrated antimony pentoxide is doubtful, although this content can be defined for specific heating temperatures and times.

Extensive studies of the materials obtained by heating the different antimonic acids have been carried out by Abe and Ito with X-ray, IR, and chemical analysis,[134,136] and with X-ray analysis and Mössbauer spectra by Stewart et al.[135] Typical DTA curves for the three different antimonic acid are illustrated in Figure 14. Large differences can be seen in the individual antimonic acids.

Thermogravimetric curves (TG), shown in Figure 15, correlate the endothermic peaks with the loss of water or oxygen by the samples. The weight of C−SbA heated to 200°C returns to its initial value by adsorbing moisture in air on keeping at room temperature, and no changes occur in its X-ray diffraction patterns and IR spectra.

In order to clarify the processes of thermal decomposition, a systematic study has been carried out by chemical analysis*, Figures 16A, B, and C, X-ray analysis, Figures

---

* The chemical analysis was carried out in the following way: The heated samples were dissolved in 0.25 M HCl solution containing 1 g of KCl under nitrogen atmosphere and KI added initiating the following reactions.

$$Sb_2O_4 + 8 H^+ + 2 I^- \longrightarrow 2 Sb^{3+} + I_2 + 4 H_2O$$

$$Sb_2O_5 + 10 H^+ + 4 I^- \longrightarrow 2 Sb^{3+} + 2 I_2 + 5 H_2O$$

The liberated I_2 is titrated with a standard sodium thiosulfate solution and amounts of Sb^{3+} in the residual solution is determined iodometrically. The water content was calculated by difference.

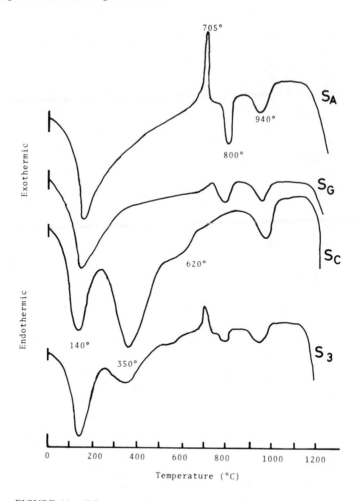

FIGURE 14.   DTA curves for various antimonic acids. Heating rate;
7°C/min, sample taken; 500 mg. Samples; S_A: amorphous, S_G: glassy,
S_C: crystalline, S_3: sample aged in 1 *M* HCl solution at 25-30°C for 3
days. (From Abe, M., *Kogyo Kagaku Zasshi*, 70, 2226, 1967. With permission.)

17A, B, and IR spectra, Figure 18, for the heated samples of three different antimonic
acids.[134, 136]

When the antimonic acids are dehydrated and deoxidized by heating, the first reproducible compound (Structure C in Figures 17A and B) appears in the range of 820 to
900°C (DTA temp.) or 700°C (for 5 hr heating) for amorphous and glassy antimonic
acid, and of 700°C to 900°C (DTA temp.) or 600 to 800°C (for 5 hr heating) for
crystalline one. Its IR spectrum and chemical analysis show no evidence of OH and
H_2O.[136] These results reveal that compound C has a stoichiometry $Sb_2O_{4.33}$ corresponding to Sb_6O_{13} but it is neither Sb_2O_5 nor Sb_3O_6OH. The X-ray powder data of structure
C, Sb_6O_{13}, ASTM card 21-51, is accurately compatible with Swanson's data (ASTM
card 11-690) listed erroneously as Sb_2O_5. The same conclusion is obtained by Stewart
et al.[135] that the Mössbauer spectrum of the $Sb_2O_{4.33}$ contains two peaks corresponding
to Sb^{III} and Sb^V, respectively, whose area ratio is 0.42.

By further heating Sb_6O_{13}, a mixture of α- and β-Sb_2O_4 is formed in the range of
1000 to 1200°C. Finally, at the temperature above 1200°C, Sb_2O_4 sublimes without
transforming first to Sb_2O_3. When heating is discontinued before all of the Sb_2O_4 had
sublimed, no weight gain occurs on cooling the remaining material. This indicates that

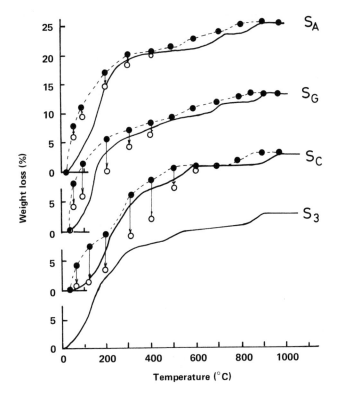

FIGURE 15. Weight loss curves for various antimonic acids at elevated temperature. TG curves heating rate 7°C/min; ● , heated at the constant temperature for 5 hr; O, keeping the heated samples in air at room temperature for 1 month. Sample designations same as for Figure 14. (From Abe, M. and Ito, T., *Bull. Chem. Soc. Jpn.*, 41, 2366, 1968. With permission.)

no oxidation takes place on cooling and the X-ray powder pattern shows only β-Sb_2O_4 to be present.[135] However, crystals of both Sb_2O_4 and Sb_2O_3 can be collected from the wall of the TGA furnace, where they have been deposited as the result of the sublimation process. When the heating is carried out in a nitrogen atmosphere, only α-Sb_2O_4 is formed in a range of 760 to 800°C (for 5 hr heating) and then sublimes at temperatures above 800°C.[134] The endothermic peak at 940°C is assigned to the transformation from Sb_6O_{13} to Sb_2O_4, regardless of the species of antimonic acid. The thermal decomposition schemes proposed for the three different antimonic acids are summarized in Table 6.[134]

The large exothermic peak at 705°C for S_A can be assigned to the crystallization of Sb_2O_5 and the deoxidization occurs simultaneously. On the DTA curve for the crystalline antimonic acid, two large endothermic peaks are found in the temperature range where no loss of oxygen occurs. The weight loss observed at a temperature below 200°C is reversible, moisture in air being absorbed at room temperature. No changes occur in the X-ray diffraction pattern (see Figure 17) and IR spectrum (see Figure 18). This first endothermic peak is assigned to the removal of free water (interstitial water). Upon increasing the temperature above 300°C, the crystalline antimonic acid begins to lose bonded water which constitutes part of the crystal structure, and the lattice constant of the heated materials begins to decrease without any change in the space group of Fd3m. A similar result was obtained by Kleshchev et al.[137] On further heating up to 400°C, the antimonic acids develop a brownish yellow color which reverts to white upon decomposition to Sb_6O_{13} at 500°C for 5 hr. Another scheme for the thermal

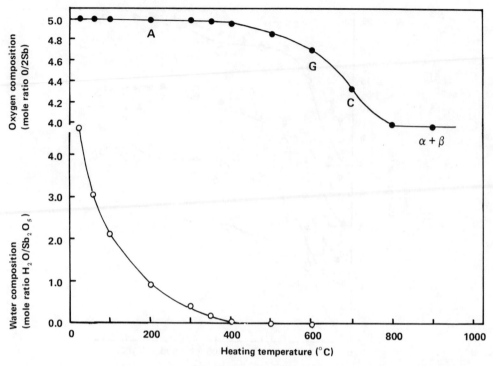

FIGURE 16A.   The changes in water and oxygen content of the amorphous antimonic acid heated at various temperatures. All samples were heated for 5 hr and cooled for 30 min. Marks of A, C, and $\alpha + \beta$ correspond to the structures in Figure 17A. (From Abe, M., *Kogyo Kagaku Zasshi*, 70, 2226, 1967. With permission.)

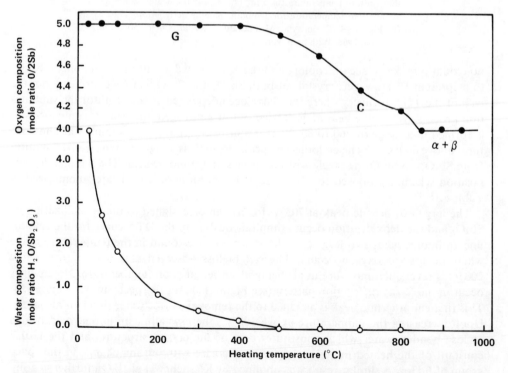

FIGURE 16B.   The changes in water and oxygen content of the glassy antimonic acid heated at various temperatures. All samples were heated for 5 hr. and cooled for 30 min. Marks of G, C, and $\alpha + \beta$ correspond to the structures of Figure 17A. (From Abe, M., *Kogyo Kagaku Zasshi*, 70, 2226, 1967. With permission.)

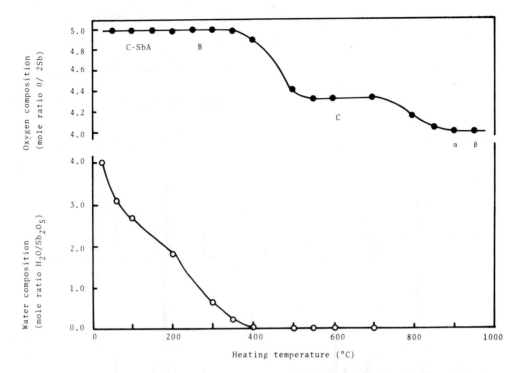

FIGURE 16C.   The changes in water and oxygen content of the crystalline antimonic acid heated at various temperatures. All samples were heated for 5 hr and cooled for 30 min. Marks of C-SbA, B, C, and $\alpha + \beta$ correspond to the structures of Figure 17B. (From Abe, M., *Kogyo Kagaku Zasshi*, 70, 2226, 1967. With permission.)

decomposition of crystalline antimonic acid, leading to the stepwise formation of H_3OSbO_3 (148°C DTA temp.), $Sb_3O_6OH(348°C)$, $Sb_6O_{13}(620°C)$, and $Sb_2O_4(940°C)$, has been reported by Novikov et al.[123] This scheme is somewhat at variance with the data in Figure 16C. In recent conclusive evidence, at least, the material heated at 700 to 800°C is neither Sb_3O_6OH, proposed by Dihlstrom and Westgrem,[120] nor "Sb_2O_5" reported by Swanson et al.,[122] but is Sb_6O_{13}.

e. IR Studies on Antimonic(V) Acids

The IR absorption bands in the region 400 to 4000 cm⁻¹ are summarized in Table 7. These data represent the results of four independent studies[136,138-140] and are of interest mainly as a means of clarifying the surface structure of the different antimonic acids, especially hydrogen bonding with Sb—O.

The well-defined IR spectra of sodium antimonate and sodium hexa-hydroxo-antimonate $Na(Sb(OH)_6$ have been included since they give useful information about the assignment of bands observed on the antimonic acids. Siebert[141] ascribes the peaks between 1030 and 1120 cm⁻¹ to δ-SbOH, and the peaks between 528 and 775 cm⁻¹ to v-SbO on $Na[Sb(OH)_6]$ in which the six OH groups coordinate with one atom of antimony octahedrally (see Figures 19A and B). This conclusion is supported from the results of substitution by deuterium (see Figure 19B). The peak at 2145 cm⁻¹ on the antimonate is probably assigned to an overtone of the SbOH deformation vibration.[141] From analogy of IR spectra between crystalline antimonic(V) acid and $Na[Sb(OH)_6]$, Abe and Ito[136] ascribe the peak at 3350 cm⁻¹ to the stretching vibration of the interstitial water, the peak at 2420 cm⁻¹ to an overtone of the SbOH deformation vibration, the peak at 1280 cm⁻¹ to SbOH deformation vibration, and peaks at 840 and 740 cm⁻¹ to the stretching vibration of SbO. When the crystalline antimonic(V) acid is exchanged with various metal ions, the deformation band of SbOH is shifted to lower vibration

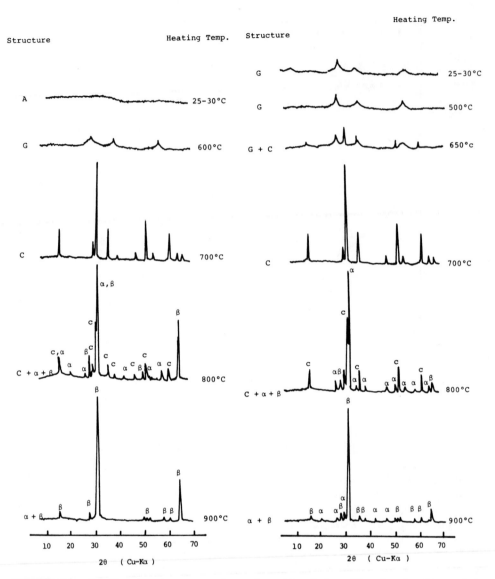

FIGURE 17A.   The X-ray powder patterns of amorphous (A) and glassy (G) antimonic acid treated thermally. Samples heated at constant temperature for 5 hr. Structure: A, amorphous; G, glassy, C, Sb_6O_{13}; α, α-Sb_2O_4 (orthorhombic-cervantite) β, β-Sb_2O_4 (monoclinic). (From Abe, M., *Kogyo Kagaku Zasshi*, 70, 2226, 1967. With permission.)

frequency, depending on the loading of the exchanged ions (Figure 19A, right) with little change in the intensities. It is known that an atom or molecule adsorbed near the surface perturbs the motion of atoms of a group, causing a shift in some group vibration frequency.[136] Such a shift is evidence that the deformation frequency at 1280 cm^{-1} on the hydrogen ion form is affected by chemically adsorbed ions. It is possible to explain a shift to lower frequency, assuming that an increase in the reduced mass occurs near the SbOH group in the crystalline antimonic(V) acid. A similar shift can be seen on the C—SbA exchanged with Ag$^+$ which is much different from Ag[Sb(OH)$_6$].[139] From these results, the following surface structure is proposed for the empirical formula of $H_2Sb_2O_5(OH)_2$ in crystalline antimonic acid. The hydrogen ions in the structure are combined as H_3O^+, and the ion exchangeable hydrogen ions are surrounded by oxygen atoms, as is Na$^+$ in Na[Sb(OH)$_6$]. In this compound, the adsorption bands of the OH group and interstitial water appear almost at the same position (3400 to

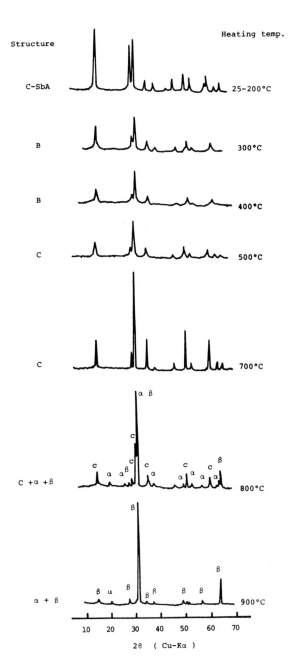

FIGURE 17B.   The X-ray powder patterns of crystalline antimonic acid treated thermally at constant temperature for 5 hr. Structure: C-SbA, crystalline antimonic acid: b, Sb_2O_5 or $Sb_3O_6(OH)$?; others are same as Figure 17A.

3500 cm^{-1}). Novikov et al.[138] ascribe the bands at 3300 and 2900 cm^{-1} to strong hydrogen bonds with water OH groups to the hydrogen-bearing oxygen of SbOH; the bands are due to the long hydrogen bonding Sb−OH...OH or Sb−OH...O/H_2. The band attributed to the hydrogen bonding at 2900 cm^{-1} decreases by ion exchange with alkali metal cations. The intensity of the bands at 2900, 2440, and 1140 cm^{-1} is not altered by heating the C−SbA up to 200°C. Then they decrease above 250°C (see Figure 18), corresponding to irreversible loss of structural water molecules accompanied by the

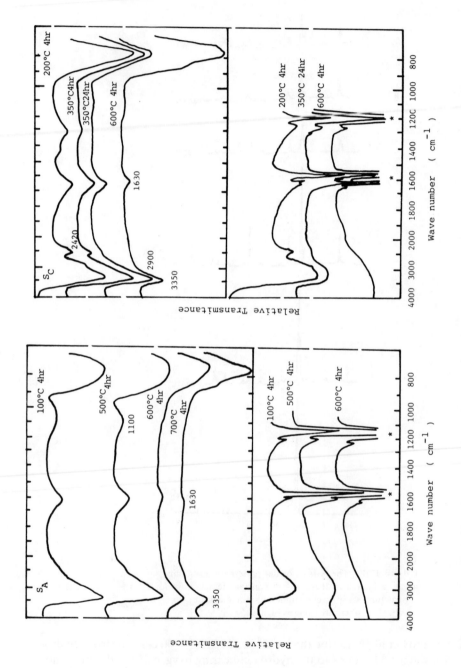

FIGURE 18. Infrared spectra of antimonic acids after heating up to 700°C. (Top) KBr disk method. (Bottom) H C.B(hexachloro-1,3-butadiene) suspension method. Left: S$_A$, amorphous antimonic acid. Right: S$_C$, crystalline antimonic acid. (From Abe, M. and Ito, T., *Bull. Chem. Soc. Jpn.*, 41, 2366, 1968. With permission.)

Table 6
THERMAL DECOMPOSITION OF THE THREE DIFFERENT ANTIMONIC ACIDS

DTA temperature (°C)[a]

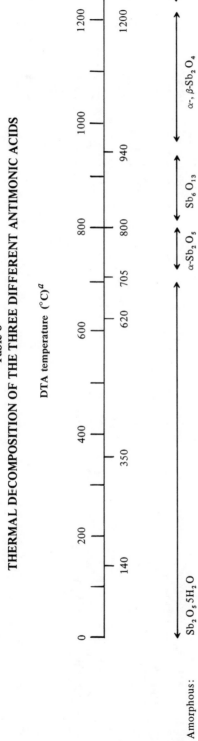
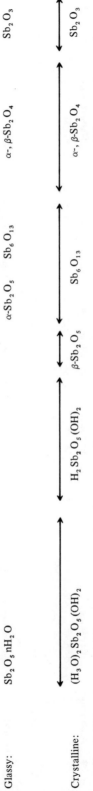

[a] Heating rate = 10°C/min.

(Original data from Abe, M., *Kogyo Kagaku Zasshi*, 70, 2226, 1967. With permission.)

Table 7
INFRARED SPECTRUM OF THE DIFFERENT ANTIMONIC ACIDS AND SODIUM ANTIMONATES

(Tentative band assignments) (cm⁻¹)

	Antimonic acid						Sodium antimonate		
	Reference 136		Reference 138	Reference 139		Reference 140	Reference 141	Reference 139	
	Amorphous	Crystalline	H⁺-form	Amorphous	Crystalline	Amorphous (?)	Na[Sb(OH)₆]	Na[Sb(OH)₆]	Na[Sb(OD)₆]
		3580(W)*	3620(VW) } ν_{H_2O} 3580(W) }						
	3350(VS) ν_{H_2O}	3350(VS) ν_{H_2O}	3300(S) $\nu_{H_3O}+$	3370(M) ν_{H_2O}	3270(S) ν_{H_2O}	3580(W) ν_{H_2O}	3400(W) ν_{H_2O}		
						3270(S) ν_{OH}	3280(VS) ν_{F_2O}	3280(VS) ν_{H_2O}	
		2850(W)	2900(W) $\nu_{H_3O}+$	3160(S) ν_{OH}	3000(VW) ν_{OH}	2920(VW) ν_{OH}	3220(VS) ν_{SbOH}	3200(S) ν_{OH}	
			1705(S) $\nu_{H_3O}+$	(2430?)	2460(W)	(2440)			2450 } ν_{OD} 2400 }
		2420(M) $2\delta_{SbOH}$					2145(M) $2\delta_{SbOH}$		
	1630(M) δ_{H_2O}	1630(M) δ_{H_2O}	1640(M) δ_{H_2O}	1630(W) δ_{H_2O}	1670(M) δ_{H_2O}		1635(VW) δ_{F_2O}	1630(VW) δ_{H_2O}	
		1280(M) δ_{SbOH}			1290(M)		1120(S)	1120	
	1100(VW)			1120(VW) δ_{SbOH}	1140(W) δ_{SbOH}		1105(S) δ_{SbOH}	1110 } δ_{SbOH}	
							1075(M)	1085	
							1030(M)	1035	
	840(VS) } ν_{SbO}	840(VS) } ν_{SbO}		830(VS) } ν_{SbO}	820(VS) } ν_{SbO}				836 823 } δ_{SbOD} 800 770 767
	740(VS) }	740(VS) }	770(VS) ν_{SbO}	775(VS) }	775(VS) }		775(M) 735(M)	735	
							695(S)	695 } ν_{SbO} 626	
							628(VS) } ν_{SbO} 600(VS) 586(VS)	597 583	605 593 } ν_{SbO} 577
								572 527	
							528(M)		

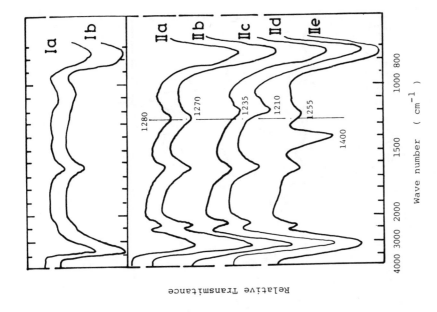

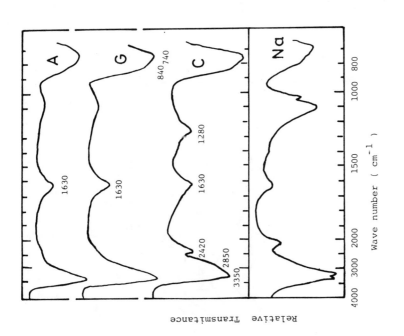

FIGURE 19A. Infrared spectra of various antimonic acids. Left, three different antimonic acids: A, amorphous G, glassy; C, crystalline acid; and Na, Na[Sb(OH)$_6$]. Right- antimonic acid ion exchanged with different elements: (top) amorphous antimonic acid: Ia, H$^+$-form; Ib, K$^+$-form. (bottom) crystalline acid; IIa. H$^+$-form; IIb, 1.1 meq K$^+$/g; IIc, 2.2 meq K$^+$/g; IId, 2.8 meq Na$^+$/g; IIe, 2.0 meq NH$_4$$^+$/g. (From Abe, M. and Ito, T., Bull. Chem. Soc. Jpn., 41, 2366, 1968. With permission.)

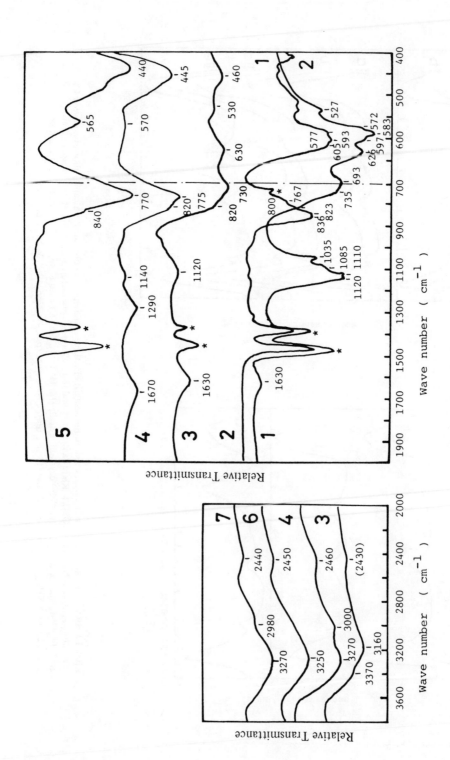

FIGURE 19B. Infrared spectra of different antimonic acids and antimonates. 1, Na[Sb(OH)₆]·0.17H₂O; 2, its substitution product with D₂O; 3, amorphous antimonic acid; 4, crystalline antimonic acid; 5, anhydrous Sb₂O₅; 6, ion-exchanged with Ag⁺; 7, regenerated with mineral acid. (From Balicheva, T. G. and Roi, N. I., *IZV, Akad. Nauk, SSSR, Neorg. Maten, 9, 277*, 1973. With permission.)

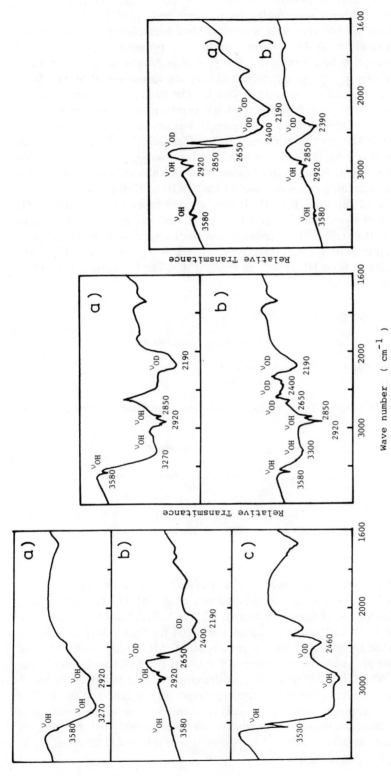

FIGURE 19C. Infrared spectra of antimonic acid substituted with heavy water. Left: a) initial antimonic acid, b) substituted strongly with heavy water, c) substituted weakly with heavy water. Middle: a) substituted partially, b) after dehydration. Right: a) substituted partially, b) after fixation of Ag⁺. (From Bourrelly, I. N., *Anal. Chem. Acta*, 94, 323, 1979. With permission.)

change in the X-ray diffraction pattern and the second peak on the DTA curves for the C−SbA. Thus the structural water molecules are combined as SbOH.

When an hexachloro-1,3-butadiene(HCB) mull method is employed instead of a nujol mull, useful information can be obtained for the absorption spectra of water and OH groups. The adsorption bands involving OH groups and water disappear by heating over 600°C (see Figure 18). As mentioned above, the formation of Sb_6O_{13} from C−SbA begins at 500°C, and is complete at 700°C. The disappearance of both OH and water bands supports the conclusion that the product heated at 700°C is not Sb_3O_6OH as reported by Dihlström and Westgren,[120] but Sb_6O_{13}. A drastic change in the maximum band at 750 cm^{-1} is attributed to the formation of Sb_6O_{13}. A similar conclusion is obtained for crystalline antimonic acid by Novikov et al.,[138] except that the product heated at 480°C is Sb_3O_6OH having the water absorption bands at 3620 and 1640 cm^{-1}, and a stretching vibration band of Sb(III)OH at 3260 cm^{-1}.

Lukina et al.[142] have reported that HAP has various types of OH groups; (1) OH_2(sorption), (2) OH_2(coordinated), and (3) SbOH acid groups and OH groups bonded by H$^+$ bond. Bourrelly[140] has reported that the IR spectra of antimonic acid and its deutrated compounds showed three types of OH groups which can be distinguished by the strength of their H$^+$ bands (see Figure 19C). The following types of OH groups can be found:

Type I — Free OH Group Compared with that of SbOH

	νOH	νOD	Isotope ratio
Sb−OH	3580 cm^{-1}	2650 cm^{-1}	1.35
H_2O	3300 cm^{-1}	2460 cm^{-1}	1.35

Type II — OH Group from Adsorbed Water or Hydrated OH Group which may be Overlapping with Former

νOH	νOD	Isotope ratio
3270 cm^{-1}	2400 cm^{-1}	1.35

Type III — SbOH Group Combined with H$^+$

νOH	νOD	Isotope ratio
2920 cm^{-1}	2190 cm^{-1}	1.35

The IR spectrum of amorphous antimonic acid is similar to those obtained for a large number of hydrous oxides such as the hydrous oxides of Zr, Ti, Sn(IV), etc., with exception of the SbO stretching vibration at 750 cm^{-1}. Balicheva[139] reported that a very weak peak at 1120 cm^{-1} can be assigned as δSbOH for $Sb_2O_5 \cdot 3H_2O$. A similar band can be seen in the IR spectrum for amorphous $Sb_2O_5 \cdot 5H_2O$ reported by Abe and Ito,[136] which was not assigned. The decrease in the intensity of OH and water bands upon heating below 600°C is attributed to the condensation of acid groups in the amorphous material. This condensation is practically irreversible on exposure to air. The IR spectra for glassy antimonic acid is essentially the same as that for the amorphous one.[136] The amorphous material is thought to be a relatively low polymer of Sb−O−Sb−O− linkage attached with OH bondings. These results led Abe and Ito to propose the structure shown in Figure 20.

3. Ion Exchange Properties of Antimonic Acid

As mentioned previously, the ion exchange behavior of antimonic(V) acid varies

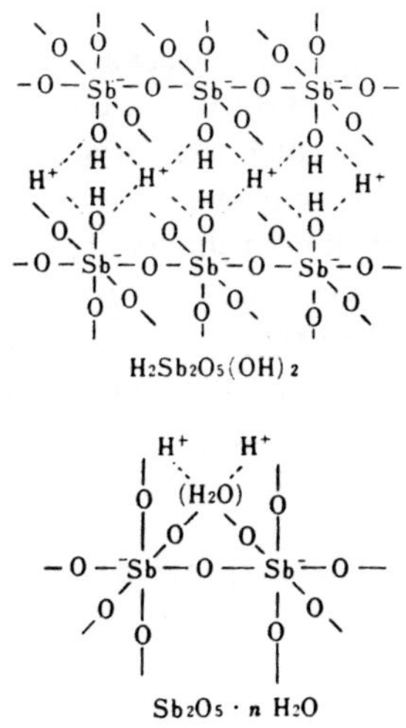

FIGURE 20. Modified surface structure of different antimonic acids. (Top: crystalline antimonic acid; (bottom) amorphous antimonic acid.

with its preparation. Antimonic(V) acid does not show swelling and shrinking in aqueous solution as do organic resins.

The pH titration curve of antimonic acid aged at different stages has been shown in Figure 5. Monomeric antimonic acid, $H[(Sb(OH)_6]$, which is known only in solution, shows a titration curve of the strongly acid type. It can be seen in Figure 5 that crystallization does not alter the total hydrogen ions capable of being neutralized and merely leads to partial hindering of dissociation of the sites with different, overlapping acidities. The backward titration curves for alkali metal ions $-H^+$ system coincide with the forward titration curve and no hysteresis is observed in the system.

Different selectivities have been reported by various authors.[97,102,104,117] The ion exchange selectivity much depends on the surface structure of the antimonic acid as well as the loading of the exchanging cations, co-ion present, temperature, etc. The selectivities of three different antimonic acids toward microamounts of alkali metal ions are shown in Section III.A.3.e. In nitric acid media, the selectivity on the amorphous exchanger increases in the order: $Li^+ < Na^+ < K^+ < Rb^+ < Cs^+$,[101] as observed on sulfonate type organic resins.[143] The selectivity on the glassy exchanger is essentially the same as that on the amorphous one. However, much different selectivity is observed on crystalline antimonic acid; $Li^+ < K^+ < Rb^+ < Na^+$ in nitric acid media and the selectivity much depends on the loading of the exchanging cations.[144] Therefore, comparisons of the selectivity should be made under the same exchange loading and pH of the aqueous solutions.

Crystalline antimonic acid has essentially a cage structure like three dimensional zeolites.[136] When small cations on crystalline antimonic acid are exchanged with large cations, the ion exchange becomes progressively more difficult as the proportion of one of the large cations in the solid phase is increased (i.e., steric effect). This may arise in a rigid structure which undergoes relatively little swelling if there is a large difference in the size of two cations. If there is no site available for the ingoing large cations within the intercrystalline volume, incomplete exchange results. When the size of the cations is much larger than that of the window of the cage structure, an ion-sieve effect will occur even if there is some lattice vibration.

222   *Inorganic Ion Exchange Materials*

a. Ion Exchange Reaction

It is very important to know how the selectivities vary with different loadings of various cations. For example, the selectivity sequences of alkali metals on C–SbA shows; $Li^+ < K^+ < Cs^+ < Rb^+ < Na^+$ for microamounts, while $Li^+ < Cs^+ < Rb^+ < Na^+$ is observed in macroamounts in nitric acid solution.[101,144]

Thermodynamic treatment of ion exchange reactions by different investigators seems to be somewhat confused because a uniform system of nomenclature has not been generally employed. The ion exchange process may be represented here by the following equation for hydrogen ions/z valent metal cations system.

$$z\,\overline{H^+} + M^{z+} \rightleftharpoons \overline{M^{z+}} + z\,H^+ \tag{18}$$

where the bar refers to solid phases and M^{z+} is a z valent metal ion. The thermodynamic equilibrium constant, K, of the above reaction can be defined as

$$K = \frac{m_{H^+}^z\,\overline{X}_{M^{z+}}\,\gamma_{H^+}^z\,\overline{f}_{M^{z+}}}{m_{M^{z+}}\,\overline{X}_{H^+}^z\,\gamma_{M^{z+}}\,\overline{f}_{H^+}^z} = K_H^M\,\frac{\overline{f}_{M^{z+}}}{\overline{f}_{H^+}^z} \tag{19}$$

Where K_H^M is defined as the corrected selectivity coefficient. The m_{H^+} and $m_{M^{z+}}$ are molalities of the cations in solution, and γ_{H+} and $\gamma_{M^{z+}}$ are the ionic activity coefficients of H^+ and M^{z+}. X_{H+} and $X_{M^{z+}}$ are the equivalent fractions of the exchanging ions in the solid phase. The ratio $\gamma_{H+}^z/\gamma_{M^{z+}}$ for uni-univalent exchange can be calculated from mean activity coefficients of pure salt solutions at the same ionic strength by the method due to Glueckauf.[145] Since these dilute solutions will not deviate greatly from the ionic strength principle in a narrow temperature range, neglect of the temperature dependence of γ_{H+}/γ_{M+} will not introduce a serious deviation in the values of K_H^M. However, in uni-multivalent ion exchange systems the ratio $\gamma_{H+}^z/\gamma_{M^{z+}}$ cannot be neglected for the calculation of the selectivity coefficients. The values of the ionic activity coefficient ratio $(\gamma_{H+}^z/\gamma_{M^{z+}})$ in solution can be calculated from the following equation.[146]

$$\log\frac{\gamma_{H^+}^z}{\gamma_{M^{z+}}} = \log\frac{\gamma_{\pm HNO_3}^{2z}}{\gamma_{\pm M(NO_3)_z}^{(z+1)}} = \frac{zS\sqrt{I}}{1+1.5\sqrt{I}} \tag{20}$$

$$\text{where } S = 1.8252 \times 10^6\left(\frac{\rho}{\epsilon^3 T^3}\right)^{1/2}$$

and ϱ is the density of water, ε is the dielectric constant of water, and T the absolute temperature of the system.

The thermodynamic equilibrium constant can be evaluated by using a simplified form of the Gaines-Thomas equation, Equation 21, assuming that the change of water

$$\ln K = -(z_M - z_H) + \int_0^1 \ln K_H^M\,d\,\overline{X}_M \tag{21}$$

content in the exchanger and the uptake of anion by the exchanger are negligible. This is the form derived by Ekedahl et al.[148] Sometimes, the graph of $\ln K_H^M$ against $\overline{X}_M$ is linear with inorganic ion exchangers (Equation 22).

$$\ln K_H^M = 4.606\,C\,\overline{X}_M + K_c' \tag{22}$$

where the term C is called Kielland's coefficient and 4.606C is the slope of the line and $K'_c = K_H^M$ when $X_M = 0$.

Some investigators have normalized the ion exchange isotherm in the case where complete exchange is not obtained. This normalization procedure involves setting the maximum limit of exchange, $(\overline{X_M})_{max}$, equal to unity and then multiplying each point of the exchange isotherm by a normalization function, f_N, such that $f_N = 1/(\overline{X_M})_{max}$. The usual procedure is then used to obtain the equilibrium constant and thermodynamic data for the exchange reaction. However, this treatment has been questioned in a recent publication that show these thermodynamic data are controversial,[149] and does not allow a comparison between specimens which are exchanged to different extents. The normalization procedure for antimonic acid is based on the assumption that one antimony gives one hydrogen ion available for ion exchange. Thus, the theoretical capacity of 5.056 meq/g is calculated from the empirical formula of $Sb_2O_5 \cdot 4H_2O$. It has been reported that 5 meq/g of Ag^+ may be exchanged for H^+ in PAA,[113,117] but that lower exchange capacities are found with other ions.

b. Maximum Degree of the Exchange on Crystalline Antimonic(V) Acid (or Polyantimonic Acid)

The cation uptakes of many inorganic ion exchangers such as hydrous oxides are known to depend upon various factors; the nature of the cationic species, temperature, concentration of cation in solution, co-ions present, pH of the solution, the method of determination (batch or column), etc. The uptake capacity data reported in the literature for polyantimonic acid are summarized in Table 8.

For the alkali metal ions on C-SbA or PAA in acidic media, the sequence of the ion exchange capacity under the stated conditions has been reported as,[117,151] $Cs^+ < Rb^+ < NH^+_4 < K^+ < Na^+$, which is parallel to the decrease in the ionic crystal radii of the alkali metals. The position of Li^+ in this sequence remains anomalous being given as $Cs^+ < Li^+ < Rb^+ < NH^+_4 < K^+ < Na^+$ by Lefebvre and Gaymard[97] and $Li^+ < Cs^+ < Rb^+ < NH^+_4 < K^+ < Na^+$ by Abe.[101,144]

In alkaline solution, the selectivity sequences show; KOH < NaOH < LiOH at pH 12 to 13 by Lefebvre and Gaymard[97] and CsOH < LiOH < KOH < NaOH by Novikov et al.[42] For the alkyl ammonium ions on C−SbA, the following series has been reported:[158] $(C_2H_5)_4N^+ < (CH_3)_4N^+ < (CH_3)_3NH^+ < $ iso-$C_3H_7NH^+_3 < (CH_3)_2NH^+_2 < C_2H_5NH^+_3 < CH_3NH^+_3 \lll NH^+_4$.

This is parallel to the decreasing order of van der Waals' dimensions of the organic cations.[158] When the cation has dimensions smaller than 6 Å in two directions, the cation may pass the window of the cage of C−SbA structure without any resistance. A cation, such as $(CH_3)_3NH^+$, having only one such dimension less than 6 Å, can pass through the window with some distortion due to lattice vibrations. Cations such as $(CH_3)_4N^+$ and $(CH_3)_4N^+$ and $(CH_3)_4N^+$, being larger than 6 Å in three directions, cannot enter into the cage of the structure and are adsorbed only on the surface of the C−SbA.

The exchange loadings achieved under specific conditions varies with the species of antimonic acid and the nature of the exchanging ions; for example Li −0.72 to 0.95 meq/g on amorphous SbA and Li −0.30 to 0.33 for crystalline C−SbA (see Table 8).[38] Similar disagreement is observed for alkaline earth metal cations, viz., $Ca^{2+} < Sr^{2+} < Mg^{2+} < Ba^{2+}$ on PAA[97] $Mg^{2+} < Ba^{2+} < Ca^{2+} < Sr^{2+} <$ on C−SbA-silica gel in 0.1 M chloride solution[127] and $Mg^{2+} < Ba^{2+} < Sr^{2+} < Ca^{2+}$ on C−SbA in 0.1 M nitrate solution (see Table 8).[154,155] It has been reported recently that the sorption and desorption are extremely slow for Mg^{2+}, Ca^{2+} and Sr^{2+} requiring 20 to 80 days for attainment of equilibria at 30°C, whereas, equilibrium is attained within 2 days for Ba^{2+}.[103,154,155]

For transition metal ions on C−SbA the following series was found:[156] $Ni^{2+} < Co^{2+} < Zn^{2+} < Cu^{2+} < Mn^{2+} < Cd^{2+}$ in 0.1 M nitrate solutions. The maximum uptakes of

Table 8
ION EXCHANGE LOADINGS OF DIFFERENT HYDRATED ANTIMONY PENTOXIDES AT VARIOUS CONDITIONS

Alkali Metal Ions

Exchanger	Sequences of exchange capacity( )	In solution	Ref.
PAA	Cs(1.0)<Li(1.2)<Rb(1.7)<NH$^+_4$(2)<K(2.4)<Na(3.2)	0.1 M nitrate	97
	KOH(3.4)<NaOH(4.3)<LiOH(5)	pH 12-13	
	Ag(3.6) - (M$^+$/H$^+$ = 0.1), Ag(5.1) - (M$^+$/H$^+$ = 1.0)	0.1 M HNO$_3$	117
	Tl(3.1) − (M$^+$/H$^+$ = 0.2), Tl(5.5)−(M$^+$/H$^+$ = 1.0)	0.1 M HNO$_3$	
SbA	Li(0.72−0.95)<K(1.23-1.25) on amorphous	0.1 M nitrate	38
C−SbA	Li(0.30-0.33)<K(1.29-1.30) on crystalline	0.1 M nitrate	
HAP	Na(1.35)-retention	1 M HNO$_3$	108
C−SbA	Li(1.0)<Cs(1.2)<Rb(1.4)<NH$^+_4$(2.0)<K(2.4)<	0.1 M nitrate	101
	Na(2.8) - retention		
HAP	Cs(0.15)<Rb(1.45)<K(1.7)<Na(2.61)-retention	0.1 M HNO$_3$	150
	Cs(0.02)<Rb(0.44)<K(0.57)<Na(0.95)	0.1 M HCl	151
PAA	Na(1.44), Na(1.54)-retention	0.1 M(Na$^+$ +	126
(silica gel	Na(1.51)	HCl)	
supd.)		0.1 M Na$^+$ +	126
		0.5 HNO$_3$	
	Na(2.73)	0.1 M NaNO$^3_3$	126
HAP	Tl(0.25)-TlNO$_3$,(0.10)-Tl$_2$SO$_4$, (0.16)-Tl acetate	0.1 M HNO$_3$	152
PAA	Cs(1.58)<Na(5.1)	0.25 M(HNO$_3$	153
	Na(3.6-4.8)-total capacity 0.1(NaCl + NaOH)	+ nitrate)	
C−SbA	Li(0.44)<K(0.86)<Na(0.90); Sb/Si = 0.51	0.1 M chloride	127
(silica gel	Li(0.44)<K(1.48)<Na(2.56); Sb/Si = 13.8	0.1 M chloride	127
supd.)			

Alkaline earth metal and other ions

Exchanger	Sequences of exchange capacity( )	In solution	Ref.
PAA	Ca(0.5)<Sr(0.5)<Mg(0.6)<Ba(2.5)	0.1 M nitrate	97
	Ca(1.4)<Sr(2.3)<Ba(5.4); M(OH)$_2$	pH = 12-13	97
	Sr(3.4)-0.5N, (5.06)-2N	(H$^+$ + Sr^{2+})	117
	Pb(4.5)-(M^{2+}/H$^+$ = 0.2), (5.1)-(M^{2+}/H$^+$ = 1.0)	0.1 M HNO$_3$	117
PAA	Sr(1.42)	0.05 M Sr^{2+} +	152
(silica gel		1.5 M HNO$_3$	
supd.)			
C−SbA	Ni(0.20)<Mg(0.32)<Ca(1.64)<Ba(2.00)< Sb/Si = 0.51	0.1 M chloride	127
(silica gel	Sr(2.52)<Cd(2.72)		
supd.)			
	Mg(0.20)<Ni(0.24)<Ca(1.28)<Ba(2.96)< Sb/Si = 13.81		
	Sr(3.52)<Cd(4.18)		
C−SbA	Mg(0.61)<Ba(2.53)<Sr(3.10)<Ca(3.4)	0.1 M nitrate	154
	Mg(0.54)<Ba(2.93)<Sr(3.77)<Ca(4.06)<Pb(5.86) - retention	0.1 M nitrate	155
	Ni(0.51)<Co(0.61)<Zn(0.71)<Cu(2.53)< Mn(II) (5.97)<Ca(5.86)	0.1 M nitrate	156
	- retention		
HAP	Ta(0.15)	2.2 × 10^{-3} M +	157
		1 M HNO$_3$	

Note: ( ); meq/g, exchanger: PAA, polyantimonic acid; SbA; amorphous antimonic acid; C−SbA, crystalline antimonic acid; HAP, hydrated antimony pentoxide. Retention; retention capacity by column technique, others; batch technique.

Mn^{2+}, Pb^{2+}, and Cd^{2+} were found to be 5.86 to 5.98 meq/g which is much higher than the theoretical capacity of 5.056 meq/g.[155,156] Tl$^+$ uptake on PAA also exceeded the theoretical capacity.[117] A stoichiometric compound, having a ratio Sb/M^{2+} higher than 2, has not yet been reported for the corresponding oxide or antimonate. In the ion exchange reaction a stoichiometric relationship exists between the liberated hydrogen ions and the adsorbed metal ions.[155] However, the stoichiometry may be maintained if the ion exchange reaction takes place according to the following:

$$3\,\overline{H^+} + 2\,Cd^{2+} + H_2O \;\rightleftharpoons\; \overline{Cd^{2+} + Cd(OH)^+} + 4H^+ \qquad (23)$$

and/or

$$5\,\overline{H^+} + 3\,Cd^{2+} + H_2O \;\rightleftharpoons\; \overline{Cd^{2+} + Cd_2(OH)^{3+}} + 6\,H^+ \qquad (24)$$

Evidence is proposed for the existence of hydroxo-aquo species, $Cd(OH)^+$, in the aqueous solution at high pH or of binuclear species, $Cd_2(OH)^{3+}$, in strong solutions of Cd^{2+}.[20] The additional capacity may be explained by assuming the adsorption of the hydroxo-aquo species or polynuclear species in the exchanger at high concentrations of Mn^{2+}, Cd^{2+}, and Pb^{2+} in high pH media.[155,156]

A very limited amount of work has been carried out on the kinetic aspects of the ion exchange reactions of antimonic acid. Jolivet and Lefebvre[159] have reported that the exchange reaction rate is governed by the intercrystalline diffusion of Ag^+. Diffusion proceeds by a change in position of ion pairs in the crystal state and is more rapid when the Ag^+ concentration is greater and the of the exchanger permits the formation of a more stable Ag-antimonate.

c. Ion Exchange Isotherms

Ion exchange isotherms have been used to represent graphically experimental data pertinent to steric and ion sieve effects. The ordinate of these plots, $\overline{X_M}$, is the equivalent fraction of the ion M^{n+} in the exchanger phase, defined as:

$$\overline{X}_M = \frac{\text{meq } M^{n+}/g \text{ of exchanger}}{\text{meq of } (M^{n+} + H^+)/g \text{ of exchanger}}$$

and the abscissa, X_M, is the equivalent fraction of the M^{r+} in the solution phase, defined as

$$X_M = \frac{\text{meq of } M^{n+}/g \text{ of solution}}{\text{total meq of } (M^{n+} + H^+)/g \text{ of solution}}$$

When K_H^M does not depend on the loading of the exchanging ions, the isotherms of uni-univalent and uni-divalent exchange systems can be plotted with solid lines in Figure 21.

Cation exchange resins of the strong acid type have elastic structures and display swelling and shrinking dependent upon the nature of the exchanging cations. They display isotherms which do not deviate greatly from the ideal ones. Inorganic ion exchangers generally have rigid structures and display curves in which K_H^M varys greatly with the exchanging cations. The exchange isotherms can be classified into five types:[160] (A) higher selectivity for the entering cation over the entire range of exchanger composition; (B) entering cations show a selectivity reversal with increasing equivalent fraction in the exchanger; (C) selectivity for the leaving cations over the entire range of exchanger composition; (D) exchange does not go to completion although entering cation is initially preferred, and the degree of exchange gives a value lower than unity; and (E) hysteresis effects may result from the formation of two exchanged phases as in the case of crystalline zirconium phosphate in various cationic forms.[7]

When small cations are exchanged by large cations in inorganic ion exchangers, the ingoing ion is initially preferred and becomes progressively less preferred with increased loading. Thus, the ion exchange isotherms are of the type (B) or (D). Figures 22 to 24 illustrate some available isotherms and the change in selectivity coefficients, K_H^M, against the equivalent fraction of exchanging cations.

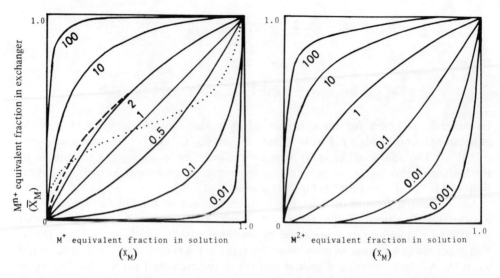

FIGURE 21. Ideal exchange isotherms for uni- and bivalent cations vs H^+. ———— : ideal isotherm for univalent (left) and bivalent (right), ---- : K^+/H^+ exchange on Amberlite IR 120.[161] ····· : Cs^+/H^+ exchange on zirconium phosphate in microcrystalline form.

Novikov, et al.[43] reported that the selectivity coefficients as a function of $\overline{X_{Na}}$ and $\overline{X_K}$ showed inflecton points at $\overline{X_M} = 0.6$, indicating the presence of different sites (see Figure 22a). They found the relative cation exchange affinity series to increase in the order: $Li^+ < K^+ < H^+ < Na^+ < Ag^+$ at both 20°C and 80°C. These results disagree with those of Abe who found that K_H^M vs $\overline{X_M}$ showed straight lines for all alkali metals.[144] His selectivity sequences as a function of X_M decreased in the order; $Li^+ < K^+ < Cs^+ < Rb^+ < Na^+$ for $\overline{X_M} = 0$ to 0.1, $Li^+ < Cs^+ < K^+ < Rb^+ < Na^+$ for 0.1 to 0.32 and $Li^+ < Cs^+ < Rb^+ < K^+ < Na^+$ for 0.32 to 1.0.

High selectivity coefficients for Ag^+/H^+ and Tl^+/H^+ systems have been reported by Baetsle and Huys[117] and by Novikov et al.[43]

C−SbA displays an ion sieve effect for large organic cations as described earlier. In a series of substituted alkylammonium ions, the degree of maximum exchange decreases with increasing size of the cation. Tetramethyl- and tetraethylammonium cations were completely excluded. The same ion sieve effect is observed in the pH titration curve with $0.1\ M(CH_3)_4NOH$ solution.[43,97]

Thermodynamic data for alkali metal ions/H^+ systems are given in Table 9. It is seen that the results from different investigators of the same exchange reaction do not agree. The major differences may be related to nonequilibrium conditions and lack of homogeneity of the exchange materials. Similar data for alkaline earth cations are shown in Table 10. Here also remarkable differences are found. From the overall thermodynamic data, the affinity series shows; $Ba^{2+} < Ca^{2+} < Sr^{2+}$ by Baetsle and Huys,[117] $Mg^{2+} < Ca^{2+} < Ba^{2+} < Sr^{2+}$ by Novikov et al.[163] and $Mg^{2+} < Ba^{2+} < Sr^{2+} < Ca^{2+}$ by Abe and Sudoh.[155] Abe[103,154] has pointed out that for exchange reactions at low loading, the concentration of the metal in the equilibrium solution is extremely low for the systems Ca^{2+}/H^+ and Sr^{2+}/H exchange, and moreover the rate of exchange of Ba^{2+} is relatively rapid, while that of Ca^{2+} and Sr^{2+} is extremely slow. Thus, the observed discrepancies may be due to a kinetic effect. The sequence, $Ca^{2+} < Ba^{2+} < Sr^{2+}$,[163] is the same as that observed for an earlier stage (a few days) of the exchange on C−SbA. The sequence, $Ba^{2+} < Ca^{2+} < Sr^{2+}$, on PAA[117] is the same as that on C−SbA for a few weeks.[155]

For transition metals, the selectivity series was observed, in terms of increasing overall selectivity, to be[156] $Zn^{2+} < Co^{2+} < Ni^{2+} < Cu^{2+} < Mn^{2+} \ll Cd^{2+}$. This series is almost

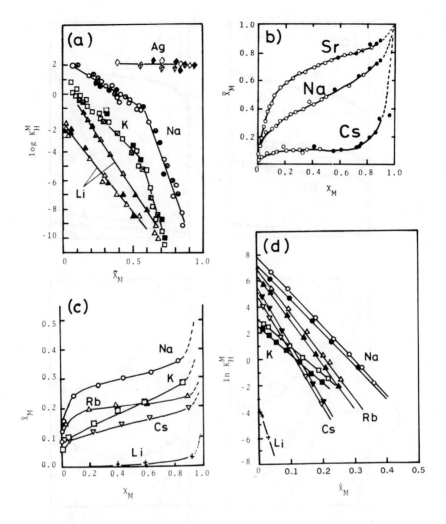

FIGURE 22.   Ion exchange isotherms for univalent ions on antimonic acid. (a) log K_H^M versus X_M at 20°C (open symbols) and 80° (filled symbols) from Reference 43; (b) and (c) isotherms and α) log K_H^M vs. $\overline{X}_M$ at 20° (open symbols) and 40° (filled symbols) from Reference 44.

parallel to the increasing order of the stability constant for hydrolysis of the metal ions, except for Mn^{2+}.[156] Cations such as Ni^{2+}, Co^{2+}, and Zn^{2+}, have an octahedral primary solvation shell in aqueous solution, while Cu^{2+} has a tetragonally distorted primary solvation shell as a consequence of the Jahn-Teller effect. If the exchanging cations maintain a similar configuration as in aqueous solution, a large steric effect may be operative for Ni^{2+}, Co^{2+}, and Zn^{2+} and a decreased steric effect, due to a larger Jahn-Teller deformation for $Cu(H_2O)^{2+}_6$. An extremely high selectivity is found for Cd^{2+}. The relation in K_H^{Cd} vs X_{Cd} is similar to that obtained in the system of Pb^{2+}/H^+ exchange,[117,154] indicating the presence of different sites or exchange of hydrolyzed species and/or polynuclear species of the cations.[155] Cations, such as Cs^{2+} and Pb^{2+}, have a large effective ionic radius and can classified as "soft" acids in the hard and soft acids and bases concept. In general, a "soft" acid is not highly hydrated in aqueous solution, because of its weak polarizing ability in the ion-water interaction. Thus, Cd^{2+} and Pb^{2+} may easily enter into the cavity of the C−SbA structure by stripping some water molecules. A similar change in the coordination of water can be found on the surface of $SiO_2 \cdot nH_2O$ and activated alumina.[164]

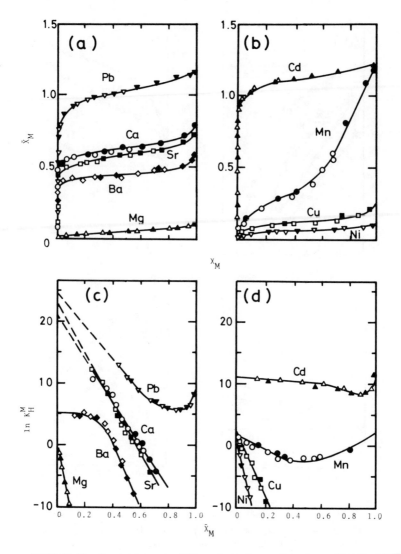

FIGURE 23.   Ion exchange isotherms of alkaline earth and transition metal ions on crystalline antimonic acid (C-SbA). Open symbols represent the forward reaction, filled symbols the reverse reaction; $\mu = 0.1$, $T = 30°C$.[155,156]

d. X-Ray Diffraction Analysis of the Antimonic(V) Acid Exchanged with Different Metals

As mentioned earlier, crystalline antimonic acid does not undergo marked swelling or shrinkage with the exchange of various cations. However, changes in the lattice constant amounting to a few percent occur upon cation exchange.* Similar behavior is established for various zeolites[165] and alumina[166] exchanged with alkali metal ions. This may be due to the fact that the C−SbA does not undergo any large dimensional change with ion exchange because of its three-dimensional framework structure. Typical examples for antimonic acid exchanged with alkali metal ions are demonstrated in Table 11.[144] A remarkable decrease in the diffraction intensities of the (111) and (311) planes was observed with an increase in the crystal ionic radii of the adsorbed metal ions, while the intensity of the (222) plane increased. Calculated values of the

---

*   Two solid phases are present in the case of Hg(II) ions.[107]

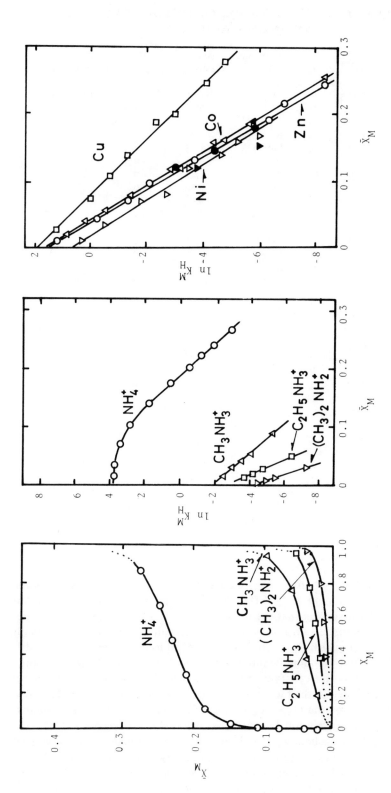

FIGURE 24. Ion exchange isotherms of organic cations and transition metal ions on crystalline antimonic acid. [156,158] Left: isotherms of organic cations, middle: selectivity coefficients of organic cations, right; selectivity coefficients of transition metal ions; $\mu = 0.1$, T = 30°C.

Table 9
UNI-UNIVALENT ION EXCHANGE REACTIONS ON CRYSTALLINE ANTIMONIC ACID

Exchange reaction	Conc.	°C	Isotherm type	$\Delta G°$ (kcal/eq)	$\Delta H°$ (kcal/eq)	$\Delta S°$ (eu/eq)	Ref.
$Li^+ \rightarrow H^+$	0.1 M	20		11.14	14.27	10.7	43
		80		10.50	14.28		
		20	C	26.			144
$Na^+ \rightarrow H^+$	0.1 M		B	4.32			117
	0.1 M	20	(Site I)	−1.07	0	3.7	43
			(Site II)	8.97	0		
		80	(Site I)	−1.29	0	18.2	43
			(Site II)	10.80	0		
	0.1 M	22	B	−0.05			153
	0.1 M	20	B	3.36[a]			144
		40	B				
$K^+ \rightarrow H^+$	0.1 M	20	(Site I)	2.41	0		
			(Site II)	14.2	0	−8.2	43
		80	(Site I)	2.41	0		
			(Site II)	17.1	0	48.4	43
		20	B	4.70[a]			144
		40	B				
$Rb^+ \rightarrow H^+$	0.1 M	20	B	5.93[a]			144
		40	B				
$Cs^+ \rightarrow H^+$	0.1 M	22	B	1.6			153
		20	B	9.3			
		40	B	9.60[a]			144
$Ag^+ \rightarrow H^+$	0.1 M	20		−2.70	0	9.4	43
		80		−3.26	0		
	0.1 M			−2.0			117
$Tl^+ \rightarrow H^+$	0.1 M			−2			117
$NH_4^+ \rightarrow H^+$	0.1 M	25	B	6.81[a]	−2.25	−30	158
		60	B				
$CH_3NH_3^+ \rightarrow H^+$	0.1 M	25	C	12.4[a]	29.3	64	158
		60	C				
$C_2H_5NH_3^+ \rightarrow H^+$	0.1 M	25	C	24[a]	32	185	158
		60	C				
$(CH_3)_2NH_2^+ \rightarrow H^+$	0.1 M	20	C	31[a]	90	197	158
		60	C				

[a]   Thermodynamic data is normalized at a temperature of 25°C.

lattice constant of the ion exchanged C−SbA are plotted against the effective ionic radii of the metal ions in Figure 25.[154] Effective ionic radii are taken from Shannon and Prewitt's table[82] by assuming that the metal ions are six-coordinate. A strong dependence of the lattice constant on ionic radii is noticed although it may be difficult to explain its relationship quantitatively because the metal ions were exchanged in different amounts. When the exchanging cations, such as Na^+ and Ca^{2+}, have an ionic radii of about 1.0 Å, the lattice constant of the exchanged C−SbA shows a minimum value. This may be attributed to the fact that such cations are exchanged in a preferable configuration in the cage of the C−SbA structure.[154] Novikov et al.[102] have pointed out that there is a good correlation between the minimum lattice constant and the maximum selectivity of the exchanging metal ions. The same conclusion was obtained for the exchange of alkaline earth and transition metals by Abe and Sudoh.[156] X-Ray diffraction analysis revealed that conversion of the cation exchanged C−SbA to the hydrogen form is indeed reversible within experimental error. However, in Ca^{2+}/H^+ and Sr^{2+}/H^+ system, irreversibility is apparently observed because of the extremely slow

Table 10
UNI-BIVALENT ION EXCHANGE REACTIONS ON CRYSTALLINE ANTIMONIC ACID

Exchange reaction	Ionic Strength	t (°C)	Isotherm type	$\Delta G°$ (kcal/eq)	$\Delta H°$ (kcal/eq)	$\Delta S°$ (eu/eq)	Ref.
$Mg^{2+} \to H^+$	0.1	30	C	13.4	15.3	6.1	155
		60	C				
$Ca^{2+} \to H^+$	0.5	20	B	1.37			117
	0.1	20	B	1.17	2.15	3.4	43
		80	B	0.97	2.15		
	0.1	30	B	-0.67^a	7.9	28.7	155
		60	B				
$Sr^{2+} \to H^+$	0.5 and 2.0	20	B	0			117
	0.1	20	B	-0.076	3.03	10.6	163
		80	B	-0.72	3.03		
	0.1	22	B	-0.075			153
	0.1	30	B	-0.527^a	4.8	17.9	155
		60	B				
$Ba^{2+} \to H^+$	0.1	20	D	2.53			117
	0.1	20		-0.045	1.95	.85	163
		80		-0.455	1.95		
	0.1	30	B	2.44^a	4.53	7.0	155
		60	B				
$Pb^{2+} \to H^+$	0.1	20		-0.76			117
	0.1	30		-3.11^a	-0.77	7.8	155
		60					
$Mn^{2+} \to H^+$	0.1	30	B	0.647^a	6.2	19	156
		60	B				
$Co^{2+} \to H^+$	0.1	30	B	12.0^a	38	88	156
		60	B				
$Ni^{2+} \to H^+$	0.1	30	C	11.3^a	19	26	156
		60	C				
$Cu^{2+} \to H^+$	0.1	30	B	6.93^a	8.0	4	156
		60	B				
$Zn^{2+} \to H^+$	0.1	30		12.4^a	45	110	156
		60					
$Cd^{2+} \to H^+$	0.1	20	B				
		80	B	-0.93	3.58	11.4	163
		30		-1.81	3.08		
		60		-2.82^a	-1.2	5.3	156

[a] Thermodynamic data is normalized at a temperature of 25°C.

rate of desorption and in addition to the extremely high adsorptive ability of C–SbA for Ca^{2+} and Sr^{2+}.[154,155] Similar phenomena is also found for the variation in the c-lattice spacing (perpendicular to the cation-containing phases) in β-alumina with the ionic radius of the contained cations.[166] The minimum occurs at sodium and silver ion. The lattice expands when large and smaller cations are inserted. This is to be expected for the large species, where the natural spacing, due to the Al–O–Al bridging groups is insufficient.[166]

It has been reported that the presence of sodium in even small amounts on PAA inhibits completely the uptake of Sr^{2+}. Effective eluants for Sr^{2+} adsorbed on PAA column are $AgNO_3 + HNO_3$ and $NaNO_3 + HNO_3$.[167,168]

e. Ion Exchange Selectivity of Antimonic Acid and Hydrated Antimony Pentoxide Towards Microamounts of Various Elements

A great many studies have been carried out for the determination of distribution

Table 11

X-RAY DIFFRACTION DATA OF THE C–SbA EXCHANGED BY DIFFERENT ALKALI METAL IONS

Exchanged	H⁺-form		Li		Na		K		Rb		Cs	
hkl	d(Å)	I/I	d(Å)	I/I	d(Å)	I/I	d(Å)	I/I	d(Å)	I/I	d(Å)	I/I
111	5.985	100	5.985	100	5.950	82	6.049	81	5.950	51	6.015	45
220											3.678	4
311	3.128	70	3.127	74	3.116	61	3.155	60	3.112	100	3.138	100
222	2.995	75	2.994	84	2.984	100	3.024	100	2.979	63	3.005	66
400	2.594	15	2.594	15	2.583_5	24	2.618	20	2.581	5	2.601	6
331	2.381	11	2.380	10	2.373	8	2.403	8	2.368_5	4	2.387_5	2
422	2.119	2	2.119	2			2.139	2				
511 / 333	1.998	17	1.997	21	1.988	17	2.015	16	1.987_8	22	2.000_8	27
440	1.836	31	1.834	38	1.828_4	45	1.850_2	42	1.826_0	35	1.838_2	36
531	1.755	22	1.754	24	1.746_6	21	1.768_4	22	1.744_6	10	1.758_0	10
533	1.583	11	1.584	10	1.576_0	10	1.597_0	18	1.575_2	12	1.585_8	11
622	1.565	24	1.564	28	1.557_8	39	1.578_6	30	1.556_1	20	1.567_6	21
444	1.498	6	1.497	6	1.492_0	10	1.510_6	8	1.490_0	6	1.500_2	2
711 / 551	1.454	12	1.453	14	1.447_2	12	1.466_0	11	1.445_8	10	1.455_5	7
731	1.352	11	1.350	13	1.346_0	11	1.362_4	10	1.344_0	14	1.354_5	16
a (Å)	10.38_1		10.37_5		10.33_5		10.47_0		10.32_3		10.40_0	

ᵃ a; mean lattice constant.

coefficients (Kd). This information is useful for the separation of trace and microamounts of the elements in the fields of analytical chemistry, radiochemistry, environmental chemistry, and bioinorganic chemistry. For most of the measurements nitric acid media have been used in order to obtain fundamental ion exchange data in a noncomplexing medium which furthermore is useful for applications to the reprocessing of nuclear fuel.

However, it is often difficult to make valid comparisons between data from different laboratories. The distribution coefficient much depends on the loading of the metal ions in the exchanger as well as the degree of crystallinity of the antimonic acid. Therefore, the initial concentration or radiometric purity must be stated along with the total volume of the solution, the weight of the exchanger used and the temperature. A typical example of concentration dependence is demonstrated for some metal ions in Figure 26. Ion exchange ideality is maintained up to relatively high concentrations of the metal ions, but the distribution coefficient increases with decreasing concentration of the metal ions.[103] Increased Kd values with increasing concentration of metal ions are also observed for the exchange reactions of large ions (Rb^+, Cs^+, etc.) on microcrystalline zirconium phosphate.[169]

A systematic study of the equilibrium distribution coefficients for various metal ions on C–SbA has been reported by Abe and co-workers.[170] The results are summarized in the Figure 27. Girardi and co-workers have reported that about 3,000 adsorption elution cycles were carried out in a standardized way over eleven adsorbents (including 9 inorganic ion exchangers) from various media for preliminary screening of possible useful materials for radiochemical separations.[150] Krishnan and Crapper[172] have also studied the retention of 20 trace elements on HAP columns (3 cm long. × 1 cm i.d.) with HCl, HNO_3, and H_2SO_4 at various concentrations. The results reported by these authors are rearranged for HAP in two compressed figures by Abe[171] (see Figures 28 and 29). A comparative study of ion exchange selectivity between crystalline anti-

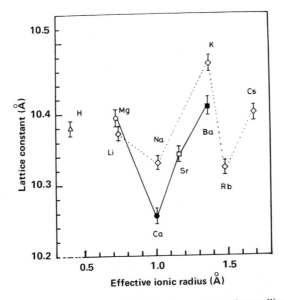

FIGURE 25. Change in the lattice constant of crystalline antimonic acid exchanged with alkali and alkaline earth metal ions. Blanket (⌷) refers to mean lattice constant of C-SbA exchanged with M^{2+} with probable experimental error. (From Abe, M., *Bull. Chem. Soc. Jpn.*, 52, 1386, 1979. With permission.)

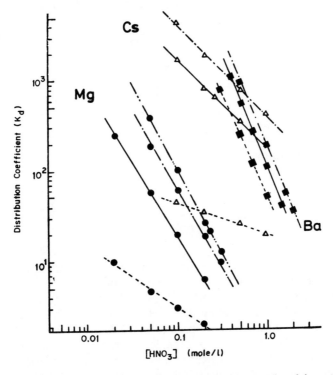

FIGURE 26. The dependence upon the initial concentration of the metals for the distribution coefficients (K_d) of Mg^{2+}, Ba^{2+}, and Cs^+ on C-SbA. Initial concentration of metals: Mg^{2+} (●), (--) 10^{-2} *M*, (—) 10^{-3} *M*, (—·) 10^{-4} *M*; (—··) 10^{-5} *M*; Ba^{2+} (■), (--) 10^{-2} *M*, (—) 10^{-3} *M*, (—·) 10^{-4} *M*; Cs^+ (△), (--) 10^{-2} *M*, (—) 10^{-3} *M*, (—) 10^{-4} *M*. (From Abe, M. and Uno, K., *Sep. Sci. Technol.*, 14, 355, 355, 1979. With permission.)

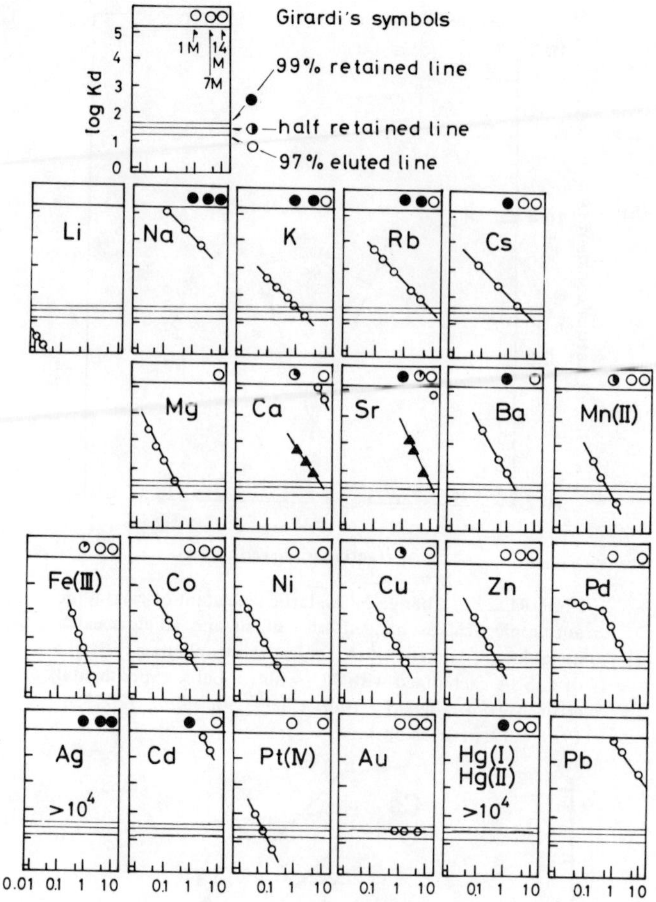

FIGURE 27. Comparison between K_d values on C-SbA and the evaluated K_d values on HAP. (▲) k_d values after 24 hr. (From Abe, M., *Sep. Sci. Technol.*, 15, 23, 1980. With permission.)

monic(V) acid (C−SbA) and hydrated antimony pentoxide(HAP) reported by Girardi et al.[150] was carried out by Abe.[170] The extended plate theory was applied for evaluating the values of the distribution coefficients of various metal ions on HAP from their retention results. The evaluated selectivities of HAP are essentially compatible with those of C−SbA for 17 or 20 metal ions.

1. Alkali Metal Ions

For alkali metal ions (except Cs^+) on C−SbA, the rate of exchange is relatively rapid, about 24 hr being required for attainment of equilibrium.

The selectivity sequence is: $Li^+ \ll K^+ < Cs^+ < Rb^+ < Na^+$ in nitric acid solution and $Li^+ \ll K^+ < Rb^+ < Cs^+ < Na^+$ in ammonium nitrate solution. The alkali metal ions on A−SbA show the following selectivity order; $Li^+ < Na^+ < K^+ < Rb^+ < Cs^+$ in nitric acid solution, which is the same as that on organic ion exchange resins of the strong acid type, and $Li^+ < Na^+ < K^+ = Cs^+ < Rb^+$ in ammonium nitrate solution. On HAP, the selectivity sequence of alkali metal ions is approximately; $Cs^+ < K^+ = Rb^+ < Na^+$ in nitric acid solution and $K^+ < Cs^+ < Rb^+ < Na^+$ in hydrochloric acid solution. An extremely high value of Kd is observed for Na^+ on both exchangers. The adsorbed Na^+ cannot be removed from the column of C−SbA or HAP, even with concentrated so-

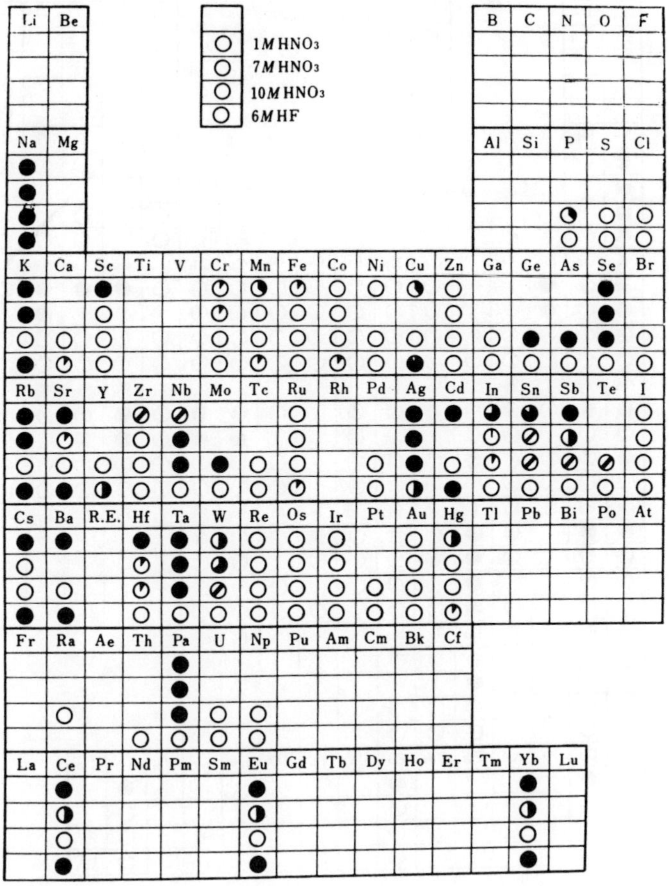

FIGURE 28.   Retention of inorganic ions on HAP with HNO_3 and HF.
●, completely retained (over 99%); ◐, partially retained (the black area is proportional to the amount retained); ○, completely eluted over 97%), ○ behavior not well reproducible (From Abe, M., *Bunseki Kagaku*, 23, 1254, 1974. With permission. Figure based on information given in Reference 150.)

lutions of HCl, HNO_3, H_2SO_4, and $HClO_4$.[126] However, Na^+ on C—SbA column can be removed with 1 $M NH_4NO_3$ solution as an eluant.[100, 101,175,176]

When the C—SbA is heated at different temperatures, the Kd values of alkali metal ions increase slightly up to 200°C and markedly at 240°C.[175,177] Maximum values are obtained for the sample heated at 330°C. This sample shows the same selectivity sequence as that of air-dried C—SbA, while the sample heated above 380° gives the selectivity series of $K^+ < Rb^+ < Cs^+ < Na^+$. The uptake of macroamounts of K^+ is changed very little by heating the air dried C—SbA up to 200°C but then decreases markedly with increasing the temperature above 300°C. [177] No adsorptive property is found on the sample heated at 700°C for which the composition corresponds to Sb_6O_{13}. An extremely high value (4.6×10^5 mℓ/g) of Kd for Na^+ is observed on the sample heated at 330°C in 10 M HNO_3 soution. Thus, irreversibility for Na^+/H^+ exchange may be the result of extremely high values of the Kd in mineral acid solutions. When the lattice constants of the heated sample are plotted against the temperature of the thermal treatment for C—SbA,[137,177] the changes indicate an inverse relationship with changes in the Kd values. If the distance between adjacent sites decreases by shrinkage of the crystal lattice, the electrostatic force may increase due to increasing

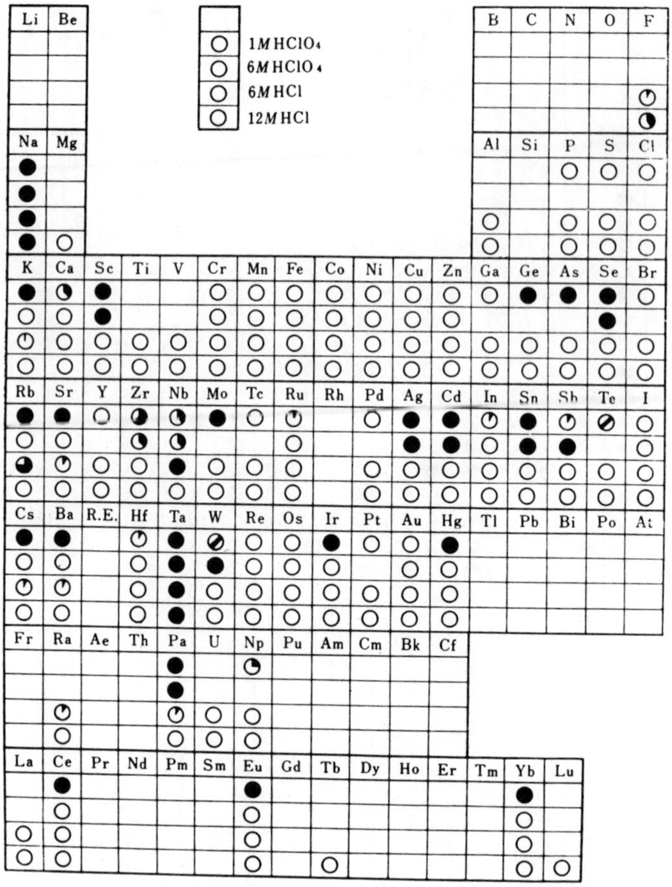

Legend:

- ○ 1 M HClO$_4$
- ○ 6 M HClO$_4$
- ○ 6 M HCl
- ○ 12 M HCl

FIGURE 29.　Retention of inorganic ions on HAP with HClO$_4$ and HCl. Symbols are the same as Figure 28. (From Abe, M., *Bunseki Kagaku,* 23, 1254, 1974. With permission. Figure based on information given in Reference 150.)

electron density of sites. Thus, increased adsorption ability may be explained in terms of the increased electrostatic force on adjacent sites in the heated samples.[177] Abe and Itoh[177] pointed out that the selectivity, $K^+ < Rb^+ < Cs^+$, found for the heated sample at 500°C may be ascribed to the presence of hydrated Sb_2O_5.

Kd values of heated A—SbA also increase with increasing temperature up to 330°C and then decrease at above this temperature.[175] The heated A—SbA shows increased adsorption for Na^+ even after 50 hr, but decreased gradually for K^+ in 0.4 M HNO$_3$. This behavior is due to the transformation from amorphous material to C—SbA.[101,175] The same explanation explains deviations from "1:1" exchange ideality (plot of log Kd vs. log HNO$_3$ with slope 1) reported for the Na^+/H^+ system[126] and for the Cs^+/H^+ system.[151]

Schunk and Vukov[179] have determined the adsorption capacity of Na^+ on HAP as a function of drying temperatures and concentration of acid. The optimum temperature was 270°C and an increase in acid concentration of 12 M HCl increased the selectivity.

Hypothetical thermodynamic data at infinitesimal loading were calculated for the interpretation of selectivity data of alkali metal ions in the trace amount on C—SbA.[144] The values of $(\ln K)_{\bar{x}_M \to o}$ were estimated by extrapolating to "zero loading" the curves of Figure 22. The calculated $(\Delta H°)_{\bar{x}_M \to o}$ and $(\Delta S°)_{\bar{x}_M \to o}$ increase with increasing ionic

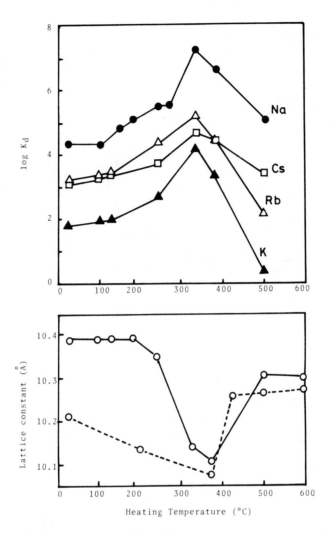

FIGURE 30.   Change in the Kd values (for alkal metals) and lattice constant of C-SbA heated at different temperatures. Kd values; 0.5 M HNO$_3$, K$^+$, Rb$^+$ and Cs$^+$,[177] Na$^+$ (interpolated from Reference 175). Lattice constant -O- from Reference 177, —O—, from Reference 137.

radii of the alkali metals. An inverse relationship is found for Dowex® 50-X12[146] and microcrystalline zirconium phosphate.[180] As shown by Sherry and Walton,[181]

$$\Delta S° = \Delta S°_{ex} + \Delta S°_{hydr} \qquad (25)$$

where $\Delta S°_{ex}$ represents the entropy differences between the two ionic forms of the exchanger and $\Delta S°_{hydr}$ the difference in entropies of hydration of the exchanging ions.* The values of $\Delta S°_{hydr}$ can be found from Rosseinsky's table.[182] The calculated $(\Delta S°)_{\bar{x}_M \to 0}$ are shown plotted against effective ionic radii in Figure 31. For Dowex® 50-X12[146] and ZrP,[180] the calculated values of $(\Delta S°_{ex})$ gave 1.9, 9.4, 10.5, and 9.93 e.u. (Dowex), and −7.9, −7.4, −8.3, and 7.8 e.u. (ZrP) with nearly constant values for H$^+$/Na$^+$, H$^+$/K$^+$, H$^+$/Rb$^+$, and H$^+$/Cs$^+$, respectively. The organic resins have essentially an elastic

---

*   M$^+$ (aq) + H$^+$ (gas) → M$^+$ (gas) + H$^+$ (aq) − Δ S° hydr

M$^+$ (gas) + H$^+$ → M $^{-+}$ + H$^+$ (gas) Δ S° ex

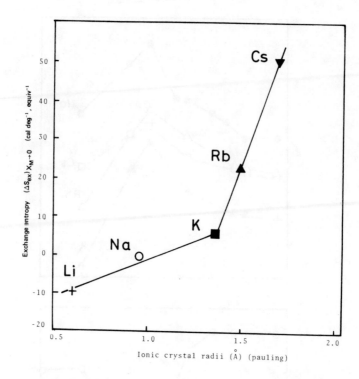

FIGURE 31.   Exchange entropy, $(\Delta S^\circ_{ex})_{\bar{x}_M}\to 0$, as a function of ionic crystal radii. (Reprinted with permission from *J. Inorg. Nucl. Chem.*, Vol. 41, Abe, M., Ion-exchange equilibria of crystalline antimonic (v) acid with alkali metal ions, Copyright 1979, Pergamon Press, Ltd.)

structure even for a high degree of crosslinkage and the hydration number of the exchanging ions may be nearly the same as that of the ions in the aqueous solution. Microcrystalline ZrP may have an essentially two-dimensional layered structure,[183] which, through changes in the c-dimension, allows hydration of the exchanging ions with nearly the same number of the water molecules as the ions in aqueous solution. Thus, the $(\Delta S^\circ)_{\bar{x}_M, o}$ may be independent of the crystal ionic radii for these exchangers. C—SbA has a rigid structure and does not undergo any appreciable dimensional change during ion exchange. At "zero loading" when highly hydrated cations go to the weakly hydrated sites without water loss, the degree of freedom may decrease in the system. However, when less hydrated cations, Cs^+ and Rb^+ are the ingoing cations, the degree of freedom may increase. The high selectivity coefficient of sodium is due to the highly negative value of $(\Delta H^\circ)_{\bar{x}_M, o}$ and the small contribution of the $(\Delta S^\circ_{ex})_{\bar{x}_M, o}$. This suggests a much stronger bond between the sodium ions and the sites of C—SbA than other alkali metal ions.

2. Alkaline Earth Metal Ions

For trace amounts of alkaline earth metal ions, the affinity series on PAA may be written as: $Ra^{2+} < Ba^{2+} < Ca^{2+} < Sr^{2+}$ in nitric acid media.[117] Sr^{2+} is the most strongly bound ion, surpassing all other alkaline earth metals. The same selectivity series is also reported on C—SbA; ($Mg^{2+} < Ba^{2+} < Ca^{2+} < Sr^{2+}$). The equilibrium of Ba^{2+} —H^+ exchange was attained within 24 hr, as observed for macroamounts of Ba^{2+}, but the exchange reaction of other alkaline earth metals is very slow.[103] Much higher values were obtained for the equilibrium Kd of Ca^{2+} and Sr^{2+} on C—SbA than on PAA.[104,117]

3. Transition Metal Ions

The following series was found on C–SbA: $Ni^{2+} < Mn^{2+} < Zn^{2+} < Co^{2+} < Cu^{2+} \ll Cd^{2+}$ in nitric acid media. Cd^{2+} is more strongly adsorbed than any other transition metal.[106,156] The selectivity series, $Zn^{2+} < Cu^{2+} < Cd^{2+}$, can be found in the retention behavior on HAP.[108] The exchange reaction of the transition metals on C–SbA are slow, about 4 days being required for attainment of equilibrium in the cases of Cu^{2+}, Zn^{2+}, and Mn^{2+} and one month for Ni^{2+} and Co^{2+}. In 2 M HCl solution, the Kd values of Cd^{2+}, Zn^{2+}, and Cu^{2+} decrease markedly due to formation of their chloro complexes. In 2 M HCl–80% acetone solution, the affinity series shows; $Zn^{2+} < Cd^{2+} < Cu^{2+}$. [105]

A study of the hypothetical thermodynamic data at infinitesimal load revealed that the calculated $(\Delta H^{\circ}_{ex})_{\bar{x}_M \to 0}$ values are almost parallel to the ΔH°_{hydr} in magnitude.[156] This indicates that the ion exchanged cations maintain almost the same structure of the aqueous octahedrally hydrated cations, except in the case of Mn^{2+} and Cd^{2+}. The increased $(\Delta s^{\circ}_{ex})_{\bar{x}_M}$ for Cd^{2+} and Mn^{2+} can be interpreted in terms of the entropy-producing process by the net transfer of water molecules from exchanger to the solution phase.[156] The high selectivity coefficient of Cd^{2+} may be due to the contribution of a highly negative value of $(\Delta H^{\circ})_{\bar{x}_M \to 0}$ and a low contribution of $(\Delta S^{\circ})_{\bar{x}_M \to 0}$.

The affinity sequences for tervalent metals can be summerized as follows: $Al^{3+} \ll Ga^{3+} < Yb^{3+} < Fe^{3+} < La^{3+} < In^{3+}$, in nitric acid media on crystalline antimonic acid. The maximum Kd value was found for the ions having the effective ionic radii of 1 Å, as observed for alkali and alkaline earth metal ions.[178]

For other metals, extremely high retention properties were found for the elements such as Ag, Ta, Pa, Se, As, and Ge on HAP,[150] and Hg(I) and Hg(II) on C–SbA in nitric acid media.[107] Ta is strongly retained on HAP, even with 10 M HNO$_3$ or 12 M HCl solution as the eluants.[152] Balantseva et al.[184] have studied the presence of PrOH in the solution containing various cations, such as Fe(III) Fe(II), Ni(II), Co(II), Cu(II), Al, Bi(III), and Zn(II). The sorption increased with increasing concentration of PrOH in the solution. Vialatt et al.[185] have reported that it is possible to hold F^- on $Sb_2O_5 \cdot nH_2O$ in concentrated hydrochloric acid and consequently improve the sensitivity of F^- determinations.

The Kd values reported and the separation factors, $\alpha(A/B)$, where A and B are neighboring metal ions, are summarized in Table 12, the values reported on Amberlite® IR 120 and AG 50W–X8 being included for comparison. The separation factors on C-SbA are generally larger than those on organic resins.

4. Separation of Various Metals on Antimonic Acid

a. Mutual Separation of Alkali Metal Ions

The mutual separation of microamounts was performed successfully on a small column of C–SbA (6.0 × 0.8 cm i.d.) by Abe and Ito.[100,101] Typical elution curves for alkali metal ions are illustrated in Figure 32. Na^+ is strongly adsorbed on the C–SbA column and cannot be eluted even if concentrated mineral acid is used as the eluant. The adsorbed Na^+ can be eluted easily with an ammonium nitrate solution. A slightly different order of elution is found with ammonium nitrate solution; $Li^+ < K^+ < Rb^+ < Cs^+ < Na^+$. Incomplete separation is obtained for Rb–Cs pair with this eluant on C-–SbA.

On amorphous material, the elution order is the same as that observed on organic resins of the strong acid type. The separation of Li^+, Na^+, and K^+ can be performed on a column of A–SbA with nitric acid solution as the eluant.[101] However, Na^+ becomes difficult to remove from the column with a few cycles of regeneration or with increasing time of immersion in nitric acid solution, because of its gradual transformation to C–SbA.[101,174]

Table 12
DISTRIBUTION COEFFICIENTS (K_d) AND SEPARATION FACTORS (α) FOR VARIOUS METALS ON A-SbA, C-SbA, and PAA IN NITRIC ACID MEDIA

Exchanger	Solution	Parameter	Li	Na	K	Rb	Cs	Ref.
A-SbA	0.1 M HNO$_3$	K_d	6.4	27.8	123	196	226	
		α		4.3	4.4	1.6	1.2	
G-SbA	0.1 M HNO$_3$	K_d	10.4	37.4	167	238	318	101
		α		3.6	4.4	1.4	1.3	
Amberlite® IR-120	0.2 M HNO$_3$	K_d	19.5	30	64	85.5	100	
		α		1.5	2.1	1.3	1.2	

Exchanger	Solution	Parameter	Li	K	Cs	Rb	Na	Ref.
C-SbA	0.1 M HNO$_3$	K_d	0.33	4.5×10^2	1.4×10^3	8.1×10^3	8.3×10^4	101 (217)
		α		1.4×10^3	3.1	5.8	10.2	
PAA	1 M HNO$_3$	$K_d{}^a$			2.0×10^2	1.6×10^2	1.0×10^3	117
		α				1.25	6.25	

Exchanger	Solution	Parameter	Mg	Ba	Ca	Sr	Ref.
PAA	1 M HNO$_3$	$K_d{}^a$		26	5.2×10^3	2.1×10^4	117
		α			200	4.0	
C-SbA	1 M HNO$_3$	$K_d{}^b$	0.02	1.1×10^2	2.6×10^6	2.2×10^7	103
		α		5.9×10^2	3.9×10^3	5.2	

Exchanger	Solution	Parameter	Mg	Ca	Sr	Ba	Ref.
AG 50W-X8	1 M HNO$_3$	K_d	22.9	35.5	39.2	68	143
		α		1.6	1.1	1.73	

Exchanger	Solution	Parameter	Ni	Mn(II)	Zn	Co	Cu	Cd	Ref.
C-SbA	0.2 M HNO$_3$	K_d	17	170	220	400	800	1.9×10^5	106
		α		10	1.3	1.8	2.0	240	

Exchanger	Solution	Parameter	Zn	Cu	Ni	Mn(II)	Cd	Co	Ref.
AG 50W-X8	0.2 M HNO$_3$	K_d	352	356	384	389	392	392	143
		α		1.01	1.09	1.01	1.01	1.00	

Note: A-SbA, amorphous antimonic acid; G-SbA, glassy antimonic acid; C-SbA, crystalline antimonic acid; and PAA, polyantimonic acid.

[a] K_d values were calculated on the basis of the selectivity quotients from Table 5 in Reference 117.
[b] Table 1, in Reference 103.

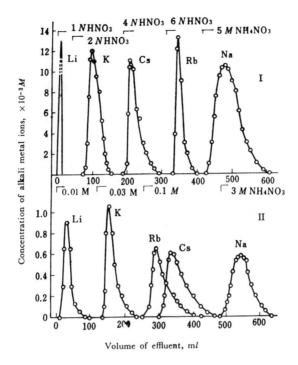

FIGURE 32. The separation of alkali metal ions on crystalline antimonic acid with nitric acid and ammonium nitrate as eluants. (From Abe, M., *Bull. Chem. Soc. Jpn.*, 42, 2683, 1969. With permission.)

b. Alkaline Earth Metal Ions

A column separation of ^{90}Sr from its fission products has been reported by Baetsle and Huys.[117] ^{90}Sr recovery from acid solutions after fuel reprocessing has also been preported by Aubertin et al.[167] Based on a study of Kd values of alkaline earth metals, $Mg^{2+}-Cs^+-Ba^{2+}$ were separated on a small column (2.0 × 0.4 cm i.d.) of C–SbA.[103] A satisfactory separation of Cs^+ from Sr^{2+} is achieved under usual column operation conditions while Ca^{2+} if present is eluted with Cs^+.[103] However, if elution was started after keeping the adsorbed metal ions on the top of the C–SbA column for about 15 hr, the Cs^+ was separated without elution of Ca^{2+}. In order to obtain more rapid separations heated columns have been used.[103] The separation of Mg^{2+} and Cs^+ from Ca^{2+} and Sr^{2+} is performed quantitatively, but the adsorbed Ca^{2+} and Sr^{2+} cannot be removed with concentrated nitric acid, 10 M NH_4NO_3 and 0.2 M EDTA adjusted to pH 10.

c. Separation of Transition Metal Ions

A satisfactory separation is achieved with 99% recovery of pure Ni^+ and Cu^{2+} by using an eluant of 0.1 and 6 M HNO_3 on the C–SbA column (2.0 × 0.4 cm i.d.).[106] Cd^{2+}, adsorbed on a C–SbA column cannot be removed completely due to a tailing effect,[105] even with acetone-HCl mixtures for which Kd = 1. A slightly improved elution curve is obtained for a column heated at 50°C, but the tailing effect is still observed. When an eluant containing 0.5 M KCl in 1 M HCl-acetone solution is used, the tailing of Cd^{2+} is eliminated completely.[105] The Cd^{2+} in the last 50 mℓ of its elution peak remains below the detection limit of the atomic absorption method (0.01 ppm). Zn^{2+} and Cu^{2+} show no tailing effect. Thus, quantitative separation is performed with 99 to 100% recovery for Cd^{2+} from Zn^{2+} and $Cu.^{2+}$. The K^+ adsorbed on the C–SbA during the elution of Cd^{2+} can be easily removed with 3 M HNO_3. The C–SbA column therefore can be used repeatedly with usual column operation conditions.

The lattice constant of the C–SbA in the hydrogen form is decreased from 10.38 Å to 10.26 Å by the ion exchange of Cd^{2+}, while there is an increase to 10.47 Å by K^+. The rapid elution of Cd^{2+} by addition of KCl may be due to this lattice expansion.[105,106] It has been known that the separation of Cd^{2+} from Zn^{2+} and Cu^{2+} is very difficult on an anion exchange resin when using HBr as the eluant.[186,187] This separation was demonstrated with 4×10^{-4} mmol of Cd^{2+} and 0.04 mmol each of Zn^{2+} and Cu^{2+} under almost the same conditions on C–SbA.[106]

Belinskaya et al[188] have reported that PAA can be used for removal of Ag^+ and Cd^{24} from concentrated radioisotope solutions containing various ions.

d. Gas-Solid Chromatography

A limited number of adsorbents are used in gas-solid chromatography, mainly alumina, silica gel, molecular sieves, and porous polymer, (e.g., Poropak), so that a search for new chromatographic materials is particularly useful when new properties are exhibited. The chromatographic column has been used as a catalytic reactor.[189] Inorganic ion exchangers give promise of functioning both as a catalyst for reactions and as a separating phase for the products and reactants.

Some gas chromatographic separations have been performed successfully on well defined crystalline exchangers, such as zirconium phosphate and arsenate. Lykourghiotis et al.[190] have reported that rapid determinations can be achieved with selective retention of some organic compounds on HAP. At the same temperature, the logarithm of the corrected retention volume of compounds belonging to the same homologous series is a linear function of the number of carbon atoms, as is usually the case in gas-liquid chromatography. The eluted chromatographic peaks are usually symmetrical. A good separation was performed for various pairs with similar chromatographic properties. In addition, the more specific properties are that it can retain completely alkenes and alkynes, and this can be used to separate saturated from unsaturated hydrocarbons. The parameters, ΔH°_{ad}, ΔS°_{ad}, and activation energy, for the adsorption of some representive organic compounds on HAP were obtained.

5. Applications of HAP and C–SbA to Real Samples

Many naturally occurring samples, including most of the biological, mineral, sea water, and glassy types, contain a large quantity of sodium as compared with those of other metals. Neutron activation analysis (NAA), with its high sensitivity for many elements, should be a suitable method for simultaneous determination of trace elements. However, the detection and determination of trace elements in the ppb level are often made difficult or impossible by the presence of a radiosodium background. The elimination of radiosodium without affecting the concentration of other cations would in many cases permit the simultaneous determination of many trace elements by instrumental means. Girardi and co-workers[108,150,191,192] have developed a method using HAP for the removal of radiosodium from mixed radio tracer solutions obtained by wet digesting the irradiated samples. After removal of sodium with 14 M HNO_3, ^{42}K and ^{64}Cu can be detected. The concentration of ^{42}K is, however, sufficiently high to mask the radioactivity of other nuclides. The ^{42}K can be removed by means of a HAP column, using a lower acid concentration (1 M HNO_3). ^{82}Br can now be detected. After the decay of the latter, ^{65}Zn, ^{59}Fe, and ^{80}Co can be detected. More selective separations can be obtained by using a combination of columns of different selective adsorbents. For example, high activity nuclides in neutron activated biological samples are separated selectively on HAP (^{24}Na), ZrP(^{32}P) and Ti–P(^{42}K) with a decontamination factor better than 10^{-4}, 10^{-3}, and 10^{-2} respectively.[172,205]

Table 13
APPLICATION TO REAL SAMPLES BY MEANS OF HAP AND C–SbA

Element	Separation from	Eluant	Elution order	Exchanger[a]	Sample	Note	Ref.
Na	Other elements	6—10 MHCl or HNO$_3$	Na retain	HAP	Biol.	For NAA	108,150,152, 192–198
Na, K	Other elements	10 MHCl	Na retain	HAP/resin	Biol.	For NAA	201–203
Na	Transition metals	7—10 MHCl	Na retain	HAP/TiP/ZrP	Biol.	For NAA	172,204,205
Na	43 elements	7 MHCl	Na retain	HAP/Al$_2$O$_3$	Biol.	For NAA	206
Na	25 elements	Various	Element isolate	HAP/Various exchangers	Biol.	For NAA	207
Na	Transition metals	6 MHCl	Na retain	HAP	Rock	For NAA	193,208,209
Li	Na, K, Ca etc	0.4 M	Li isolate	C–SbA	Rock	For determination Li	210
Na	Transition metal	12 MHCl	Na retain	HAP	opt. glass	For NAA	211,212
Na	Other elements	12 MHCl	Na retain	HAP	pure metals	For NAA	191,213
Na	Cu,Mn,Co,Fe,Cr	12 MHCl	Na retain	HAP	pure metal carbonate	For NAA	214
Na	Alkali metals	HCl	Na isolate	HAP	pure water	For detn. Na,Cl	215
^{43}K	Other elements	HNO$_3$	^{43}K isolate	HAP	V target	For isolation	216
Na,K	Li	0.1 MHNO$_3$	Na,K,Ca retain	C–SbA	LiCl	For purification	217
Na,K	Other elements	9 MHCl	Na, K retain	HAP/KPW	K salt	Removal radio K	218
^{68}Ga	^{68}Ge	0.2% Na-oxalate	^{68}Ga elute	HAP	generator	^{68}Ga/^{68}Ge	219

a Exchanger: HAP = hydrated antimony pentoxide; C-SbA = crystalline antimonic (V) acid; TiP = titanium phosphate; ZrP = zirconium; KPW = potassium phosphomolybdate.

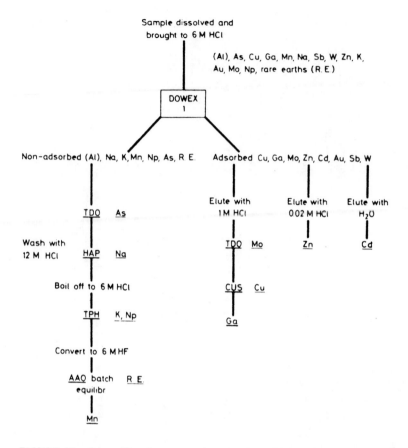

FIGURE 33.   Scheme for the systematic separation of impurities giving rise to radionuclides with half-lives shorter than a few days, in neutron- activated high-purity aluminum. TDO, tin dioxide; HAP, hydrated antimony pentoxide; TPH, titanium phosphate; AAO, aluminum oxide; CUS, copper sulfide. (From Cuypers, J., Girardi, F., and Mousty, F., *J. Radioanal. Chem.*, 17, 115, 1973. With permission.)

The applications of HAP and C—SbA to other samples of interest are summarized in Table 13. It can be seen in the table that a large number of applications of HAP are in regard to the separation of radiosodium. The simultaneous determinations of multielements is not so effective without separation of radiosodium and/or bromine. As all radiochemists know, the development of a separation procedure is often a long and painful experience. Cuypers et al.[191] have set up schemes for the systematic analysis of trace impurities in high purity Al and Zn metals using inorganic exchangers. A typical separation scheme is shown in Figure 33. Tjioe et al.[194] have also developed an automated chemical separation in routine NAA for biological samples on the basis on a combination of distillation and HAP and Dowex® 2–X8. Schuhmacher et al.[207] have reported recently a semiautomated and non-time-consuming radiochemical separation scheme for determination of 25 trace elements in biological specimens by means of 16 different organic and inorganic ion exchangers. Total time needed for one separation amounts to 3 hr and simultaneous processing of four samples only takes 4.5 hr.

Lithium in the ppm level usually occurs along with a large quantity of sodium, calcium, and other metals in rock samples and sea water. The chromatographic separation of lithium from sodium on sulfonated cation exchangers is not favorable because of the low values of the separation factor (between 1.5 and 2.0). C—SbA exhibits extremely large separation factors, $\alpha(Na^+/Li^+) = 2.6 \times 10^5$ and $\alpha(K^+/Li^+) = 1.5 \times 10^3$.

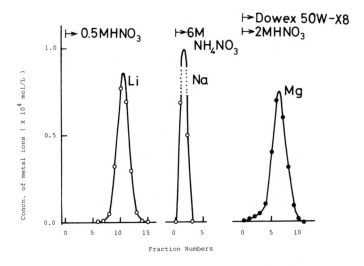

FIGURE 34. Separation of Li$^+$, Na$^+$ and Mg$^+$ with double column consisting of Dowex 50W-X8 (14 × 1.0 cm i.d.)-upper and C-SbA column (2.2 ×
0.8 cm i.d.)-bottom. Fraction 2.3 mℓ, flow rate; 0.9 mℓ/min, loading; 1 ×
10^{-3} mmol of each metal ions. (From Abe, M., Ichsan, E. A. W. A., and
Yayashi, K., *Anal. Chem.*, 52, 524, 1980. With permission.)

This indicates that selective separation is feasible for lithium from these metals. A very
favorable separation is obtained by simple injection of the lithium chloride solution
containing microamounts of sodium, potassium, and calcium, dissolved in 0.1 M nitric
acid solution, on a C–SbA column of 6.0 × 0.8, i.e., as compared with that on organic
resin of the same column size.[217] If the C–SbA column is applied to the separation of
lithium in environmental samples containing large amounts of Na$^+$, Mg^{2+}, and Ca^{2+},
these metal ions can be separated in principle. However, the separation procedure is
not effective because of tailing of Mg^{2+}, and moreover incomplete regeneration is obtained for C–SbA exchanged with Ca^{2+} of the slow rate of desorption of Ca^{2+}.[103]

The Kd values of multivalent cations are much higher than those of Na$^+$ and K$^+$ on
sulfonated cation exchange resins in nitric acid media.[143] The double column used to
obtain rapid separation of these elements in HCl consists of an upper column (14.0
cm long × 1.0 cm i.d.) of Dowex® 50W-X8 and a lower column (2.2 cm long × 0.8
cm i.d.) of C–SbA.[210] A solution (3 mℓ) containing 1.0 × 10^{-3} mmol of each of the
metals was added on the top of the double column. The Li$^+$ was eluted with 0.5 M
HNO$_3$ solution. The Na$^+$ was retained by the C–SbA column and the Mg^{2+} by Dowex®
50W-X8 up to 100 mℓ of the injection of the 0.5 M HNO$_3$. After removing the upper
column, the Na$^+$ adsorbed was eluted with 6 M NH$_4$NO$_3$ solution as an eluant, and
the Mg^{2+} adsorbed was eluted with 2 M HNO$_3$ (see Figure 34).

Similar procedures can be applied to the separation of lithium from a large amount
of other cations.[210] When a solubilized mineral sample was added to the top of the
resin column with 0.2 M HNO$_3$, and then the column was washed with 0.5 M HNO$_3$
in order to remove phosphate and perchlorate ions, all metal cations were retained on
the top of the resin column. After connecting the C–SbA column to the lower end of
the resin column, the elution of lithium ions was carried out by continuous injection
of 0.5 M HNO$_3$. A quantitative separation is performed effectively with 99 to 100%
recovery of Li$^+$ in a relatively short time.

A potential application of inorganic ion exchangers, is the possible use as radioisotope generator systems. An alumina column is generally employed for this purpose.
Arino et al.[219] have developed a new ^{68}Ge/^{68}Ga generator system using HAP. They

postulated that HAP could selectively adsorb Ge and ^{68}Ga was eluted with 2% sodium oxalate solution. This miniaturized generator (2%) can provide a high recovery (80 ± 10%) with 99.9% radionuclide purity.

Attention has been directed to the application of inorganic ion exchangers to water electrolysis, and production of sodium and chlorine gas. One of the main problems in the development of advanced alkaline water electrolysis, which operates at about 150°C, is to find a replacement for chrysotile asbestos which is currently used as the gas separator material. Vandenborre and Leysen[221] attempted to develop an electrolysis cell which is based on PAA. They obtained thin sheets of PAA with a thickness of 0.025 cm and a surface area of 500 cm^2. An evaluation of the PAA membrane under electrolysis conditions has been performed on an electrolysis unit cell (EUC) having a commercial 5% Pt catalyst a support as the cathode and a 50 mesh nickel grid as the anode. The results indicate that the PAA membrane resists chemical degradation in hot alkaline solution up to 150°C, and in contrast to nafion, no special corrosion problem will have to be faced for a period of 300 hr continuous operation at room temperature. The ohmic drop in the cell was low as a result of using a thin membrane which possesses excellent conducting properties.

B. Hydrous Oxides of Niobium and Tantalum

A limited amount of the work has been carried out on the ion exchange properties of hydrous niobium and tantalum oxides. These compounds are potentially useful as ion exchanges materials because of their high capacity, reasonable rate of ion exchange and high resistance to chemical reagents, as described in Section II of this chapter.

1. Preparation and Properties of Hydrous Niobium(V) Oxide
a. Preparation

Hydrous Nb_2O_5 is obtained when $NbCl_5$ or $NbOCl_3$ is hydrolyzed in water or by adding aqueous ammonia. A niobate salt may also be used to obtain a white gelatinous precipitate by addition of HCl or HNO_3. Treatment of the solution of niobium pentachloride with ammonia yields gel-like precipitates containing different quantities of water. It is very difficult to remove traces of chloride ion from the precipitated oxide. Different properties are exhibited by precipitates which have been regarded as hydroxide, hydrated pentoxide, and niobic acid.[222] Zakharov and co-workers[223-225] have recently studied the topochemical formation of niobium hydroxide by the action of ammonia on niobium pentachlorides and of nitric acid on potassium niobate. The solid niobium pentachloride (0.0037 mol) was treated with equal volumes (50 mℓ) of aqueous ammonia at concentrations of 0.12 to 12 M.[223] The mixture was stirred vigorously for 1 min and the apparent volume of the precipitate was determined after allowing to settle for 20 min. At low concentrations of ammonia and nitric acid (up to 0.3 M and 0.1 M, respectively) gel-like precipitates are formed, as in the precipitation of niobium and tantalum hydroxides. With increase in the concentrations, the precipitates become denser, and their apparent volume decreases sharply. The solid-phase breakdown of the molecular structure of the pentachlorides is accompanied by a disordered formation of diol bridges in various directions, which is responsible for the amorphous character of the hydroxide. When acid acts on potassium niobate, the protons of the former obviously interact with the hydroxo-groups in the structure of the latter. This results in the formation of amorphous phases of variable composition containing hydroxo-, oxo-, and aquo-groups.[224]

b. Physical and Chemical Properties

Under equilibrium conditions, K_2NbOF_5 and K_2TaF_5 are present in the (Nb, Ta)$_2O_5$–HF–KF–H_2O systems containing up to 1 to 2 M hydrofluoric acid.[225] Therefore, the fluoride ion replaces oxo- and hydroxo-groups completely in tantalum compounds and to a certain extent in niobium compounds. Under conditions of low acidity it is probably not the oxo-group but hydroxo-groups that are replaced by fluoride ions in the niobium and tantalum hydroxides. Thus, hydroxo-groups can be determined by substitution with fluoride ions. The rate of substitution for an aged sample decreases with duration of aging, but the total quantity of determinable hydroxo-group is almost unchanged. However, the hydroxo-content decreases for niobium hydroxide aged for 24 hr in concentrated perchloric acid. Thus, oxolation is practically irreversible under the given conditions. The dehydration curve for the amorphous material is a smooth curve showing no indication of a definite hydrate.[222,226] However, Galanova[227] has reported that the niobic acid precipitated from strong salt solution at pH 3.5 to 5.5 gives a series of new hydrates, indicating the presence of $Nb_2O_5 \leqslant 0.2\ H_2O$ at 200°C. On the other hand the curve for the precipitation made by heating the oxide with water at 150°C in a bomb, shows a point of inflection which suggests the existence of either a monohydrate or hemihydrate. Since none of the hydrous precipitates give an X-ray pattern, the formation of a hydrate has not been established with certainty.[228]

Izumi and Kodama[229] have recently reported that triniobium hydroxide heptaoxide, $Nb_3O_7(OH)$, can be prepared hydrothermally by heating niobic acid or triniobium chloride heptaoxide, Nb_3O_7Cl, with 3.0 $M\ H_2SO_4$ at 250 to 350°C.

c. Thermal Analysis of Hydrous Niobium(V) Oxide

Comparison of the thermal analyses reported in the available literature yields a very contradictory picture for the dehydration of niobium hydrous oxide and its transformation from amorphous to crystalline Nb_2O_5. Holtzberg et al.[230] have found an endothermic peak at 210°C (dehydration), and a large exothermic peak at 580°C which was reduced to 520°C at a slower heating rate. The hydroxide obtained by topochemical reaction gave a large exothermic peak at 590°C.[223] On the other hand, other workers,[231-233] have obtained an endothermic peak (dehydration) at around 200°C, a small exothermic peak at 375 to 470°C, and a large one at 550 to 609°C. Sathyanarayama and Patel have explained that the former exothermic peak is attributed to the formation of δ-phase and the latter to β-phase.[232]

Differences in thermograms can be due to the different water contents and the presence of impurities. Sakharov et al.[223] proposed the following thermal decomposition process from the results of thermal and X-ray analysis:

$$Nb_2O_5 \cdot nH_2O \rightarrow Nb_2O_5\ (amorphous) \rightarrow \gamma\text{-}'Nb_2O_5 \rightarrow \gamma\text{-}'Nb_2O_5(T) \rightarrow \alpha\text{-}Nb_2O_5(H).$$

Groult et al.[233] have proposed the decomposition process

$$Nb_2O_5\ (amorphous) \longrightarrow \delta \longrightarrow \gamma \longrightarrow \alpha$$

It is known that the polymorphism of Nb_2O_5 is subject to considerable debate.[234] The origin of the confusion is that Nb_2O_5 appears to give a number of metastable polymorphs based upon the complexity of the X-ray patterns under variable heating conditions. Holtzberg et al.[230] have claimed that the σ- and γ- modifications represent different degrees of crystallinity of the same polymorph. In addition to this, amorphous material converts exothermally and irreversibly to a crystalline phase at as low as 200°C when contaminated with NH_4Cl, and generally in the vicinity of 440°C when free of detectable contaminants. The effect of alkaline earth impurities on the thermograms has also been noted.[235,236]

d. IR Absorption Spectra

Balukova et al.[224] have studied IR spectra of a niobium hydroxide obtained by the topochemical reaction between niobium(V) chloride and concentrated aqueous ammonia. The absorption bands in a range of 550 to 700 cm^{-1} are typical of polymeric oxides (see Figure 35). At the same time the intense narrow adsorption band in the range of 920 to 950 cm^{-1} due to the Nb = O vibration is absent.[237, 238] Hence the complex nature of the adsorption band in the range 700 to 900 cm^{-1} (presence of two absorption bands at 780 and 880 cm^{-1}) suggests the presence of bridging metal-oxygen bonds which form polymeric chains. Here the absorption which appears as a shoulder at 1120 cm^{-1}, had been assigned to the incipient formation of a crystal lattice, which is not observed by X-ray diffraction. The absorption at 1645 cm^{-1} is due to the deformation vibrations of water molecules, which can be coordinated with niobium atoms or adsorbed by niobium hydroxide (see Table 14). The adsorption band with a maximum at 3200 cm^{-1} is due to the OH stretching vibrations and the diffuse band at 3400 cm^{-1} shows the presence of an OH group partaking in hydrogen bonding. In the IR spectrum of the aged hydroxide there is an absorption band with a maximum at 1160 cm^{-1}. An absorption in this range can be assigned to the deformation vibrations of bridging OH groups.

The IR spectrum of niobium hydroxide exchanged with alkaline earth metal ions shows an increase in intensity of the band at 3400 cm^{-1}, and a decrease at 3200 cm^{-1}, corresponding to the stretching vibration of OH groups.* Zakharov and co-workers have proposed that the hypothetical mechanism for the interaction of the hydroxides can be represented schematically as follows:[224]

Some[232] consider that niobium hydroxide is a high polymer having the structure:

---

*   It has been known that the presence of broad bands shifted to lower wave numbers led investigators to suggest that the solid acid was composed of strongly hydrogen-bonded three-dimensional aggregates, although the actual structure is not determined.[19,20]

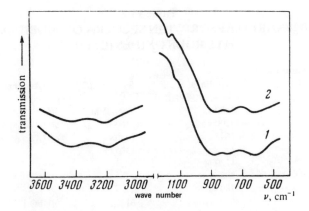

FIGURE 35. Infrared absorption spectra of (1 freshly obtained niobium hydroxide; (2) niobium hydroxide aged in air. (From Balukova, V. D., Ermolaev, V.M, Zakharov, M. A., and Nazarova, R. I., *Zhur. Neorg. Khim.*, 20, 3297, 1975. With permission.)

Others[239] tend to regard the niobium hydroxide as a polymer without participation of the ol bonds.*

$$\left[\begin{array}{ccc} & \overset{\displaystyle O}{\underset{\displaystyle \|}{}} & \\ HO - Nb - OH & ----- & HO - Nb - OH \\ & \overset{\displaystyle \|}{\underset{\displaystyle O}{}} & \end{array} \right]_\infty$$

2. Preparation and Properties of Hydrous Tantalum Pentoxide
a. Preparation of Hydrous Tantalum Oxide

Gelatinous hydrous tantalum pentoxide or tantalic acid, is obtained by hydrolysis of tantalum pentachloride with an excess of water or by treating sodium tantalate with acid[242] or CO_2.[243,244]

In 1875, Santesson indicated that the compounds prepared in different ways possessed variable water contents when dried at 100°C.[242] The hydrous oxides investigated by Jander and Schulz[245] were prepared by adding an excess of dilute nitric acid to a solution of sodium tantalate or $K_7Ta_5O_{16} \cdot 20H_2O$, at 0 and 100°C. From the pH titration curve of potassium tantalate with HCl (see Figure 36) Britton and Robinson[246] indicated that there is no evidence for the formation of $K_2Ta_5O_{16}$, as suggested by Jander and Schulz,[245] nor of K_3TaO_4 and $K_2Ta_2O_7$. The forward-titration curve exhibits two steps. However, the broken curve in Figure 36 indicates pH changes of the solution in which the precipitated tantalic acid was suspended on back-titration with KOH. It indicates that a small amount of interaction occurs between KOH and freshly precipitated tantalic acid. Thus, Britton and Robinson[246] concluded that the first part of the titration consists of the neutralization of free alkali.

There is an important difference in the precipitation of hydrous Ta_2O_5 and Nb_2O_5. Whereas, in the titration of the niobate solutions, a turbid unfilterable suspension was first formed which flocculated sharply at the end-point of the reaction, with the tan-

---

*

$$\overset{\diagdown}{\underset{\diagup}{M}} \overset{OH}{\underset{OH}{\diagup\diagdown}} \overset{\diagup}{\underset{\diagdown}{M}}$$

Table 14
INFRARED ABSORPTION SPECTRA OF NIOBIUM HYDROUS OXIDES (CM⁻¹)

Sathyanarayana et al.[232]	Balukova et al.[224]	Sych et al.[236]	Assignment
3400 s	3400 vs	3000-3500	$\upsilon(H_2O)$
	3200 vs	3160 s	$\upsilon(OH)$ or $\upsilon(NbOH)$
1640 m	1645 s	1630 s	$\delta(H_2O)$
		1405 m	
1080 w	1120 w		
1000-600 s	880 vs		
	780 vs		
	550- vs 700	612	$\upsilon(NbO_6)$

talate solutions the majority of the precipitate was immediately flocculated and could be filtered off, leaving only a very small suspension in the filtrate.

b. Thermal Analysis of Hydrous Tantalum Oxide

Thermograms reported in the literature differ markedly as regards the number and type of the thermal effects. Three different types of behavior have been observed in the DTA curves.[223,233,249]

The hydrous tantalum pentoxides formed by topochemical reaction show an endothermic peak due to dehydration at 250 to 350°C.[223] The resulting amorphous pentoxides contain excess energy; spontaneous incandescence, with considerable evolution of heat as the oxides crystallize, occurs when the hydrous oxides are heated. Formation of Ta_2O_5 is immediately followed by two exothermic peaks, at 330 to 440°C and 695 to 720°C.

The DTA curves of the hydrous oxide aged under ammonia for 2 to 4 hr shows a gradual disappearance of the first exothermic peak at 415°C. Despite the obvious restructuring all specimens of tantalum pentoxide remain amorphous towards X-rays up to the exothermic peak at 695 to 720°C. Hence, the first exothermic peak represents a phase transition from amorphous(I) to amorphous(II) (see Figure 37).

The thermal changes of the hydrous tantalum pentoxides can be represented by the scheme:[223]

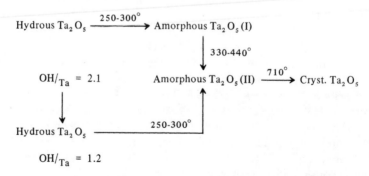

Thus, the existence of a low temperature amorphous phase of tantalum pentoxide is connected with a high content of hydroxo-groups in the heated hydrous oxide. On the aged hydrous Ta_2O_5 precipitates it is difficult to observe the exothermic peak at 330 to 440°C, and the fresh precipitates are amorphous regardless of the precipitation methods.[247] Aging in a sealed tube at 190°C for 30 days does not induce crystallization.

Khomutnikov et al.[248] have reported that the density and particle size of the hydrox-

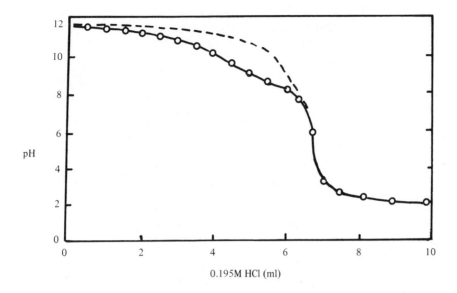

FIGURE 36. The pH titration curve of 100 mℓ of a solution of 0.00663 M K$_2$O and 0.00494 M Ta$_2$O$_5$ at 25°C. ——— forward titration, - - - back titration. (From Britton, H. T. S. and Robinson, R. A., *J. Chem. Soc.*, 419, 1933. With permission.)

ides of tantalum pentoxide increased and the solubility decreased with aging and increased heating temperature. The density of Ta(OH)$_5$ was 3.01 and 6.42 g/cm^3 after 14 hr and 30 days holding at 25°C, respectively.

Titova et al.,[249] have prepared hydrous tantalum pentoxide by adding a potassium hexatantalate solution to nitric acid at a specified pH, which was regulated by periodic addition of HNO$_3$ to the reaction mixture. The duration of contact between the precipitate and mother liquor was 1 hr. The precipitates were separated by centrifugation, carefully washed with water, and dried in air to constant weight (10 days at 22 to 25°C). The air-dried samples showed the same composition corresponding to the empirical formula Ta$_2$O$_5$·3.9H$_2$O in the pH range 2 to 5.5. The content of potassium increased with increasing pH of the preparation. All the samples prepared were amorphous to X-rays in the air-dried state. However, diffuse diffraction patterns were obtained by electron diffraction indicating small crystallites (see Table 15).

Comparison of the results of electron and X-ray diffraction data for tantalum pentoxide leads to the conclusion that the crystal structure of air-dried tantalum hydroxide resembles that of the low temperature β-Ta$_2$O$_5$ heated at 900°C.[248,250,251] Figure 38 shows the DTA and TG curves for tantalum hydroxide dried in air and also partly dehydrated. The DTA curves for all test samples reflect the dehydration process by an endothermic process. As the initial water content in the preparation diminishes, there is an increasingly evident splitting of the endothermic effect and its displacement towards higher temperatures. The two water elimination stages are clearly revealed also by thermogravimetric curves for the partially dehydrated samples, whose composition are in the range Ta$_2$O$_5$·0.97H$_2$O—Ta$_2$O$_5$·0.7H$_2$O. Complete dehydration took place above 700°C on conversion of the X-ray-amorphous preparation into the low-temperature modification (β) of Ta$_2$O$_5$.

Titova et al.[249] found a single, narrow derivative resonance absorption line for the protons in the NMR spectrum recorded at room temperature. A decrease of temperature leads to the appearance of a second, broader component in the spectrum, the intensity of which increases as the temperature is reduced (see Figure 39). The curve

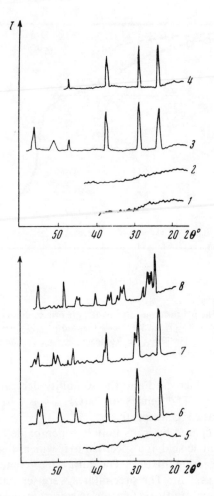

FIGURE 37.   X-ray diffractogram of products of the heating of hydroxides to different temperatures (°C): 1) Ta 20; 2) Ta 600; 3) Ta 720; 4) Ta 1000; 5) Nb 20; 6) Nb 620; 7) Nb 800; 8) Nb1100. The hydroxide was obtained by topochemical formation. (From Sakharov, V. V., Ivanova, N. E., Korovin, S. S., and Zakharov, M. A., *Zh. Neorg. Khim.*, 19, 579, 1974. With permission.)

representing the temperature variation of the second moments of the NMR spectra show that below 110 K the second moment M_2 remains constant.

The spectra of all the test samples consist of a broad ($\Delta H = 12$ to 12.8 G, $M_2 = 24$ to 26.5 G^2) and narrow ($\Delta H = 2.7$ to 3.5G, $M_2 = 1.5$ to 3.5 G^2) components. The former characterizes the proton of the water molecules and the latter the isolated protons of the hydroxy-groups. After partial dehydration of tantalum hydroxide at 200°C, the content of the molecular water in it diminishes sharply and the ratio OH:Ta falls appreciably. This leads to an increase of the distances between the protons in adjacent water molecules (r) and between the protons of the residual hydroxyls(X). The second dehydration stage evidently involves the elimination of water by condensation of hydroxyl groups, the process beginning at a temperature near 250°C. The decrease in the content of OH groups in the partially hydrated samples is probably due to the fact that prolonged exposure of the specimens to high temperatures promotes aging, which is accompanied by the elimination of water formed from the OH groups. This agrees with the dehydration curve obtained already by Laptskii et al.[252] in which it was shown that half of the H$_2$O was lost more readily than the rest.

Table 15
ELECTRON DIFFRACTION
DATA FOR THE AIR-DRY
TANTALUM HYDROXIDE
AND THE LOW-
TEMPERATURE
MODIFICATION OF
TANTALUM PENTOXIDE

$Ta_2O_5 \cdot 3.9H_2O$		Low-temperature modification of Ta_2O_5	
I	d, Å	I	d, Å
s.	3.85	s.	3.85
		w.	3.30
s.	3.11	s.	3.00
s.	2.42	s.	2.41
w.	2.01	w.	2.00
med.	1.92	med.	1.92
med.	1.80	med.	1.82
		w.	1.78
med.	1.63	med.	1.64
w.	1.56	w.	1.56
		w.	1.48
w.	1.45	w.	1.45
		w.	1.39
w.	1.31	w.	1.32
w.	1.28		
w.	1.20		
		w.	1.19
w.	1.18		

When the pyrochlore $Tl_2(Ta_2O_6)$ is treated with a sulfuric acid solution, the pyrochlore $H_2(H_2O)Ta_2O_6$ is obtained by the exchange of Tl^+ with H^+(aq). This compound has a density of 5.38 g/cm³ and a cubic lattice with a lattice constant of 10.580 Å.[253] The DTA and TGA curve show two dehydration steps, indicating the following scheme;[233]

$$H_4OTa_2O_6 \longrightarrow H_2Ta_2O_6 + H_2O \qquad (26)$$

$$H_2Ta_2O_6 \longrightarrow Ta_2O_5 + H_2O \qquad (27)$$

The sample heated at 310°C has a cubic lattice with a = 10.61 Å which is similar to that of air-dried $H_2(H_2O)Ta_2O_6$. Amorphous material is obtained by complete dehydration at 450°C but it crystallizes to δ-Ta_2O_5 after 610°C. δ-Ta_2O_5 is transformed to β-Ta_2O_5 by further heating.

3. Ion Exchange Properties of Hydrous Niobium and Tantalum Pentoxides
a. Hydrous Niobium Pentoxide

It has been known that large amounts of phosphate ions are carried down with hydrous niobium pentoxide precipitated from various aqueous solutions. Schoeller and Webb[254] showed that small quantities of phosphoric acid are almost quantitatively co-precipitated with niobium pentoxide.

Abe and Ito[22] have reported that hydrous niobium oxide exhibits cation exchange

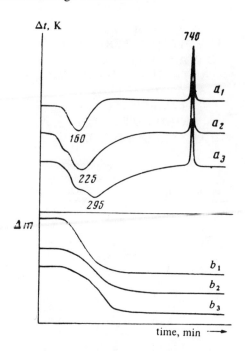

FIGURE 38.   DTA (a) and weight loss (b) curves for $Ta_2O_5 \cdot 3.9H_2O$ (a_1 and b_1), $Ta_2O_5 \cdot 2.2H_2O$ (a_2 and b_2), and $Ta_2O_5 \cdot 0.97H_2O$ (a_3 and b_3). (From Titova, V. A., Kozel, V. E., Slatinskaya, I. G., Panko, G. F., and Pitsyuga, V. G., *Zh. Neorg. Khim.*, 21, 308, 1967; *Russ. J. Inorg. Chem.*, 21, 165, 1976. With permission.)

properties with a relatively large capacity (see Section II) for potassium ions at higher pH. Thus, hydrous niobium pentoxide acts both as a cation and an anion exchanger, selective for $Cr_2O_7^{2-}$, paramolybdate, tungstates, and ferrocyanide ions.[255,256]

The niobium hydroxide obtained by topochemical reaction adsorbs Sr^{2+} and Ba^{2+} from solutions of strontium and barium hydroxide. The relation between the adsorbed metal ions and the decreased OH^- groups in the oxide indicates a stoichiometric ion exchange reaction for the systems.[235] However, a negligible amount of Sr^{2+} and Ba^{2+} exchange is observed from solutions of their chlorides.

The exchange capacity of the heated hydroxides decreases markedly with elevated temperature (see Table 16).[235] An extensive study of the exchange reactions for various ions, such as $Cr_2O_7^{2-}$, WO_4^{2-}, $Fe(CN)_6^{4-}$, VO_3^-, Ni^{2+}, and Co^{2+}, was carried out by Egorov and co-workers.[255-261] Hydrated niobium pentoxide exchanges the anions at relatively low pH($<$2).[256-261] The adsorbed anions can be eluted with aqueous ammonia. The ion exchange capacity for polyvanadate and ferrocyanide ions depends on the degree of crosslinking and peptization of the hydrated niobium pentoxide.[261] When hydrated niobium pentoxide was prepared by co-precipitation of $K_4Fe(CN)_6$ with potassium niobate, the sample had a flaky structure.[260] The sorption of $Cr_2O_7^{2-}$ follows the Freundlich equation, whereas, the sorption on hydrated Nb_2O_5 is controlled by a Langmuir equation. Freundlich sorption occurred on the sample with anisotropic surface properties whereas Langmuir sorption indicates an isotropic surface.

When pyrochlore $H_2(H_2O)Nb_2O_6$ is refluxed with a solution of bivalent metal nitrate at 100°C for 24 hr, the hydrogen ions in the pyrochlore are exchanged with the bivalent cations without any change in the crystal system.[262] The degree of ion exchange, x, depends on the cationic species: complete exchange for Cd^{2+} and Pb^{2+}, and partial exchange for Ca^{2+}, Sr^{2+}, and Ba^{2+} occur.

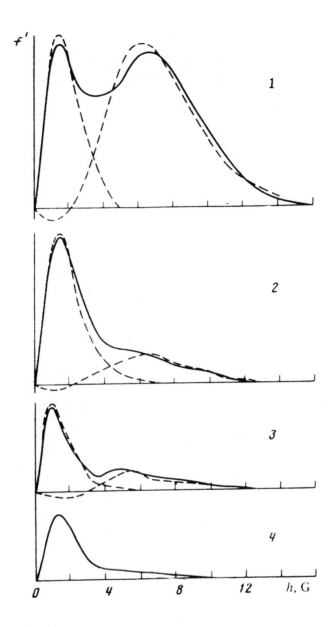

FIGURE 39. ^{1}H NMR spectra of air-dry and partly dehydrated tantalum hydroxide. (1) $Ta_2O_5 \cdot 3.9H_2O$ dried at 20-25°C; 2) $Ta_2O_5 \cdot 1.3H_2O$ dried at 150°C; 3) $Ta_2O_5 \cdot 0.7H_2O$; 4) $Ta_2O_5 \cdot 0.5H_2O$ dried at 250°C. (From Titova, V. A., Kozel, V. E., Slatinskaya, I. G., Panko, G. F., and Pitsyuga, V. G., *Zh. Neorg. Khim.*, 21, 308, 1967; *Russ. J. Inorg. Chem.*, 21, 165, 1976. With permission.)

These reactions can be represented by

$$H_2(H_2O)M_2O_6 + A^{2+} \rightleftharpoons AM_2O_6 \cdot H_2O + 2H^+ \qquad (28)$$

$$H_2(H_2O)M_2O_6 + xB^{2+} \rightleftharpoons B_xH_{2-2x}(H_2O)M_2O_6 + 2xH^+ \qquad (29)$$

(A = Cd, Pb; B = Ca, Sr, Ba; M = Nb, Ta)

Table 16

THE INTERACTION OF WEAKLY HYDRATED NIOBIUM
OXIDES WITH 0.03 *M* SOLUTIONS OF STRONTIUM AND
BARIUM HYDROXIDES[a]

Sample No.	Temperature (°C)	Composition of hydrated hydroxide (mol/mol)		Composition after ion exchange (mol/mol)		Crystallization
		OH/Nb	H_2O/Nb	Sr/Nb	Ba/Nb	
1	20	1.06	2.05	0.55	0.52	
2[b]	20	0.60	1.89	0.43	0.38	Amorphous
3	300	0.30	0.02	0.12	0.13	
4	550	0.18	—	0.04	0.04	
5	600	0.10	—	0.02	0.02	Crystalline

[a]   Reaction time; 1 hr, initial ratio M_{soln}: Nd_{solid} = 3:1.
[b]   Aged for 24 hr in 10 *M* aqueous ammonia, other samples 0.5 *M* in the same solution.

The distribution of the ingoing ions and water molecules in the structure has been studied and discussed by Grout et al.[262]

b. Adsorption of Various Elements on Crystalline Niobium and Tantalum Pentoxides

The ion exchange capacities of the hydrous oxides of niobium and tantalum decrease with increased heating temperature. The specific surface area of $Ta_2O_5 \cdot nH_2O$ decreases on heating while the pore dimensions increase.[263] Eventually the amorphous oxides of both niobium and tantalum are transformed into crystalline materials at elevated temperatures. When the crystalline material is immersed in water, OH groups may be formed on the surface of the oxides, although the interior remains anhydrous as shown by infrared measurements.

Ganzerli-Valentini et al.[264] have examined the exchange behavior for 55 ions on hydrous Nb_2O_5 and Ta_2O_5. The Ta_2O_5 was the β-form and Nb_2O_5 a complex mixture of three possible crystal forms (probably α, β, and γ). It was first necessary to determine the solubilities of the oxides in the media used for exchange. The solubilities in water were found to be and 1.81×10^{-6} *M* for Ta_2O_5 as compared to 1.36×10^{-5} for TiO_2 and below the detection limit of activation analysis for Nb_2O_5. About 10 times lower solubilities were observed for Ta_2O_5 than those for TiO_2 in nitric acid solutions at different concentrations.

The exchange experiments were carried out in solutions containing radio tracer in 0.1, 1.4, and 8 *M* nitric acid. Concentrations were always kept below 10^{-6} *M* and batch equilibrations were carried out by shaking 0.25 g of oxide with 10 m*l* of the solution at room temperature for 2 hr. The variation of Kd with nitric acid concentration is illustrated in Figures 40 and 41.[264]

In order to obtain a better understanding of the mechanism of both cation and anion exchange the adsorption of Ag^+ and Mo(VI) anion were examined in detail. The variation of K_d values of Ag^+ vs. nitric acid concentration is shown in Figure 42. The curves for the three oxides almost have the same shape; K_d is independent of HNO_3 concentration in a range of 10^{-3} to 10^{-1} *M*; there is then a decrease with a minimum at about 1 *M* HNO_3 followed by an increase. The known ability of silver to form mixed oxides with the oxides used explains its adsorption at low HNO_3 concentration. Different factors may contribute to the adsorption increase at higher acidity; the increase in the adsorbing surface and the formation of anionic silver complexes with nitric acid, which

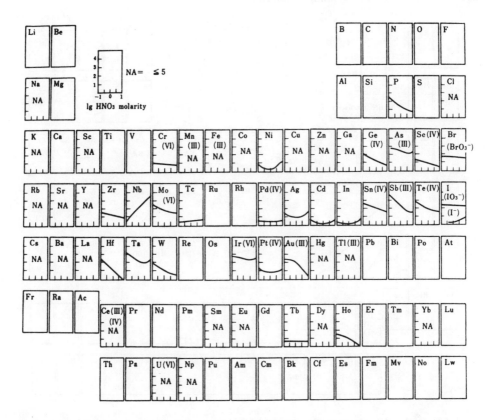

FIGURE 40. Adsorption of elements on Nb$_2$O$_5$ from nitric acid solutions. Roman numerals refer to the oxidation state in the initial solution. (From Ganzerli-Valentini, M. T., Meloni, S., Maxia, V., and Pisani, U., *J. Radioanal. Chem.,* 16, 191, 1973. With permission.)

may be adsorbed on the oxides because of their amphoteric behavior. Uptake curves as a function of Ag^+ concentration (in 0.1 M HNO$_3$) showed an almost linear increase up to 10^{-3} M beyond which the uptake remained constant (maximum uptake for Ta$_2$O$_5$ is 5×10^{-3} meq/g).

The variation of K_d for molybdate ions in nitric acid of increasing concentration is complex and ascribed to the formation of polymeric forms of molybdate ions. Maximum uptakes of MoO_4^{2-} on Nb$_2$O$_5$ and Ta$_2$O$_5$ are about 5×10^{-3} meq/g, which is almost the same as that of Ag^+.

c. Applications to Real Samples

Hydrous Ta$_2$O$_5$ is a cation exchanger suitable for the purification of nuclear reactor cooling waters at temperatures up to 300°C. Experiments were run in a high-temperature, high-pressure exchange column connected to a pressure pump and to 2 feed tanks.[265] Radioactive feed solutions were used so as to obtain fast, accurate analysis of the materials. Hydrated Ta$_2$O$_5$ was found to have a capacity of 1.37 meq/g at 300°C. A solution containing 395γK$^+$/mℓ, passed through tantalum oxide in the Na$^+$/NH$_4^+$ form, showed a rapid decrease in pH at first then more slowly to pH 5. When metal ions, such as Na$^+$, Cs$^+$, Sr^{2+}, or Ba^{2+}, were used as feed solution, the oxide in the K$^+$ form showed a similar capacity for both bivalent and univalent ions. Hydrous Ta$_2$O$_5$ takes up most of the radionuclides present in coolant water at high temperature.[266]

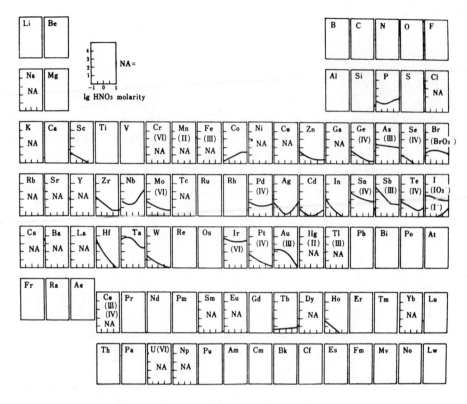

FIGURE 41.   Adsorption of elements on Ta_2O_5 from nitric acid solutions. Roman numerials refer to the oxidation state in initial solution. (From Ganzerli-Valentini, M. T., Meloni, S., Maxia, V ., and Pisani, U., *J. Radioanal. Chem.*, 16, 191, 1973. With permission.)

C. Hydrous Tungsten Oxide "Tungstic(V) *Acid*"
1. Preparation of Tungstic Acid

As mentioned in Section II, two different tungstic acids, white and yellow, are known.[267] An insoluble monohydrate H_2WO_4 usually known as yellow tungstic acid, is formed by boiling a mixed solution of a tungstate with an excess of mineral acid. The yellow tungstic acid has essentially a crystalline nature with definite composition.

Huttig and Kurre[268] dissolved the yellow tungstic acid in ammonia, cooled the solution to 0°C, and added hydrochloric acid dropwise with rapid stirring. A white voluminous precipitate was obtained under these conditions. Morley[269] obtained a pale yellow powder which contained a little more water than corresponds to $WO_3 \cdot 2H_2O$. Polyakov[270] has reported that an increase in the amounts of HCl or HNO_3 decreases the tungsten content in the solution and that without boiling a white acid is precipitated completely only in the presence of HCl.

Dehydration isobars show that the yellow acid is a monohydrate and that the white acid is hydrous, the water content of which varies continuously with change in temperature.[268,271] X-Ray analysis of several preparations confirmed the above conclusion that the deep yellow acid has a crystalline structure entirely different from that of hydrous tungsten trioxide.[269] It was further shown that the white acid is amorphous to X-rays and that the lemon-yellow acid, has a composition formulated as $WO_3 \cdot 2H_2O$ or $H_2WO_4 \cdot H_2O$. However, Burger claimed that the white acid analyzed for $WO_3 \cdot 2H_2O$ and give a definite X-ray diffraction pattern.[271] He was probably talking about what Morley called the lemon-yellow hydrate, which seems to be different from the white preparation, although this difference could be one of the particle size. The

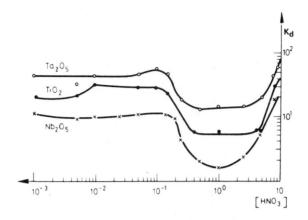

FIGURE 42. Variation of K_d with HNO_3 concentration for Ag^+ exchange on three oxides. (From Ganzerli-Valentini, M. T., Meloni, S., Maxia, V., and Pisani, U ., *J. Radioanal. Chem.,* 16, 191, 1973. With permission.)

lemon-yellow compound is not stable and goes over to the deep yellow monohydrate on aging.

Little is known about the structure of tungstic acid. The X-ray diffraction pattern is listed on the ASTM card file 18-1418 as tungsten oxide hydrate, $WO_3 \cdot 2H_2O$, but the crystal system is not assigned. WO_3 is monoclinic at ordinary temperatures and tetragonal above 710°C.[272]

The yellow acid sometimes takes on a greenish color especially on ignition because of the formation of a lower oxide, as a result of a small amount of some reducing impurity in the precipitate. A tungstic acid jelly is obtained by adding mineral acid to 3 to 10% sodium tungstate solutions until the acid concentration of the mixture is between 0.1 and 0.5 *M*, and allowing to stand. The homogeneous jelly can be broken down, washed and activated like silica gel to make it into an adsorbent.[271]

2. Physical and Chemical Properties of Tungstic Acid

a. Chemical Stability

Tungstic acid is stable in nitric acid solution, but soluble in alkaline solution.[82 221,273,274] When tungstic acid is immersed in pure water for a long time, peptization occurs.[82] Therefore, this exchanger can be used only under limited conditions; in acidic media or in the presence of a buffer solution at pH below ~5. This exchanger is also stable towards alcohol and acetic acid.[82] Both white and yellow tungstic acids change to a greenish or bluish color by the action of reducing agents.

b. Infrared Spectra

The IR spectra of white tungstic acid shows bands at 1410, 1200, and 1100 cm⁻¹ in the frequency region 1000 to 1700 cm⁻¹ (see Figure 43).[275] These bands indicate the presence of different types of hydroxyl groups bonded with the W atom. The bands at 1200, and 1100 cm⁻¹ are very weak. The most intense band is at 1410 cm⁻¹, which can be assigned to a complex vibration arising from interaction of hydroxyl group vibrations with a W−O bond. The band at 1100 cm⁻¹ can be assigned to vibrations of hydronium ions present in approximately the same state as in $(H_3O)Cl$, $(H_2O)Br$, etc.[276,277] Thus, there are three types of bound water in this compound. (1) water in the form of hydroxyl bonded to a W atom; (2) water molecules present as water of hydration inside the crystal lattice or in the adsorbed state; and (3) hydronium ions.

The spectra of yellow tungstic acid contains no bands corresponding to a deforma-

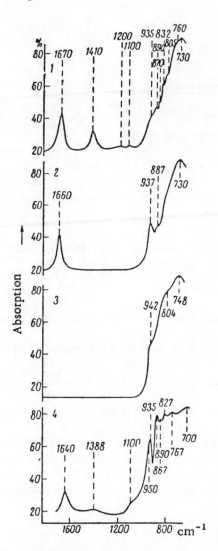

FIGURE 43. Infrared absorption spectra of tungsten compounds. 1) White tungstic acid; 2) yellow tungstic acid; 3) tungsten trioxide; 4) sodium paratungstate. (From Kabanov, V. Ya. and Spitsyn, V. I., *Dokl. Akad. Nauk.*, 148, 109, 1963; *Dokl. Chem.; Proc. Akad. Sci. SSSR, Chem. Sec.*, 148, 26, 1963. With permission.)

tion vibration of hydroxyl groups or of oxonium ions. Consequently, in this compound only one type of water, water of crystallization, which corresponds to the band at 1660 cm^{-1} is present. In the range of tungsten-oxygen bridge vibrations (650 to 1000 cm^{-1}), the spectrum of yellow tungstic acid is similar to that of WO_3 (the slight difference may be due to the influence of H_2O molecule on the lattice vibrations of WO_3). Therefore, yellow tungstic acid is similar to hydrated tungsten trioxide.

Schwarzmann and Glemser[278] reported that the ir spectra showed bands at 3560, 3420, 3180, 1600, 1005, 945, and 918 cm^{-1} for $WO_3 \cdot 2H_2O$; 3200, 1620, and 948 cm^{-1} for $WO_3 \cdot H_2O$; and of 820 and 770 cm^{-1} for WO_3. The bands found at 3560, 3420, and 3180 cm^{-1} were attributed to the OH groups which show bands in the 3600 to 3000 cm^{-1} region. $^1_1$H NMR spectra (17.5 MC/sec, T = 290, and 77 K) were obtained. The secondary moments found with both compounds were 25.5 ± 1.5 and 24.5 ± 1.5 gauss, respectively, which corresponds to an H–H distance of about 1.56 Å in both cases,

Table 17
CATION EXCHANGE CAPACITY OF W(VI) OXIDE AT DIFFERENT pH[a]

Batch No.	pH of solution: Initial	pH of solution: Final	Exchange capacity (in meq of H^+/g)
1[b]	2	1.8	0.20
1	3	2.7	0.3
1	4	3.65	0.35
1	5	4.55	0.92
1	6	5.2	2.12
3[c]	2	1.8	0.2
3	3	2.7	0.3
3	4	3.6	0.4
3	5	4.3	2.76
3	6	4.9	2.98

[a] With NaCl solutions.
[b] Batch 1; 0.1 *M* Na_2WO_3(100 mℓ) + 3 *M* HCl(100 mℓ), aged for 2 hr.
[c] Batch 3; 0.1 *M* Na_2WO_3(100 mℓ) + Conc. HCl(50 mℓ), aged for 4 hr.

indicating the presence of crystalline water. The spectra are similar to those of $CaSO_4 \cdot 2H_2O$ in which the water has been established to be crystalline water. The possibility of $WO_3 \cdot H_2O$ being $WO_2(OH)_2H_2O$ was excluded by comparing its NMR spectrum with that of $MoO_3PO_3(OH)H_2O$. No similarity was found and a comparison with the spectrum of H_3OClO_4 excluded the possibility of H_3O^+.

On the basis of IR spectral studies Kabanov and Spitsyn[275] have proposed the presence of the following unstable poly compounds:

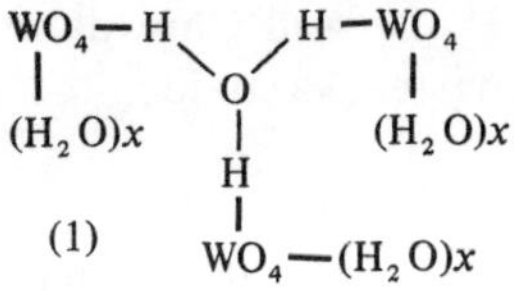
(1)

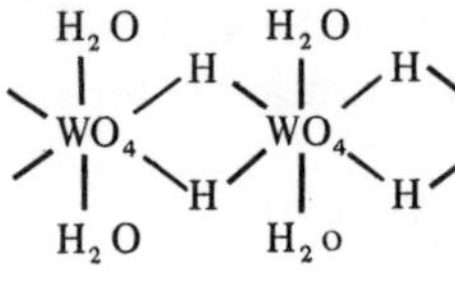
(4)

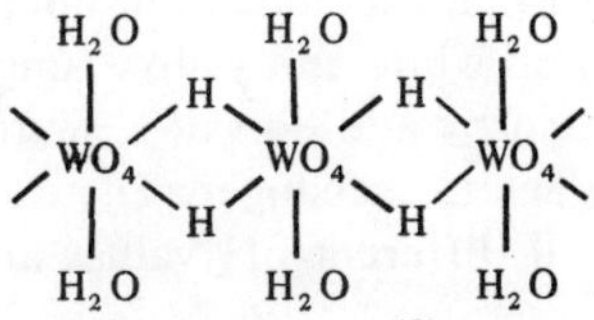
(2)

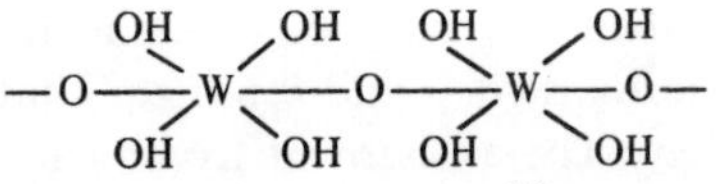
(5)

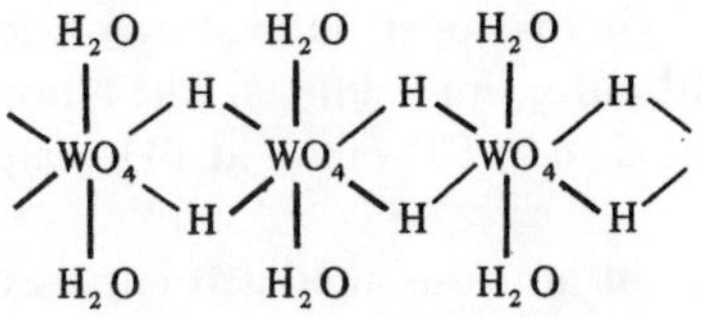
(3)

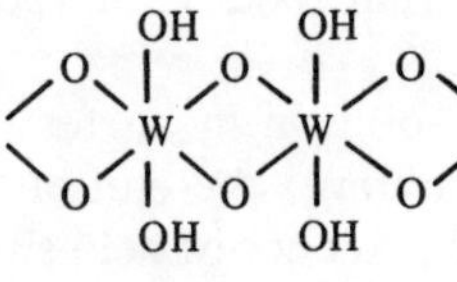
(6)

In the first group, WO_4^{2-} anions are hydrogen bonded to H_3O^+ cations. In the second group there are molecules of tungstic acid and WO_4^{2-} ions, and the third group con-

Table 18

DISTRIBUTION
COEFFICIENT OF SOME
METAL IONS

Metal ion	K_d values	
	Batch No. 1	Batch No. 3
Zn^{2+}	51.37	21.6
Cu^{2+}	52.23	46.97
Co^{2+}	35	12
Ca^{2+}	134	104.2
Sr^{2+}	116	91.5
Ba^{2+}	28.57	12.51
Mg^{2+}	8.7	4.132
Ni^{2+}	TA[a]	TA
Mn^{2+}	TA	TA

Note: Batch Numbers 1 and 3 are the same as in Table 17.

[a]   TA = total adsorption.

tains HWO^-_4 ions. Units of types (1) and (2) are relatively more important at high pH, and the number of units of types (3) and (4) increase with a decrease in pH. The metastable compound gradually undergoes rearrangement in solution, apparently with the initial formation of linearly condensed chains in which units of types (5) and (6) play a substantial part. With further interaction of the hydroxyl groups, elimination of water molecules takes place accompanied by a transformation from the linear to a three-dimensional structure with octahedral coordination of oxygen around the W.

3. Ion Exchange Properties of Tungstic Acid

Amphlett et al.,[273] and Abe and Ito[22] indicated that tungstic acid exhibits a pH titration curve with a break point, indicating both an ion exchange reaction at pHs below 5 and the dissolution of the exchanger at higher pH. De and Chowdhury[81] found no break point in the pH-titration curve for hydrous tungsten(VI) oxide.

a. Ion Exchange Capacity

Because of its solubility in alkaline solution, the capacity of this exchanger must not be determined above pH 5. Abe and Ito[22] reported that the maximum uptakes for K^+ was about 0.4 meq/g and 0.6 meq/g (at $\mu = 0.1$) on white and yellow tungstic acids, respectively. The amount of hydrogen ions liberated by addition of a neutral salt solution is very small because of the oxides weakly acidic exchanger. The exchange capacities of two different oxides for sodium ions at different pH values are given in Table 17.[82]

When 2 *M* NaCl solution in buffer media at pH 6 is passed through the hydrous tungstic(VI) oxide column, the elution curve of hydrogen ions shows a long tailing effect because of the presence of acid sites with different acidities. The anion exchange capacity for bath No. 1 is 0.13, 0.08, and 0.05 meq Cl^- per g at pH − 0, 1, and 3, respectively.

Szalav and Bartha[279] studied the equilibria in aqueous media for the exchange of K^+, Tl^+, and Tl^{3+} on the yellow acid and a blue acid ($WO_{2.87} \cdot H_2O$). The equilibria can be characterized by a Langmuir-Hueckel isotherm. At 25°C, the adsorption is dependent on the HCl concentration. Tl^{3+} did not adsorb on the yellow acid but was adsorbed on the blue acid as Tl(I) as a result of a redox process. From the isotherm, the number

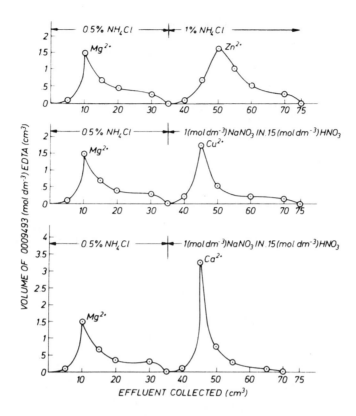

FIGURE 44. Separation of Zn^{2+}, Cu^{2+} and Ca^{2+} from Mg^{2+} on a tungsten(VI) oxide column (Batch No. 1). (From De, A. K. and Chowdhury, K., *Chromatographia*, 11, 586, 1978. With permission.)

of active sites on the surface was calculated and from this and the lattice constant of the oxide, the active specific surface for K^+ was found to be 9.4, 2.7, and 0.4 m² g⁻¹ in 0, 0.5, and 2.87 M HCl, respectively. These values were 1.8, 0.1 and 0.04, for the yellow acid. The values for Tl^+ were 1.0(0.5 M HCl) and 0.8 (2.87 M HCl) for the yellow acid, and 10 (0.5 M) and 8.7 (2.87) for the blue acid. Under the same acid conditions, Tl^{3+} gave values of 1.0 and 0.2 on the blue acid.

b. Ion Exchange Separations

The distribution coefficients of metal ions have been determined and possible separations on hydrous tungstic(IV) acid have been studied by De and Chowdhury.[82] The exchanger (0.5 g) is immersed in 50 mℓ of a solution containing 2×10^{-4} M metal ions in 1 M NaCl solution adjusted at pH 5 with a buffer solution. Ni^{2+} and Mn^{2+} are completely adsorbed not only in this concentration range, but also when higher concentrations are used. The results obtained are summarized in Table 18.

Some useful separations can be achieved for Mg^{2+} from Zn^{2+}, Cu^{2+}, Ca^{2+}, Sr^{2+}, Mn^{2+}, and Ni^{2+} (see Figure 44) and Co^{2+} from Ni^{2+} and Mn^{2+} by using a glass column of 1.5 cm diameter containing about 5 g of the exchanger. A very effective separation of Ca^{2+} has been carried out from a large amount of Mg^{2+} (see Figure 44).

The adsorption capacities of Np(IV) on tungstic acid (prepared as a bluish green glassy gel) were dependent upon the concentrations of both HNO_3 and Np. The adsorption of V on tungstic acid was considerably less than that of Np. The breakthrough points of Np were 2400 or 1000 column volumes at 1 or 2 M HNO_3 with 1×10^{-2} mol/ℓ of V, respectively. Thus, the tungstic acid exchanger was suitable for separation of Np from $VO_2(NO_3)_2$ solutions.[280]

REFERENCES

1. Carlson, T. A., Kraus, K. A., Johnson, J. S., Jr., and Phillips, H. O., Adsorption of rare earths on inorganic materials, *ORNL,* 1583, 203, 1955.
2. Kraus, K. A. and Phillips, H. O., Anion exchange studies. XIX. Anion exchange properties of hydrous zirconium oxide, *J. Am. Chem. Soc.,* 78, 249, 1956.
3. Kraus, K. A., Phillips, H. O., Carlson, T. A., and Johnson, J. S., Jr., Ion exchange properties of hydrous oxides, *Proc. 2nd Intl. Conf. Peaceful Uses of Atomic Energy,* Vol. 28, Paper No. 15/p/ 1832, United Nations, Geneva, 1958, 3.
4. Amphlett, C. B., Inorganic ion exchangers, in *Topics in Inorganic and General Chemistry,* Robinson, P. L., Ed., Elsevier, Amsterdam, 1964, chap. 5.
5. Fuller, M. J., Inorganic ion-exchange chromatography on oxides and hydrous oxides, *Chromatogr. Rev.,* 14, 45, 1971.
6. Vesely, V. and Pekarek, V., Synthetic inorganic ion-exchangers I, hydrous oxides and acid salts of multivalent metals, *Talanta,* 19, 219, 1972.
7. Clearfield, A., Nancollas, G. H., and Blessing, R. H., Inorganic ion-exchangers, in *Ion Exchange and Solvent Extraction,* Marinsky, J. A. and Marcus, Y., Eds., Marcel Dekker, New York, 1973, chap. 1.
8. Abe, M., Analytical applications of synthetic inorganic ion-exchangers. I. Hydroxides and hydrous Oxides, *Bunseki Kagaku,* 23, 1254, 1974.
9. De, A. K. and Sen, A. K., Synthetic ion exchangers, *Sep. Sci. Technol.,* 13, 517, 1978.
10. Clearfield, A. and Vaughan, P. A., The crystal structure of zirconium chloride octahydrate and zirconium bromide octahydrate, *Acta Cryst. Allagn.,* 9, 555, 1956.
11. Clearfield, A., Structural aspects of zirconium chemistry, *Rev. Pure Appl. Chem.,* 14, 91, 1964.
12. Alekseeva, I. I., Nemzer, I. I., and Yuranova, L. I., State of zirconium and hafnium in perchlorate solution, *Zh. Neorg. Khim.,* 20, 92, 1974.
13. Johnson, J. S. and Kraus, K. A., Hydrolytic behavior of metal ions. VI. Ultracentrifugation of zirconium(IV) and hafnium(IV). Effect of acidity on the degree of polymerization, *J. Am. Chem. Soc.,* 78, 3937, 1956.
14. Makherji, A. K. *Analytical Chemistry of Zirconium and Hafnium,* Pergamon Press, New York, 1970, chap. 1.
15. Fratiello, A., Vidulich, G. A., and Mako, F., A direct nuclear magnetic resonance cation hydration study of zirconium perchlorate and zirconium nitrate solution in water-hexamethyl phosphoramide-acetone mixture, *Inorg. Chem.,* 12, 470, 1973.
16. Baglin, F. G. and Breger, D., Identification of the zirconium sulphate species in highly acidic aqueous solution by Raman spectroscopy, *Inorg. Nucl. Chem. Lett.,* 12, 173, 1976.
17. Bragina, M. I. and Bobyrenko, Yu, Ua., Infrared adsorption spectra of titanium (IV) sulfate and chloride aqueous solution, *Zh. Neorg. Khim.,* 17, 117, 1972; *Russ. J. Inorg. Chem.,* 17, 61, 1972.
18. Sheytanov, C. E. and Rizov, N., On the behavior of titanium (IV) in aqueous medium. I. The polymerization processes in the system: Ti (IV)-HClO$_4$-H$_2$O, *Inorg. Nucl. Chem. Lett.,* 6, 785, 1970.
19. Feitknecht, W., Giovanoli, R., Michaelis, W., and Müller, M., Hydrolysis of iron (III) salt solution. II. Changes in the hydrolyzed products, *Z. Anorg. Allgem. Chem.,* 417, 114, 1975.
20. Burgess, J., *Metal Ions in Solution,* Ellis Harwood, London, 1978, chap. 10.
21. Abe, M. and Ito, T., Ion adsorptive properties of insoluble bi- and tervalent metal hydrous oxides and hydroxides, *Nippon Kagaku Zasshi,* 86, 817, 1965.
22. Abe, M. and Ito, T., Ion adsorptive properties of insoluble quadri-, quinque-, and sexi-valent metal hydrous oxides, *Nippon Kagaku Zasshi,* 86, 1259, 1965.
23. Bye, G. C., Robinson, J. G., and Sing, K. S. W., The characterization of aluminium hydroxide gels by nitrogen adsorption, *J. Appl. Chem.,* 17, 138, 1967.
24. Gregg, S. T. and Hill, K. J., The production of active solid by thermal decomposition. II. Ferric oxide, *J. Chem. Soc.,* 3945, 1953.
25. Gregg, S. J. and Hill, K. J., Electronic properties of transition-metal complex ions adsorbed on silica gel. II. Cobalt (II) and cobalt (III), *J. Chem. Soc. A,* 1183, 1969.
26. Rutledge, J. L., Surface parameters of stannic oxide in powder, ceramic, and gel forms by nitrogen adsorption techniques, *Proc. Okla. Acad. Sci.,* 46, 137, 1966; *Chem. Abstr.,* 67, 36632e, 1966.
27. Mikhail, R. Sh. and Fahim, R. B., Thermal treatment of thorium oxide gel at low temperatures, *J. Appl. Chem.,* 17, 147, 1967.
28. Mikhail, R. Sh., Gabr, R. M., and Fahim, R. B., Surface area and pore structure of ceric oxide, *J. Appl. Chem.,* 20, 222, 1970.
29. Unger, K. and Vydra, F., The sorption of Zn(NH$_3$)$^{2+}_4$ and Zn(en)$^{2+}_3$ on silica gels of various specific surfaces. The determination of specific surface area of silica gel by sorption of Zn(en)$^{2+}_3$, *J. Inorg. Nucl. Chem.,* 30, 1075, 1968.

30. **Kozawa, A.**, Ion-exchange adsorption of zinc and copper ions on silica, *J. Inorg. Nucl. Chem.*, 21, 315, 1961.

31. **Abe, M.**, Unpublished results.

32. **Kirichenko, L. F., and Vysotskii, Z. Z.**, Sorption of cations by silicas in the acid region, *Dokl. Akad. Nauk. SSSR*, 175, 635, 1967.

33. **Chidley, B. E., Parker, F. L., and Talbot, E. A.**, Properties of Hydrated Titanium Dioxide and Hydrated Tantalum Pentoxide as High Temperature Ion-exchange Materials, U.S.A.E.A., Rep. AERE-R5220, Atomic Energy Research Establishment, Harwell, Berks., 1966.

34. **Heitner-Wirguin, C., and Albu-Yaron, A.**, Hydrous oxides and their cation exchange properties. *J. Appl. Chem.*, 15, 445, 1965.

35. **Heitner-Wirguin, C. and Albu-Yaron, A.**, Hydrous oxides and their cation exchange properties, II. Structure and equilibrium experiments, *J. Inorg. Nucl. Chem.*, 28, 2379, 1966.

36. **Abe, M., Nasir, B. A., and Yoshida, T.**, Chromatographic separation of trace amounts of transition metals from large amounts of calcium with hydrous zirconium dioxide as ion-exchanger, *J. Chromatogr.*, 153, 295, 1978.

37. **Knight, R. J. and Sylva, R. N.**, Precipitation in hydrolysed iron (III) solutions, *J. Inorg. Nucl. Chem.*, 36, 591, 1974.

38. **Abe, M. and Ito, T.**, Preparation and properties of "so-called" antimonic(V) acid, *Bull. Chem. Soc. Jpn.*, 41, 333, 1968.

39. **Breeuwsma, A. and Lyklema, J.**, Interfacial electrochemistry of haematite (α-Fe$_2$O$_3$), *Discuss. Faraday Soc.*, 52, 324, 1971.

40. **Levine, S. and Smith, A. L.**, Theory of the differential capacity of the oxide/aqueous electrolyte interface, *Discuss. Faraday Soc.*, 52, 290, 1971.

41. **Parks, G. A.**, The isoelectric points of solid oxides, solid hydroxides and aqueous hydroxo complex systems, *Chem. Rev.*, 65, 177, 1965.

42. **Novikov, B. G., Materova, E. A., and Belinskaya, F. A.**, Nature and stability of precipitated polyantimonic acid, *Zh. Neorg. Khim.*, 20, 1566, 1975; *Russ. J. Inorg. Chem.*, 20, 876, 1975.

43. **Novikov, B. G., Belinskaya, F. A., and Materova, E. A.**, Structure and ion-exchange properties of crystalline antimonic acid cation exchanger. Exchange of monopositive cations, *Vestn. Leningrad Univ. Fiz. Khim.*, No. 4, 29, 1971.

44. **Bailar, J. C., Emeléus, H. J., Nyholm, S. R., and Trotman-Dickenson, A. F.**, Eds., *Comprehensive Inorganic Chemistry*, Vol. 1, Pergamon Press, New York, 1973, 560.

45. **Mercer, R. M. and Miller, R. P.**, The preparation and properties of some hydroxy compounds of beryllium, *J. Inorg. Nucl. Chem.*, 28, 61, 1966.

46. **Wells, A. F.**, *Structural Inorganic Chemistry*, 4th ed., Oxford University Press, New York, 1975, 521.

47. **Elleman, D. D. and Williams, D.**, Proton positions in brucite crystals, *J. Chem. Phys.*, 25, 742, 1956.

48. **Dean, J. A.**, *Chemical Separation Methods*, van Nostrand Reinhold, New York, 1969, 142.

49. **Churms, S. C.**, The effect of pH on the ionexchange properties of hydrated alumina. I. Capacity and selectivity, *J. S. African Chem. Inst.*, 19, 98, 1966.

50. **Bailar, J. C., Emeléus, H. J., Nyholm, S. R., and Trotman-Dickenson, A. F.**, Eds., *Comprehensive Inorganic Chemistry*, Vol. 1, Pergamon Press, New York, 1973, 1094.

51. **Busev, A. I.**, *The Analytical Chemistry of Indium*, Pergamon Press, Oxford, 1962, 28.

52. **Roy, R. and Shafer, M. W.**, Phases present and phase equilibrium in the system In$_2$O$_3$–H$_2$O, *J. Phys. Chem.*, 58, 372, 1954.

53. **Christansen, A. N. and Broch, N. C.**, Hydrothermal investigation of the systems In$_2$O$_3$–H$_2$O–Na$_2$O and In$_2$O$_3$–D$_2$O–Na$_2$O. The crystal structure of Rhombohedral In$_2$O$_3$ and In(OH)$_3$, *Acta Chem. Scand.*, 21, 1046, 1967.

54. **Christansen, A. N., Groenbaek, K. P., and Rasmussen, S. E.**, The crystal structure of InOOH, *Acta Chem. Scand.*, 18, 1261, 1961.

55. **Moore, T. E., Ellis, M., and Selwood, P. W.**, Solid oxides and hydroxides of Manganese, *J. Am. Chem. Soc.*, 72, 856, 1950.

56. **Dachs, H.**, Neutron and X-ray diffraction of manganite MnOOH, *Z. Kryst.*, 118, 303, 1963.

57. **Mellor, L. M.**, *A Comprehensive Treatise on Inorganic and Theoretial Chemistry*, Vol. 9, Longmans, London, 1952, 625.

58. **Huttig, G. F., Tsuji, T., and Steiner, B.**, Oxyhydrate and active oxides. XLVI. On the system of Bismuth(III) oxide/water, *Z. Anorg. Allg. Chem.*, 200, 74, 1931.

59. **Mambetov, A. A. and Nabiev, M. I.**, Formation conditions, composition, and physico-chemical properties of bismuth acids formed at pH 9.3 and 11.5, *Dokl. Akad. Nauk, Azerb. SSR*, 25, 20, 1969; *Chem. Abstr.*, 73, 38947j, 1970.

60. Ito, T. and Kenjo, T., Effects of organic impurities on the anion-exchange properties of bismuth hydroxide, *Nippon Kagaku Zasshi,* 88, 1120, 1967.
61. Ito, T. and Yoshida, T., Reversibility of adsorption of chloride ion on bismuth(III) hydroxide, *Nippon Kagaku Zasshi,* 91, 1054, 1970.
62. Doležal, J., Horáček, J., Šramek, J., and Šulecek, Z., Silica gel in inorganic analysis. Separation and determination of small amounts of zirconium, *Microchim. Acta,* 1966, 38.
63. Bannasch, W., Behavior of silica gel as ion exchanger in separation of lead(Pb-212)/Bismuth (Bi-212)/ thallium(Tl-208), *USAEC,* AEC Accession No. 41562, Rep. No. KFK-215, 1964, *Chem. Abstr.,* 62, 10021h, 1965.
64. Parks, G. A., Aqueous surface chemistry of oxides and complex oxide minerals. Isoelectric points and zero point of charge; *Adv. Chem. Ser.,* No. 67, 121, 1967, *Chem. Abstr.,* 67, 47538e, 1967.
65. Covington, A. K., Cressey, T., Lever, B. G., and Thirsk, H. R., Standard potential of the β-manganese dioxide electrode, *Trans. Faraday Soc.,* 58, 1975, 1962.
66. Vol'khin, V. V. and Leont'eva, G., Physical-chemical study of the ion exchange properties of manganese dioxide, *Izvest. Akad. Nauk SSSR, Neorg. Mater.,* 5, 1224, 1969; *Chem. Abstr.,* 71, 95273u, 1969.
67. Davies, R. V., Kennedy, J., McLroy, R. W., Spence, R., and Hill, K. M., Extraction of uranium from sea water, *Nature,* 203, 1110, 1964.
68. Ogata, N., Collection of uranium in seawater. VI. Adsorption of Uranium in seawater with titanic acid, *J. Atom. Energy Soc. Jpn.,* 13, 121, 1971.
69. Kanno, M., Technical problems on the extraction of uranium from seawater, *Bull. Soc. Sea Water Sci. Jpn.,* 31, 115, 1977.
70. Ninomiya, A., Sugasaka, K., and Fujii, A., Recovery of metal ion by active carbon-metal hydroxide adsorbents, *Kogyo Kagaku Zasshi,* 74, 1486, 1971.
71. Weiser, H. B. and Milligan, W. O., X-ray studies on the hydroxides IV. Titanium dioxide, *J. Phys. Chem.,* 38, 513, 1934.
72. Levi, von H. W. and Schiewer, E., Cation-exchange on TiO_2 aq. II. Determination of equilibrium constants for Cs-H and Na-H exchange, *Radiochim. Acta,* 9, 160, 1968.
73. Schiewer, E., Austauschadsorption von Kationen an Titandioxidhydrat, Dissertation, Technischen Universitat, Berlin, 1967.
74. Inoue, Y. and Tsuji, M., Studies of hydrous titanium oxide ion exchange II. The equilivanlence of the exchange adsorption of cations and the dissociation constant, *Bull. Chem. Soc. Jpn.,* 49, 111, 1976.
75. Keen, N. J., Studies on the extraction of uranium from sea water, *J. Br. Nucl. Soc.,* 7, 178, 1968.
76. Clearfield, A., Crystalline hydrous zirconia, *J. Inorg. Chem.,* 3, 146, 1964.
77. Amphlett, C. B., McDonald, L. A., and Redman, M. J., Synthetic inorganic ion-exchange materials II. Hydrous zirconium oxide and other oxides, *J. Inorg. Nucl. Chem.,* 6, 236, 1958.
78. De, A. K. and Das, S. K., Synthetic inorganic ion-exchangers. VIII. Hydrous cerium(IV) oxide: Synthesis, properties, and ion-exchange separations, *Sep. Sci. Technol.,* 13, 465, 1978.
79. Cotton, F. A. and Wilkinson, G., *Advanced Inorganic Chemistry,* 2nd ed., Interscience, New York, 1966, 937.
80. Mellor, L. M., *A Comprehensive Treatise on Inorganic and Theoretical Chemistry,* Vol. 11, Longmans, London, 1954, 762.
81. De, A. K. and Chowdhury, K., Synthetic ion exchangers. X. Hydrous tungsten(VI) oxides: synthesis, physico-chemical properties and ion exchange separations, *Chromatographia,* 11, 586, 1978.
82. Shannon, R. D. and Prewitt, C. T., Effective ionic radii in oxides and fluorides, *Acta Crystallagr.,* B 25, 925, 1969.
83. Abe, M. and Ito, T., The acidities of hydrous oxides as cation-adsorbents, *Nippon Kagaku Zasshi,* 87, 417, 1966.
84. Kossiakoff, A. and Harker, D., The calculation of ionization constants of inorganic oxygen acids from their structures, *J. Am. Chem. Soc.,* 60, 2047, 1938.
85. Cartledge, G. A., Studies on the periodic system. III. The relation between ionizing potentials and ionic potentials, *J. Am. Chem. Soc.,* 52, 3076, 1930.
86. Möeller, T., *Inorganic Chemistry, An Advanced Textbook,* John Wiley & Sons, New York, 1952, chap. 9, (especially 318-321).
87. Pauling, L., *The Nature of the Chemical Bond,* 3rd ed., Cornell University Press, Ithaca, N. Y., 1960, 276, 557.
88. Helfferich, F., *Ion Exchange,* McGraw-Hill, New York, 1962, 84.
89. Ahrland, S., Grenthe, I., and Noren, B., The ion exchange properties of silica gel. I. The sorption of Na^+, Ca^{2+}, Ba^{2+}, $UO^{2+}{}_2$, Gd^{3+}, Zr(IV), Nb(V), U(IV) and Pu(IV), *Acta Chem. Scand.,* 14, 1059, 1960.

90. Graham, K. and Madeley, J. D., Relation between the zeta potential of rutile and its flotation with sodium dodecyl sulphate, *J. Appl. Chem.*, 12, 485, 1962.

91. Jander, G. and Simon, A., Formation kinetics of antimony pentoxide hydrate, *Z. Anorg. Allg. Chem.*, 127, 68, 1923.

92. Jander, G., Antimony and antimonates, *Kolloid. Z.*, 23, 122, 1919.

93. Gohsh, S. and Dhar, N. R., Investigation on the colloidal behavior of antimony pentoxide, *J. Ind. Chem. Soc.*, 6, 17, 1929.

94. Ito, T. and Abe, M., Ion-exchange properties of "so-called" antimonic acid, The 15th. National Meeting of Japan Chemical Society, Japan Chemical Society, Tokyo, April 1962, Abstr. p. 58.

95. Abe, M. and Ito, T., Cation exchange properties of antimonic(V) acid, *Nippon Kagaku Zasshi*, 87, 1174, 1966.

96. Lefebvre, J., Antimonic acid as ion exchanger, detection and character of exchange, *Compt. Rend.*, 260, 5575, 1965.

97. Lefebvre, J. and Gaymard, F., Antimonic acid as ion exchanger, capacities and selectivities for alkali and alkaline earth metals, *C. R. Acad. Sci. Paris*, 260, 6911, 1965.

98. Baetsle, L. H., van Deyck, D., Huys, D., and Guery, A., The use of inorganic exchanger in acid media for recovery of Cs and Sr from reprocessing solution, *USAEC*, AEC Accession No. 7613, Rep. No. BLG. 267, 1964.

99. Baetsle, L. H., van Deyck, D., Huys, D., and Guery, A., Separation of ^{137}Cs and ^{90}Sr from fission products in an acid medium on mineral exchangers, *USAEC*, AEC Accession No. 3871, Rep. No. EUR 2497c, 1975.

100. Abe, M. and Ito, T., Mutual separation of alkali metals with antimonic(V) acid, *Bull. Chem. Soc. Jpn.*, 40, 1013, 1967.

101. Abe, M., The mutual separation of alkali metals with three different antimonic(V) acids, *Bull. Chem. Soc. Jpn.*, 42, 2683, 1969.

102. Novikov, B. G., Materova, E. A., and Belinskaya, F. A., Nature and stability of precipitated polyantimonic acid, *Vestn. Lingrad. Univ. Fiz. Khim.*, 22, 97, 1976.

103. Abe, M. and Uno, K., Ion-exchange behavior and separation of alkaline earth metals on crystalline antimonic(V) acid, *Sep. Sci. Technol.*, 14, 355, 1979.

104. Konečný, C. and Kourin, V., Recovery of Sr by means of a polyantimonic/V/acid cation exchanger, *Radioanal. Radiochem. Lett.*, 2, 47, 1969.

105. Abe, M., Selective separation of cadmium from zinc and copper(II) with crystalline antimonic(V) acid as a cation-exchanger, *Chem. Lett.*, 1979, 561.

106. Abe, M. and Kasai, K., Distribution coefficients and possible separation of transition metals on crystalline antimonic(V) acid, *Sep. Sci. Technol.*, 14, 895, 1979.

107. Abe, M. and Akimoto, M., Ion-exchange properties of crystalline antimonic(V) acid towards noble metals in nitric acid media, *Bull. Chem. Soc. Jpn.*, 53, 121, 1980.

108. Girardi, F. and Sabbioni, E., Selective removal of radio-sodium from neutron-activated materials by retention on hydrated antimony pentoxide, *J. Radioanal. Chem.*, 1, 169, 1968.

109. Mellor, J. W., Antimony, in *A Comprehensive Treatise on Inorganic and Theoretical Chemistry*, Vol. 9, Longmans, London, 1952, chap. 102.

110. Meyer, R. J. and Pietsch, E. H. E., Antimon (B), in *Gmelins Handbuch der Anorganischen Chemie*, No. 18, Gmelin-Institut Fur Anorganische Chemie und Grenzgebiete in der Max-Planck-Gesellschaft, Frankfurt am Main, West Germany, 1949, 376.

111. Simon, A. and Thaler, E., Contribution to the knowledge of hydrous gels. ITI. About hydrated antimony pentoxide, *Z. Anorg. Allg. Chem.*, 161, 113, 1927.

112. Natta, G. and Baccaredda, M., Interstitial chemical compounds. The structure of hydrated antimony pentoxide and some antimonates, *Gazz. Chim. Ital.*, 66, 308, 1936.

113. Colin, J. M. and Lefebvre, L., Preparation of amorphous antimonic acid from freshly prepared antimonic acid solution, *C. R. Acad. Sci. Paris*, 268, 1760, 1969.

114. Cahuzac, S. and Lefebvre, J., Effect of antimonic acid preparation method on the capacity of exchange with different cations, *C. R. Acad. Sci. Paris, Ser. C*, 267, 1127, 1968.

115. Lefebvre, J. and Lemerle, J., Crystallizable high polymers in antimonic acid solution, *C. R. Acad. Sci. Paris, Ser. C*, 267, 604, 1968.

116. Cahuzac, S. and Lefebvre, J., Aging of antimonic acid in aqueous media, *Bull. Soc. Chim. Fr.*, 771, 1969.

117. Baetsle, L. H. and Huys, D., Structure and ion-exchange characteristics of polyantimonic acid, *J. Inorg. Nucl. Chem.*, 30, 639, 1968.

118. Jansen, M., Preparation and crystal structure of $Sb_2O_5 \cdot 3/5H_2O \equiv Sb_5O_{12}(OH)H_2O$, *Rev. Chim. Miner.*, 15, 242, 1978.

119. Natta, G. and Baccaredda, M., Composition and structure of antimony pentoxide hydrate, *Gazz. Chim. Ital.*, 66, 308, 1936.

120. Dihlström, K. and Westgren, A., About the construction of so-called antimony tetroxide and the isomorphous compound BiTa₂O₆F, *Z. Anorg. Allg. Chem.*, 235, 153, 1937.
121. Hanawalt, D. J., Rinn, H. W., and Frevel, L. K., Chemical analysis by X-ray diffraction. Classification and use of x-ray diffraction patterns, *Ind. Eng. Chem. Anal. Ed.*, 10, 457, 1938.
122. Swanson, H. E., Cook, M. I., Evans, E. H., and De Groot, J. H., Antimony(V) oxide, Sb₂O₅(cubic), *Natl. Bur. Stand. (U.S.) Circ.*, 539, 10, 10, 1969.
123. Novikov, B. G., Belinskaya, F. A., and Materova, E. A., Preparation and some properties of a crystalline antimonic acid cation exchanger, *Vestn. Leningrad. Univ. Fiz. Khim.*, 2, 97, 1969.
124. Oleñkova, I. P. and Plyasova, L. M., Pyrochlore motif in the structure of antimony oxides, *Zh. Strukt. Khim.*, 19, 1040, 1978; *Chem. Abstr.*, 90, 110576h, 1978.
125. Doležal, J., Stejskal, J., Tympl, M., and Kouřin, V., Improved inorganic ion-exchangers. II. Ammonium molybdophosphate-silica gel system, *J. Radioanal. Chem.*, 21, 381, 1974.
126. Caletka, R., Konečný, C., and Šimková, M., Removal of sodium from mineral acid solutions by adsorption on modified polyantimonic(V) acid, *J. Radioanal. Chem.*, 10, 5, 1972.
127. Novikov, B. G., Belinskaya, F. A., and Materova, E. A., Study of the sorption properties of silicon antimony cation exchanger, *Vestn. Leningr. Univ. Fiz. Khim.*, (1), 94, 1976; *Chem. Abstr.*, 84, 170124v, 1976.
128. Laskorin, B. N., Bondarenko, L. I., Strelko, V. V., Kulbich, T. S., and Denisov, V. I., Characteristics of the sorption of divalent cations by ion exchanger based on antimonic acid, *Dokl. Akad. Nauk SSSR*, 229, 1411, 1976.
129. Kouřin, V., Stejskal, J., and Santarová, M., Improved inorganic ion-exchangers. III. polyantimonic and mixed sulphate-silica gel systems, *J. Radioanal. Chem.*, 30, 147, 1976.
130. Taushkanov, V. P., Polkhitonov, Y. A., Kuzin, L. A., and Allabergenov, Y. A., Selective properties of active coals modified by antimony compounds, *Zh. Prikl. Khim. (Leningrad)*, 49, 470, 1976.
131. Szilagyi, J., Contribution to the knowledge of antimony dioxide, *Z. Anal. Chem.*, 57, 23, 1918.
132. Goto, H., Determination of platinum group and antimony. Gravimetric analysis by using thermal balance, *Nippon Kagaku Zasshi*, 55, 326, 1934.
133. Simon, A. and Thaler, E., A study on antimony oxide, *Z. Anorg. Allg. Chem.*, 162, 253, 1927.
134. Abe, M., Thermal decomposition of three different antimonic acids, *Kogyo Kagaku Zasshi*, 70, 2226, 1967.
135. Stewart, D. J., Knop, O., and Ayasse, C., Pyrochlores. VII. The oxides of antimony; an x-ray and Mössbauer study, *Can. J. Chem.*, 50, 690, 1972.
136. Abe, M. and Ito, T., Some observation on surface structure and cation exchange behavior of three different antimonic(V) acids, *Bull. Chem. Soc. Jpn.*, 41, 2366, 1968.
137. Kleshchev, G. V., Trofimov, V. G., and Kleshchev, D. G., and Sheinkman, A. I., Structural studies of the hydrate of antimony pentoxide, *Kristallografiya*, 21, 832, 1975; *Sov. Phys. Crystallogr.*, 21, 475, 1976.
138. Novikov, B. G., Belicheva, T. G., Belinskaya, F. A., and Materova, E. A., IR spectra of crystalline antimonic acid exchanger, *Vestn. Leningrad Univ. Fiz. Khim.*, (4), 110, 1969.
139. Balicheva, T. G. and Roi, N. I., Infrared spectra and ion exchange properties of antimonic acid, *Izv. Akad. Nauk SSSR. Neorg. Mater.*, 9, 277, 1973.
140. Bourrelly, I. N., Study of the effect of various factors on the retention characteristics of potassium and rubidium by antimonic acid in nitric acid, *Anal. Chim. Acta*, 94, 323, 1977.
141. Siebert, H., Infrared spectra of telluric acids, tellurates, and antimonates, *Z. Anorg. Allg. Chem.*, 301, 161, 1959.
142. Lukina, A. G., Speranskaya, E. F., and Drachevskaya, R. K., Study of the structure of hydrated antimony pentoxide, *Prikl. Teor. Khim.*, 5, 30, 1974.
143. Strelow, F. W. E., Rethemeyer, R., and Bothma, C. J. C., Ion exchange selectivity scales for cations in nitric acid and sulfuric acid media with a sulfonated polystyren resin, *Anal. Chem.*, 37, 106, 1965.
144. Abe, M., Ion-exchange equilibria of crystalline antimonic(V) acid with alkali metal ions, *J. Inorg. Nucl. Chem.*, 41, 85, 1979.
145. Glueckauf, E., Activity coefficients in concentrated solutions containing several electrolytes, *Nature*, 163, 414, 1949.
146. Kraus, K. A. and Raridon, R. J., Temperature dependence of some cation exchange equilibria in the range 0 to 200°, *J. Phys. Chem.*, 63, 190, 1959.
147. Gaines, G. L., Jr. and Thomas, H. C., Adsorption studies on clay minerals. II. A formulation of the thermodynamics of exchange adsorption, *J. Chem. Phys.*, 21, 714, 1953.
148. Ekedahl, E., Hogfeldt, E., and Sillén, L. G., Activities of the components in ion exchangers, *Acta Chem. Scand.*, 4, 556, 1950.
149. Breck, D. W., *Zeolite Molecular Sieves, Structure, Chemistry and Use*, John Wiley & Sons, New York, 1974, 533.
150. Girardi, F., Pietra, R., and Sabbioni, E., Radiochemical separations by retention on ionic precipitate. Adsorption tests on 11 materials, *J. Radioanal. Chem.*, 5, 141, 1970.

151. Bourrelly, I. N. and Deschamps, N., Behavior of alkali metals on hydrated antimony pentoxide, *J. Radioanal. Chem.*, 8, 303, 1971.

152. Furler, R., Licht, I. E. C. P. M., and van Heijst, J. P. M., The exchange of inorganic thallium compounds on hydrated antimony pentoxide/HAP/, *Radiochem. Radioanal. Lett.*, 16, 323, 1974.

153. Konečvný, C. and Hartl, I., Studies on the sodium(cesium and strontium)-polyantimonic(V) acid ion-exchange equilibria in dilute nitric acid solutions, *Z. Phys. Chem. (Leipzig)*, 256, 17, 1975.

154. Abe, M., Ion-exchange properties of crystalline antimonic(V) acid with alkaline earth metal ions, *Bull. Chem. Soc. Jpn.*, 52, 1386, 1979.

155. Abe, M. and Sudoh, K., Ion-exchange equilibria of alkaline earth metals and hydrogen ions on crystalline antimonic(V) acid, *J. Inorg. Nucl. Chem.*, in press.

156. Abe, M. and Sudoh, K., Ion-exchange equilibria of transition metals and hydrogen ions in crystalline antimonic(V) acid, *J. Inorg. Nucl. Chem.*, 42, 1051, 1980.

157. Püschel, S. M. P. and Lima, F. W., Retention of tantalum by hydrated antimony/V/oxide in strong acid media, *Radiochem. Radioanal. Lett.*, 6, 313, 1971.

158. Abe, M., Yoshigasaki, K., and Sugiura, T., Ion-exchange equilibria of crystalline antimonic(V) acid with organic cations, *J. Inorg. Nucl. Chem.*, 42, 1753, 1980.

159. Jolivet, J. P. and Lefebvre, J., Crystalline antimonate as ion exchangers. II. kinetics aspects of silver fixation by potassium antimonate and antimonic acid, *Rev. Chim. Miner.*, 10, 423, 1973.

160. Breck, D. W., *Zeolite Molecular Seives, Structures, Chemistry and Use,* John Wiley & Sons, New York, 1974, p. 532.

161. Abe, M., Unpublished result.

162. Harkin, J. P., Nancollas, G. H., and Paterson, R., The exchange of caesium and hydrogen ions on zirconium phosphate, *J. Inorg. Nucl. Chem.*, 26, 305, 1964.

163. Novikov, B. G., Belinskaya, F. A., and Materova, E. A., Ion exchange of dipositive cations on a crystalline antimonic cation exchanger, *Vestn. Leningrad. Univ. Fiz. Khim.*, 35, 1971.

164. Tsvetkov, V. K., Pak, V. N., and Aleskovskii, V. B., Study of products of the ion-exchange of Co(II) sorption by the surfaces of $SiO_2 \cdot nH_2O$, $Al_2O_3 \cdot nH_2O$, $TiO_2 \cdot nH_2O$ and antimony pentoxide ($Sb_2O_5 \cdot nH_2O$) using diffuse reflection spectra, *Zh. Prikl. Khim.*, Leningrad, 49, 519, 1976; *Chem. Abstr.*, 85, 11385f, 1976.

165. Sherry, H. S., The ion-exchange properties of zeolite, in *Ion Exchange,* Vol. 2, Marinsky, J. A., Ed., Marcel Dekker, New York, 1969, chap. 3.

166. Whittingham, M. S., Mechanism of fast ion transport in solids, *Electrochim. Acta,* 20, 575, 1975.

167. Aubertin, C., Lefebvre, J., and Galand, G., Separating Sr from Fission Product Solutions, U.S. Patent 3399030(Cl 23-102), 1969; *Chem. Abstr.*, 70, 16481, 1969.

168. Murthy, T. S., Balasubramaian, K. R., Ananthakrishnan, M., Varma, R. N., and Mathai, C., Fixation studies of fission product elements and U on inorganic exchangers, *Proc. Chem. Symp. 2nd* 1970, 2, 171, 1971; *Chem. Abstr.*, 76, 147869t, 1972.

169. Ahrland, S. and Albertsson, J., Inorganic ion exchangers. III. Equilibrium studies on zirconium phosphate gels, *Acta Chem. Scand.*, 18, 1861, 1964.

170. Abe, M., A study on ion-exchange properties of crystalline antimonic(V) acid and hydrated antimony pentoxide for various metal ions in nitric acid media, *Sep. Sci. Technol.*, 15, 23, 1980.

171. Abe, M., Analytical applications of inorganic ion-exchangers I. hydroxide and hydrous oxide of metals, *Bunscki Kagaku,* 23, 1254, 1974.

172. Krishnan, S. S. and Crapper, D. R., Sodium removal by hydrated antimony pentoxide in neutron activation analysis, *Radiochem. Radioanal. Lett.*, 20, 287, 1975.

173. Nagy, L. G., Török, G., Fóti, G., Tóth, T., and Feuer, L., Investigation on the preparation and application of some inorganic separators for the removal of the matrix activity in neutron activated biological samples, *J. Radioanal. Chem.*, 16, 245, 1973.

174. Nagy, L. G., Török, G., and Fóti, G., Investigation on the structure and sorption properties of removal of radiosodium, *Proc. Int. Conf. Colloid Surf. Sci.*, 1, 33, 1975; *Chem. Abstr.*, 85, 68760h, 1975.

175. Abe, M. and Tsuji, M., The ion exchange properties of Na^+ and K^+ ions on crystalline and amorphous antimonic(V) acids treated thermally at elevated temperatures, *J. Radioanal. Chem.*, 54, 137, 1979.

176. Higuchi, H. and Takehira, T., Removal of sodium from HAP, *Bunseki Kagaku,* 21, 808, 1972.

177. Abe, M. and Itoh, T., Change in the ion exchange selectivity by thermal treatment of crystalline antiomonic(V) acid towards alkali metal ions, *J. Inorg. Nucl. Chem.*, 42, 1641, 1980.

178. Abe, M., Tsuji, M., and Kimura, M., Ion exchange behavior of tervalent metals and rare earth elements on crystalline antimonic(V) acid cation exchanger, *Bull. Chem. Soc. Jpn.*, 54, 130, 1981.

179. Schunk, J. and Vukov, I., Utilization of ion-selective oxide hydrate sorption agents, *Magy. Kem. Lapja,* 31, 469, 1976; *Chem. Abstr.*, 86, 177920b, 1976.

180. Baetsle, L., Ion-exchange properties of zirconyl phosphate, III. Influence of temperature on tracer ion equilibria, *J. Inorg. Nucl. Chem.*, 25, 271, 1963.

181. Sherry, H. S. and Walton, H. F., The ion exchange properties of zeolite. II. Ion exchange in the synthetic zeolite Linde 4A, *J. Phys. Chem.,* 71, 1457, 1967.
182. Rosseinsky, D. R., Electrode potential and hydration energies. Theories and correlations, *Chem. Rev.,* 65, 467, 1965.
183. Clearfield, A. and Smith, G. D., The crystallography and structure of α-zirconium bis(monohydrogen orthphosphate) monohydrate, *Inorg. Chem.,* 8, 431, 1969.
184. Balantseva, V. M., Zhuiko, G. G., and Drachevskaya, R. K., Sorption of metals on antimony(V) oxide and hydroxide, in *Khim. Met. Metall. Khim. Technol. Silik Mendeleevsk. Sězd. Obshch. Prikl. Khim.,* Kozlov, V. V. and Rozinskaya, V. N., Eds., Nauka, Moscow, 1974, 85; *Chem Abstr.,* 85, 1311065, 1974.
185. Vialatt, B., Barrandon, J. N., Alekandsov, S., Bourrelly, I. N., Cleyreegue, C., Deschamps, N., and Jaffrezic, H., Fixation of F⁻ on Sb_2O_5 in HCl media, *Radiochem. Radioanal. Lett.,* 5, 59, 1970.
186. Fritz, J. S. and Rettig, T. A., Separation of metals by cation exchange in acetone-water-hydrochloric acid, *Anal. Chem.,* 40, 2021, 1968.
187. Strelow, F. W. E., Improved separation of cadmium-109 from silver cyclotron targets by anion exchange chromatography In nitric acid-hydrobromic acid mixtures, *Anal. Chim. Acta,* 97, 87, 1978.
188. Belinskaya, F. A., Materova, E. A., Militsina, E. A., Karmanova, L. A., and Novikov, B. G., Production ion exchange properties and possible usage of cation exchangers based on polymeric antimony, *Nauka Leningr. otd, Leningrad,* 14, 1975; *Chem. Abstr.,* 85, 96498x, 1976.
189. Langer, S. H., Yurchak, J. Y., and Patton, J. E., The gas chromatographic column as a chemical reactor, *Ind. Eng. Chem.,* 61, 11, 1969.
190. Lykourghiotis, A., Hadzistelios, I., and Katsanos, N. A., Chromatographic and adsorption properties of antimony pentoxide, *J. Chromatogr.,* 110, 287, 1975.
191. Cuypers, J., Girardi, F., and Mousty, F., The application of inorganic exchangers to radiochemical separations on neutron-activated high-purity materials, *J. Radioanal. Chem.,* 17, 115, 1973.
192. Pietra, R., Sabbioni, E., and Girardi, F., Determination of Ca, Mg, Ni, and Si in biological materials by neutron activation and Čerenkov counting, *Radiochem. Radioanal. Lett.,* 22, 243, 1975.
193. Ralston, H. R. and Sato, E. S., Sodium removal as an aid to neutron activation analysis, *Anal. Chem.,* 43, 129, 1971.
194. Tjioe, P. S., DeGoeij, J. J. M., and Houtman, J. P. W., Automated chemical separation in routine activation analysis, *J. Radioanal. Chem.,* 16, 153, 1973.
195. Ching-Wang, H., Higuchi, H., and Hamaguchi, H., Multielement neutron activation analysis of human hair samples; Application of the low temperature ashing and HAP treatment, *Bunseki Kagaku,* 22, 1586, 1973.
196. Buenafama, H. D. and Rudelli, M. D., Determination of Cs, Rb and Ba in neutron activated biological materials, *J. Radioanal. Chem.,* 16, 269, 1973.
197. Török, G., Fóti, G., Nagy, L. G., Tóth, T., and Feuer, L., Use of selective sorption of methods for removal of high activity compounds of neutron-activated biological samples, *Magy. Kem. Foly,* 78, 277, 1972; *Chem. Abstr.,* 77, 331155y, 1972.
198. Bird, E. D., Emery, J. F., Lupica, S. B., and Lyon, W. S., Antimony pentoxide for sodium removal in neutron-activated drain, *USAEC,* ORAU107, 245, 1968.
199. Velandia, J. A. and Perkons, A. K., An ion-exchange group-separation scheme for rapid analysis of the components of neutron-activated biological tissues, *J. Radioanal. Chem.,* 20, 473, 1974.
200. Schelhorn, H., Pfrepeer, G., and Geisler, M., Determination of trace element in biological materials with neutron-activation analysis, *J. Radioanal. Chem.,* 33, 187, 1976.
201. Platin, L. O., A method for the determination of Mn, Cu, Zn, K, and Na in small tissue biopsies by neutron activation analysis, *J. Radioanal. Chem.,* 12, 441, 1972.
202. Velandia, J. A. and Perkons, A. K., Survey of 33 constituent elements in heart tissue by instrumental activation analysis, *J. Radioanal. Chem.,* 14, 171, 1973.
203. Lievens, P., Cornelis, R., and Hoste, J., A separation scheme for the determination of trace elements in biological materials by neutron activation analysis, *Anal. Chim. Acta,* 80, 97, 1975.
204. Török, G., and Diehl, J. F., Preparation and properties of Sb(V) aquoxide for separation of sodium in activation analysis, *Radiochim. Acta,* 15, 96, 1971.
205. Török, G., Schelenz, R., Fischer, E., and Diehl, J. F., Separation of Na, K, and P by means by inorganic separators in the neutron-activation analysis of biological materials, *Fresenius' Z. Anal. Chem.,* 263, 110, 1973.
206. Maziere, B., Gaudray, A., Stanilewicz, W., and Comar, D., Possibilities and limits of the multi-elemental determinations in biological samples by neutron activation analysis with and without chemical separation, *J. Radioanal. Chem.,* 16, 281, 1973.
207. Schuhmacher, J., Maier-Borst, W., and Hauser, H., A half automated, non time consuming radiochemical separation scheme for determination of 25 trace elements in biological specimens, *J. Radioanal. Chem.,* 37, 503, 1977.

208. Treuil, M., Jaffrezic, H., Deschamps, N., Derre, C., Guichard, F., Joron, J. L., Pelletier, B., and Courtois, C., Analysis of lanthanides, hafnium, scandium, chromium, manganese, cobalt, copper and zinc in the minerals and rocks by neutron activation, *J. Radioanal. Chem.*, 18, 55, 1973.

209. Tshiashala, M. D. and DeMicheli, F. O., Separation of K from rock samples in neutron activation analysis, *Radiochem. Radioanal. Lett.*, 25, 101, 1976.

210. Abe, M., Ichsan, E. A. W. A., and Hayashi, K., Ion-exchange separation of lithium from large amounts of sodium, calcium, and other elements by a double column of Dowex 50W-X8 and crystalline antimonic(V) acid, *Anal. Chem.*, 52, 524, 1980.

211. Gills, T. E., Marlow, W. F., and Thompson, B. A., Determination of trace elements in glass by activation analysis using hydrated antimony pentoxide for sodium removal, *Anal. Chem.*, 42, 1831, 1970.

212. Kudo, K., Kobayashi, K., and Shigematsu, T., Substoichiometric and non-destructive determinations of trace impurities in high-purity optical glasses by neutron activation analysis, *J. Radioanal. Chem.*, 27, 329, 1975.

213. Yoshida, H. and Yonezawa, C., Determination of sodium in high-purity zinc and selenium by neutron activation, *Bunseki Kagaku*, 22, 929, 1973.

214. Mitchell, J. W., Riley, J. E., and Northover, W. R., Determination of trace transition elements in ultra high purity sodium and calcium carbonates by neutron activation analysis, *J. Radioanal. Chem.*, 18, 133, 1973.

215. Higuchi, H., Nonaka, N., Hamaguchi, H., and Tomura, K., Determination of sodium and chlorine in pure water by neutron activation analysis, *J. Radioanal. Chem.*, 36, 457, 1977.

216. Casella, V. R., Grant, P. M., and O'Brien, H. A., Jr., The quantitative recovery and purification of spallogenic ^{43}K for nuclear medicine; A radiochemical procedure for V targets bonbarded with medium-energy protons, *J. Radioanal. Chem.*, 36, 337, 1977.

217. Abe, M., Chromatographic separation of microamounts of sodium and potassium from a large quantity of lithium chloride by using crystalline antimonic(V) acid as a cation exchanger, *Sep. Sci. Technol.*, 13, 347, 1978.

218. Massart, D. L., The elimination of potassium activity in activation analysis by isotopic exchange on column, *J. Radioanal. Chem.*, 4, 265, 1970.

219. Arino, H., Skraba, W. J., and Kramer, H. H., A new $^{68}Ge/^{68}Ga$ Radioisotope generator system, *Int. Nat. J. Appl. Radiat. Isot.*, 29, 117, 1978.

220. Nattall, L. J. and Titterington, W. A., *Electric Production of Hydrogen,* City University Press, London, 1975.

221. Vandenborre, H. and Leysen, R., On inorganic-membrane-electrolyte water electrolysis, *Electrochim. Acta,* 23, 803, 1978.

222. Mellor, J. W., Columbium, in *A Comprehensive Treatise on Inorganic and Theoretical Chemistry,* Vol. IX, Longmans, London, 1952, chap. 55.

223. Sakharov, V. V., Ivanova, N. E., Korovin, S. S., and Zakharov, M. A., Topochemical precipitation of niobium and tantalum hydroxides from various compounds, *Zh. Neorg. Khim.*, 19, 579, 1976; *Russ. J. Inorg. Chem.*, 19, 313, 1974.

224. Balukova, V. D., Ermolaev, V. M., Zakharov, M. A., and Nazarova, R. I., Problem of interaction of polymeric niobium hydroxide with solutions of alkaline earth elements, *Zh. Neorg. Khim.*, 20, 3297, 1975; *Russ. J. Inorg. Chem.*, 20, 1822, 1975.

225. Nikolaev, N. S. and Buslaev, Y. A., Solubility and hydrolysis in the system $HF-NbF_5-H_2O$, *Zhur. Neorg. Khim.*, 4, 205, 1959; *Chem. Abstr.*, 53, 11972b, 1959.

226. Mambetov, A. A., Abbasova, F. G., and Aliev, S. T., Dehydration of a hydrated gel of peroxoniobic acid at constant temperature as a function of the vapor pressure of water in the atmosphere, *Uch. Zap. Azerb. Gos. Univ.*, 16, 1967; *Chem. Abstr.*, 69, 90090f, 1968.

227. Galanova, M. A., Composition of niobic acid precipitated from buffers I, *Tr. Voronezh. Technol. Inst.*, 17, 203, 1968; *Chem. Abstr.*, 72, 136976s, 1970.

228. Weiser, H. B., The hydrous oxides and hydroxides, *Inorganic Colloidal Chemistry, Vol. II,* John Wiley & Sons, London, 1935, 298.

229. Izumi, F. and Kodama, H., Hydrothermal synthesis and characterization of triniobium hydroxide heptaoxide, *Z. Anorg. Allg. Chem.*, 441, 196, 1978.

230. Holtzberg, F., Reisman, A., Berry, M., and Berkenblit, M., Chemistry of group V_B pentoxide. VI. The polymorphism of Nb_2O_5, *J. Am. Chem. Soc.*, 79, 2039, 1957.

231. Lapitskii, A. V., Simanov, Y. P., and Yarembash, E. I.., Some properties of niobium pentoxide, *Zh. Fiz. Khim.*, 26, 56, 1952; *Chem. Abstr.*, 46, 10995h, 1952.

232. Sathyanarayana, D. N. and Patel, C. C., Studies on hydroxide and peroxide of niobium, *Z. Anorg. Allg. Chem.*, 353, 103, 1967.

233. Groult, D., Michel, C., and Raveau, B., Thermal decomposition of oxonium and ammonium pyrochlore H_3MWO_6, H_4OMO_6, and NH_4MWO_6 (M = Nb,Ta), *J. Inorg. Nucl. Chem.*, 36, 61, 1974.

234. Reisman, A. and Holtzberg, F., Nb$_2$O$_5$ and Ta$_2$O$_5$ structure and physical properties in high temperature oxides, in *High Temperature Oxides, Part II, Oxides of Rare Earths, Titanium, Zirconium, Hafnium, Niobium, and Tantalum*, Alper, A. M., Ed., Academic Press, New York, 1970, 218.

235. Spitsyn, V. I., Ermolaev, V. M., Sakharov, V. V., and Zakharov, M. A., The formation of the amorphous hydroxides (Nb,Sr,Ba) (O,OH)$_m$· nH$_2$O, *Zh. Neorg. Khim.*, 19, 3237, 1974; *Russ. J. Inorg. Chem.*, 19, 1773, 1974.

236. Sych, A., Novik, T. V., and Eremenko, L. A., Mechanism of the formation of cerium group rare earth orthoniobates from co-precipitated hydroxides, *Izv. Akad. Nauk SSSR Neorg. Mater.*, 13, 2046, 1977.

237. Barrachlough, C. C., Lewis, J., and Nyholm, R. S., The stretching frequencies of metal-oxygen double bonds, *J. Chem. Soc.*, 1552, 1959.

238. Selbin, J., Metal oxocations, *J. Chem. Educ.*, 41, 86, 1964.

239. Chalyi, V. P., "Gidookisi Metallov" (Metal Hydoxides), *Izv. Naukova Damka Kiev*, 1972.

240. Williams, J. M. and Peterson, S. W., Molecular structure determination by neutron and X-ray diffraction, in *Spectroscopy in Inorganic Chemistry*, Vol. II, Rao, C. N. R. and Ferraro, J. R., Eds., Academic Press, New York, 1971, 23.

241. Pimentel, G. C. and MoClellan, A. L., *The Hydrogen Bond*, Reinhold, New York, 1960, 102.

242. Weiser, H. B., The hydrous oxides and hydroxides, *Inorganic Colloidal Chemistry*, Vol. II, John Wiley & Sons, London, 1935, 299.

243. Hahr, R., Phosphates of niobium and tantalum, *J. Am. Chem. Soc.*, 73, 5091, 1951.

244. Wedekind, E. and Maass, W., The precipitation of tantalic acid from west Australia fergusonite; sodium tantalate, *Z. Angew. Chem.*, 23, 2314, 1911; *Chem. Abstr.*, 5, 643, 1911.

245. Jander, G. and Schulz, H., About amphoteric oxide hydrate of alkaline solutions and solid salts (Isopoly acid and isopoly acid salt), *Z. Anorg. Chem.*, 144, 225, 1925.

246. Britton, H. T. S. and Robinson, R. A., Physicochemical studies of complex acids. IX. Tantalic acid, Reaction of alkali niobate and tantalate solutions with organic acids, *J. Chem. Soc.*, 419, 1933.

247. Muxart, R., Vernois, J., Arapaki-Strapeties, H., Dartige, J. M., and Kovacevic, S., Hydrated tantalum oxide precipitate, *Rev. Chim. Miner.*, 9, 905, 1972; *Chem. Abstr.*, 78, 131475s, 1973.

248. Khomutnikov, V. A., Chernya, A. S., Batsuev, A. A., Vlybina, T. I., and Iranov, O. P., Study of the composition, properties and mechanism of aging of niobium and tantalum hydroxides, Deposited Dec., VINITI 4059, 1976; *Chem. Abstr.*, 89, 114503j, 1978.

249. Titova, V. A., Kozel, V. E., Slatinskaya, I. G., Panko, G. F., and Pitsyuga, V. G., Dehydration of tantalum hydroxide, *Zh. Neorg. Khim.*, 21, 308, 1976; *Russ. J. Inorg. Chem.*, 21, 165, 1976.

250. Zaslavskii, A. I., Zvinchuk, R. A., and Tutov, A. G., X-ray studies on the polymorphism of Ta$_2$O$_5$, *Dokl. Akad. Nauk. SSSR*, 104, 409, 1955; *Chem. Abstr.*, 50, 7538f, 1956.

251. Godina, N. A., Savchenko, E. P., and Keler, E. K., Formation conditions and properties of lanthanum, cerium, praseodymium, and neodymium orthotantalates, *Izv. Akad. Nauk SSSR. Neorg. Mater.*, 4, 389, 1968.

252. Laptskii, I. A. V., Simanov, Y. P., Semenenko, K. N., and Yarembash, E. I., The properties of tantalum pentoxide, *Vestn. Moskov. Univ.*, 9, 85, 1954; *Chem. Abstr.*, 49, 3712c, 1955.

253. Hervieu, M., Michel, C., and Raveau, B., Ion exchange properties of pyrochlore type; pyrochlore H$_{1+x}$(H$_2$O) Ta$_{1+x}$W$_{1-x}$O$_6$ and NH$_4$TaWO$_6$, *Bull. Soc. Chim. Fr.*, 11, 3939, 1971.

254. Schoeller, H. R. and Webb, W. H., Investigation into the analytical chemistry of tantalum, niobium and their mineral associates. XXXII, *Analyst*, 61, 585, 1936.

255. Egorov, Yu. V. and Sukharev, Yu. I., Hydrated niobium pentoxide as an ion-exchanging ampholyte, *Izv. Akad. Nauk SSSR Neorg. Mater.*, 3, 1210, 1967; *Chem. Abstr.*, 68, 33570t, 1967.

256. Sukharev, Yu. I., and Egorov, Yu. V., Some sorption compounds of Nb(OH)$_5$, *Izv. Akad. Nauk SSSR Neorg. Mater.*, 4, 996, 1968; *Chem. Abstr.*, 69, 99774g, 1968.

257. Sukharev, Yu. I. and Egorov, Yu. V., Ion-exchange properties of hydrated niobium pentoxide, *Izv. Akad. Nauk SSSR Neorg. Mater.*, 5, 2159, 1969; *Chem. Abstr.*, 72, 83308s, 1970.

258. Sukharev, Yu. I. and Egorov, Yu. V., Thermodynamics of ion-exchange on hydrated niobium pentoxide, *Izv. Akad. Nauk SSSR Neorg. Mater.*, 7, 270, 1971; *Chem. Abstr.*, 74, 103422, 1971.

259. Sukharev, Yu. I., Reif, M. G. and Egorov, Yu. V., Polymerization of hydrated metal oxide ion-exchange matrix, *Izv. Akad. Nauk SSSR Neorg. Mater.*, 8, 1606, 1972; *Chem. Abstr.*, 78, 8323p, 1973.

260. Sukharev, Yu. I. and Egorov, Yu. V., Sorption anisotropy of an inorganic ion-exchanger as a result of application synthesis, *Zh. Fiz. Khim.*, 47, 1489, 1973; *Chem. Abstr.*, 79, 108452u, 1973.

261. Korshunova, N. K., Sukharev, Yu. I. and Egorov, Yu. V., Formation of ion-exchange precipitates of hydrated niobium pentoxide in a medium of ferrocyanide and polyvanadate ions, *Izv. Akad. Nauk SSSR Neorg. Mater.*, 13, 2052 1977; *Chem. Abstr.*, 88, 42099m, 1978.

262. Groult, D., Michel, C., and Raveau, B., New lacunar pyrochlores of bivalent ion synthesized by ion exchange, *J. Inorg. Nucl. Chem.*, 37, 2205, 1975.

263. Sharygin, L. M., Barybin, V. I., and Gonchar, V. F., Change in the physicochemical properties of hydrated tantalum pentoxide during heat treatment, *Izv. Akad. Nauk SSSR Neorg. Mater.*, 14, 1468, 1978; *Chem. Abstr.*, 89, 186482z, 1978.

264. Ganzerli-Valentini, M. T., Meloni, S., Maxia, V., and Pisani, U., Radiochemical separations by adsorption on some oxides of group IVB and VB, *J. Radioanal. Chem.*, 16, 191, 1973.

265. Chidley, B. E., Parker, F. L., and Talbot, E. A., Properties of Hydrated TiO_2 and Hydrated Ta_2O_5 as High Temperature Ion-Exchange Materials, AERE Rep. No. R5220, Atomic Energy Research Establishment, Didcot, Harwell, Berks., England, 1966.

266. U. K. Atomic Energy Authority, Inorganic ion-exchangers, French Patent 1486949, 1967, *Chem. Abstr.*, 68, 74492n, 1968.

267. Mellor, J. W., Tungsten, in *A Comprehensive Treatise on Inorganic and Theoretical Chemistry*, Vol. XI. Longmans, London, 1952, 762.

268. Huttig, G. F. and Kurre, B., For hydrate of tungsten trioxide, *Z. Anorg. Allg. Chem.*, 122, 44, 1922.

269. Morley, A. M., The structure of the tungstic acid, *J. Chem. Soc.*, 1930, 1987.

270. Polyakov, V. I., Precipitation of tungsten as tungstic acid solution, *Dokl. Akad. Nauk. Uzb. SSSR*, 27, 31, 1970.

271. Weiser, H. B., The hydrous oxides and hydroxides, *Inorganic Colloidal Chemistry, Vol. II*, John Wiley & Sons, London, 1935, 136.

272. Wells, A. F., *Structural Inorganic Chemistry*, 4th ed., Clarendon Press, Oxford, 1975, 474.

273. Amphlett, C. B., McDonald L. A., and Redman, M. J., Synthetic inorganic ion-exchange materials. II. Hydrous zirconium and other oxides, *J. Inorg. Nucl. Chem.*, 6, 236, 1958.

274. Morley, A. M., The behavior of the tungstic acids towards sodium hydroxide, *J. Phys. Chem.*, 36, 1655, 1932.

275. Kabanov, V. Ya. and Spitsyn, V. I., Investigation of the mechanism of the formation of hydrated high-molecular weight tungstates by infrared spectroscopy, *Dokl. Akad. Nauk.*, 148, 109, 1963; *Dokl. Chem.; Proc. Akad. Sci. SSSR, Chem. Sect.*, 148, 26, 1963.

276. Bethell, D. E. and Sheppard, N., The infrared spectrum of H_3O^+ in acid hydrates, *J. Chem. Phys.*, 21, 1421, 1953.

277. Ferriso, C. C. and Hornig, D. F., Infrared spectra of oxonium halides and the structure of oxonium ion, *J. Chem. Phys.*, 23, 1464, 1955.

278. Schwarzmann, E. and Glemser, O., Bonding state of water in hydrates of tungsten trioxides, *Z. Anorg. Allg. Chem.*, 312, 45, 1961.

279. Szalav, T. and Bartha, L., Ion exchange adsorption processes on tungsten oxides, *Magy. Kem. Foly.*, 81, 67, 1975; *Chem. Abstr.*, 82, 103702c, 1975.

280. Tsuboya, T., Kaya, A., and Hoshino, T., Neptunium separation from uranium nitrate-nitric acid solutions with tungstic acid exchanger, *Tokai Works Semi Annual Progress Report*, No. N 831-70-02, 1970, 72.

INDEX

A

I